The World's Landscapes
edited by J. M. Houston

Ireland

The World's Landscapes
edited by J. M. Houston

Ireland

A. R. Orme

Associate Professor of Geography
University of California, Los Angeles

ALDINE PUBLISHING COMPANY
CHICAGO

First published 1970 by
ALDINE PUBLISHING COMPANY
529 South Wabash Avenue
Chicago, Illinois 60605

and

Longman Group Ltd
London

SBN 202–10030 (clothbound edition), 202–10035 (paperbound edition)
Library of Congress Catalog
Card Number 70-91729

PRINTED IN THE UNITED STATES OF AMERICA

To Lusanne

For the plain shall be broke
  by the share of the stranger,
And the stone-mason's stroke
  Tells the woods of their danger;

The green hills and shore
Be with white keeps disfigured,
  And the Mote of Rathmore
Be the Saxon churl's haggard!

The land of the lakes
Shall no more know the prospect
  of valleys and brakes –
So transformed is her aspect!

The Gael cannot tell,
In the uprooted wildwood
  And red ridgy dell,
The old nurse of his childhood. . . .

We starve by the board,
And we thirst amid wassail –
  For the guest is the lord,
And the host is the vassal!

Through the woods let us roam,
Through the wastes wild and barren;
  We are strangers at home!
We are exiles in Erin!

Samuel Ferguson, 1834 (translated from the Irish of Ó Gnímh, c. 1580)

Editor's Preface

Despite the multitude of geographical books that deal with differing areas of the world, no series has before attempted to explain man's role in moulding and changing its diverse landscapes. At the most there are books that study individual areas in detail, but usually in language too technical for the general reader. It is the purpose of this series to take regional geographical studies to the frontiers of contemporary research on the making of the world's landscapes. This is being done by specialists, each in his own area, yet in non-technical language that should appeal to both the general reader and to the discerning student.

We are leaving behind us an age that has viewed nature as an objective reality. Today, we are living in a more pragmatic, less idealistic age. The nouns of previous thought forms are the verbs of a new outlook. Pure thought is being replaced by the use of knowledge for a technological society, busily engaged in changing the face of the earth. It is an age of operational thinking. The very functions of nature are being threatened by scientific takeovers, and it is not too fanciful to predict that the daily weather, the biological cycles of life processes, as well as the energy of the atom will become harnessed to human corporations. Thus it becomes imperative that all thoughtful citizens of our world today should know something of the changes man has already wrought in his physical habitat, and which he is now modifying with accelerating power.

Studies of man's impact on the landscapes of the earth are expanding rapidly. They involve diverse disciplines such as Quaternary sciences, archaeology, history and anthropology, with subjects that range from pollen analysis, to plant domestication, field systems, settlement patterns and industrial land use. But with his sense of place, and his sympathy for synthesis, the geographer is well placed to handle this diversity of data in a meaningful manner. The appraisal of landscape changes, how and when man has altered and remoulded the surface of the earth, is both pragmatic and interesting to a wide range of readers.

The concept of 'landscape' is of course both concrete and elusive. In its Anglo-Saxon origin, *landscipe* referred to some unit of area that was a natural entity, such as the lands of a tribe or of a feudal lord. It was only at the end of the sixteenth century that, through the influence of Dutch landscape painters, the word also acquired the idea of a unit of visual perceptions, of a view. In the German *landschaft*, both definitions have been maintained, a source of confusion and uncertainty in the use of the term. However, despite scholarly analysis of its ambiguity, the concept of landscape has increasing currency precisely because of its ambiguity. It refers to the total man-land complex in place and time, suggesting spatial interactions, and indicative of visual features that we can select, such as field and settlement patterns, set in the mosaics of relief, soils and vegetation. Thus the 'landscape' is the point of reference in the selection of widely ranging data. It is the tangible context of man's association with the earth. It is the documentary evidence of the power of human perception to mould the resources of nature into human usage, a perception as varied as his cultures. Today, the ideological attitudes of man are being more dramatically imprinted on the earth than ever before, owing to technological capabilities.

In a book of this modest length, yet covering so extensive and intricate data, much could have been said that has necessarily been omitted. And as it is a pioneer work, the author has only touched on some fields that still await more research. Enough has been said in this work, however, to indicate how persuasive has been man's influence on Ireland since he first entered the island some 8,000 years ago. As each immigrant group has entered Ireland, so new imprints on the landscape have been made, as so many strandlines on the beach of time. Unfortunately, the contemporary landscapes of Ireland are acquiring a homogeneity that is fast destroying local expressions. Careful planning is now needed to preserve the best of Ireland's heritage and yet adjust to new needs.

J. M. Houston

Contents

List of Illustrations

Acknowledgements

We are grateful to the following for permission to reproduce photographs:

Aerofilms Ltd: figs. 25, 42, 43, 61, 62, 63, 65, 67, 69; Bord na Mona: figs. 72, 73; *Irish Times:* figs. 23, 77; Northern Ireland Tourist Board: fig. 10; Shannon Free Airport Development Co. Ltd: fig. 78; Bord Fáilte Eireann: figs. 6, 8, 12, 14–16, 20, 24, 33, 35, 39, 41, 47, 48, 50, 51, 56, 57, 82; figs. 2, 5, 7, 9, 29, 30, 36, 52, 55, 60, 71, 79 are photographs by Dr J. K. St Joseph in the Cambridge University Collection (copyright reserved). Figs. 26, 54 and 64 and the cover are photographs by the author.

The author wishes to acknowledge a sincere debt of gratitude to the following scholars: to Tom Jones Hughes whose keen perception and knowledge of the Irish landscape and deep sympathy for Irish society made such lasting impressions on the author during his years in Ireland; to E. Estyn Evans, T. W. Freeman, G. F. Mitchell and many other contemporary geographers, historians, archaeologists and Quaternary scientists whose continuing researches and stimulating writings have contributed so much towards a better understanding of the changing Irish landscape; to Michael Herity and Robin Butlin for kindly commenting on Chapters 5 and 8 respectively; and to the series editor, James Houston of Oxford University, and the publishers for their help and encouragement during the preparation of *Ireland*.

Introduction

The Irish landscape has all the fascination of a well-cut diamond and, like such a diamond, owes much of its interest and individuality to the work of man. The contemporary scene, with its fields, hedgerows, farmsteads, roads, towns and industries, bears little resemblance to the thickly wooded country that man once inherited from the hand of nature. Indeed, the clearance of the native woodlands has been perhaps the most dramatic change that man has inflicted on this natural landscape but, in the space thus cleared, he has also fashioned new landscapes which are as fascinating as they are complex. For several thousand years, Ireland has been exposed to periodic immigration by peoples of differing cultural origins each motivated by distinct needs and aspirations and possessing certain traditions and technical facilities. As each immigrant group made Ireland its home, so new features of settlement and land use were added to the landscape while older features associated with earlier immigrants were either displaced by or subordinated to the needs of the new colonists. The countryside is thus rich in elements attributable to Neolithic folk, Celtic cowlords, Anglo-Norman barons, seventeenth-century planters and other colonizing forces that have played such important roles in changing the face of Ireland.

Ireland's individuality also owes much to the country's character as an outpost located towards the edge of the European continental shelf. For long periods the country lay isolated from the mainstreams of European social and economic development. It was never brought under the power of the Roman empire and, alone among the countries of Europe, was spared the fury of the barbarian invaders who swept across the continent in the years following the decline of Rome. Even the emergence of powerful European nation-states some four or five hundred years ago, the discovery of the Americas and the development of world trade had little immediate impact on Ireland because the country had few desirable resources and, for better or for worse, was about to be linked more firmly than ever to its nearest neighbour, Britain. France and Spain rarely expressed more than passing interest in remote Ireland (Irish ships played no great part either in the Newfoundland fisheries or in the growth of trade with the New World although, during the eighteenth and nineteenth centuries in particular, North America did become a major refuge for Irish people fleeing from poverty, insecurity and famine at home. Even today, despite vastly improved communications, Ireland still lies far from the industrial heartland of Europe. Nevertheless, on the two occasions when the country lay astride major migrational routes, Neolithic folk introduced farming and the Vikings introduced towns – events of great material significance to the evolving landscape.

One consequence of Ireland's comparative isolation was that the Celts who

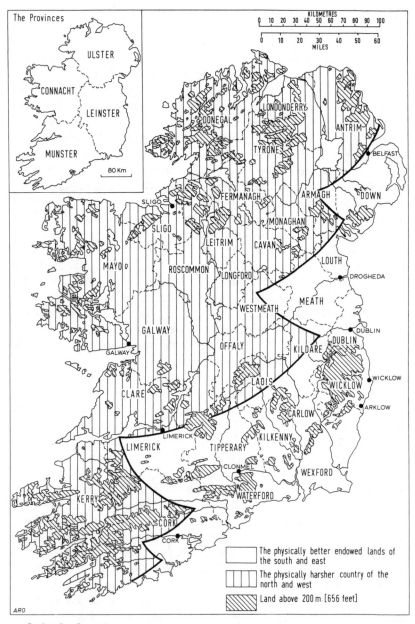

The Provinces

ULSTER

CONNACHT

LEINSTER

MUNSTER

80 Km

KILOMETRES
0 10 20 30 40 50 60 70 80 90 100

0 10 20 30 40 50 60
MILES

DONEGAL

LONDONDERRY

ANTRIM

TYRONE

BELFAST

SLIGO

FERMANAGH

ARMAGH

DOWN

SLIGO

MONAGHAN

LEITRIM

CAVAN

MAYO

ROSCOMMON

LONGFORD

LOUTH

DROGHEDA

WESTMEATH

MEATH

GALWAY

OFFALY

KILDARE

DUBLIN

DUBLIN

GALWAY

LAOIS

WICKLOW

WICKLOW

CLARE

CARLOW

ARKLOW

LIMERICK

KILKENNY

LIMERICK

TIPPERARY

CLONMEL

WEXFORD

KERRY

WATERFORD

CORK

CORK

☐ The physically better endowed lands of
the south and east

▦ The physically harsher country of the
north and west

▨ Land above 200 m [656 feet]

ARO

1. Ireland – Locations

began settling in the country around 250 B.C. had a thousand years or more in which to mould the landscape according to their needs and customs, unimpeded by any major invasion of alien peoples. They naturally came to regard the country as their home and, when invasions did eventually bring Viking, Norman, Welsh, English, Scots and other settlers to their island, they were reluctant to accept these outsiders and their institutions into the Celtic way of life. The newcomers in their turn reciprocated these feelings and the landscape became enriched, through the media of differing settlement types and land-use patterns, by the material expressions of contrasting cultures striving to maintain their separate identities. The development of the Irish landscape is thus most clearly interpreted in terms of two societies – native and colonial – with the traditional ways of the existing inhabitants periodically upset by fresh colonists intent on imposing certain material aspects of their culture on the countryside. When, as in the cases of the medieval Dublin Pale and the seventeenth-century Ulster plantation, the colonial element was sufficiently powerful to withstand native pressures, outside influences became stamped indelibly on to the landscape. Even so, once the initial flurry of colonization had passed, new settlers were often left in relative isolation; while their traditions and dialects lingered on, their settlements and farming methods came to express a subtle compromise between their inherited customs and skills on the one hand and local conditions and contacts on the other. Where colonists were insufficiently numerous to maintain separate and flourishing communities, they were either eventually assimilated by the native population or otherwise driven out. The many derelict mansions and traces of deserted villages that litter the countryside are fitting epitaphs to those peoples who failed to establish permanent roots in Ireland. The concept of two societies, frequently out of touch and out of sympathy with one another, is clearly pertinent to an understanding of the landscape as it has evolved since the Vikings first planted their coastal colonies on Celtic Ireland in the ninth century. It should not be forgotten, however, that in earlier times Neolithic farmers, certain Bronze Age folk and the Celts themselves also acted as colonists in an already inhabited country.

Ireland's nearness to Britain goes far towards explaining certain elements in the Irish landscape. Contacts between Scotland and Ireland, within sight of one another across the narrow North Channel, date back several thousand years. Ireland's fateful connection with England began in earnest with the Anglo-Norman invasion of Ireland in 1169 but the subsequent Gaelic resurgence, which nullified many of the landscape changes imposed by the Anglo-Normans, made both the English reconquest of the sixteenth century and the plantation of Scots and English settlers that followed politically desirable. For the next three centuries, Ireland was inextricably bound to Britain and most of the outside influences and events that affected the Irish landscape stemmed from the neighbouring island. Britain's control over Ireland's commercial activities and the restrictions placed on religious liberty and, thereby, on land control and social opportunity all found expression in the landscape. Even today, after half a century of political independence, Ireland still necessarily retains close economic ties with Britain. Despite these links, however, the Irish landscape could never be considered merely a detached portion of the larger island. In religious affiliations, social customs, demographic structure and mental outlook, all of which find some expression in the landscape, most Irish people differ radically from the British.

Throughout the year Ireland is a green country, the green of its lush pastures rather than its native woodlands, only a few shreds of which now remain. A moment's reflection reveals that not only are the green pastures an expression of human activity but that the other colours which periodically enliven the countryside also owe their prominence to the work of man. The golden gorse and purple heather flourish particularly on overgrazed hillsides and on acid soils exhausted by human malpractices. The hawthorn, blackthorn and elder, whose white blossoms are so conspicuous in the spring, owe much of their prominence to their use as hedgerow plants when Ireland's open fields were being enclosed. Fuchsia and rhododendron, whose rich red flowers add so much colour to coastal scenery in the west, were both introduced by man. Likewise, the dark green of the coniferous forestry plantations and the changing splendours of wayside and garden flowers are commonly associated with alien species. Such noteworthy plants often flourish through lack of competition because many species, such as oak, elm and birch which might otherwise dominate the landscape under natural conditions, have long since been cut away and controlled by man. What, therefore, was the landscape like when the first inhabitants arrived and just how have successive waves of colonists changed the scene?

When man first reached Ireland some 8,000 years ago he found a well-wooded country bathed in warm but rather damp oceanic air. The lowlands, which had been vacated by glaciers a few thousand years earlier, were clothed with mixed oak, elm, hazel and pine forests with birch trees climbing higher on the hillsides. Although these dense forests spread right across to the western seaboard, the wetter parts of the lowlands carried extensive fens, forerunners to the present raised bogs. Plants and animals were generally similar to those in Britain but poorer in species; yet they flourished in the permissive environment and there was still sufficient variety of wild life in the woods and waters to please the first hunters and fishermen. Beneath the forest cover, the widespread debris left by the glaciers provided a rich variety of soil parent materials while the underlying rocks contained a scattering of useful minerals, but these particular resources were not appreciated by man until much later. Indeed, the primitive Mesolithic hunters, fishermen and food-gatherers who first inhabited Ireland were technically too ill-equipped to make any noticeable impact on the landscape or its resources. For 3,000 years, they pursued an unprogressive way of life, wandering along the shore and through the woods in search of food, but their only legacies have been a scatter of abandoned flint tools and occasional charcoal layers in the soil denoting their small camp sites.)

Just before 3000 B.C., Neolithic farming folk began colonizing Ireland. They introduced crop cultivation, stock-rearing and permanent settlements and thus initiated the first of many revolutionary changes that were to befall the landscape at the hand of man. Using fire and stone axes, they cut inroads into the primeval forests and in the clearings they pastured cattle, grew wheat and barley, built homesteads and provided burial places. The decline of elm, the expansion of hazel and the appearance of weeds in the pollen record preserved in nearby bogs all suggest human interference. With abundant land available the colonists practised shifting cultivation, abandoning their clearings to hazel, ash and birch scrub when the soils became exhausted. Gradually, the landscape became a mosaic of virgin forests, tillage patches, rough pastures and secondary woodlands in various stages of regeneration. Around 1800 B.C., farming folk began exchanging their stone implements for more efficient bronze tools and landscape changes acquired a new quality. As a flourishing Bronze Age culture developed, cattle-rearing and tillage expanded to meet the needs of the growing farming population and of the miners, craftsmen and warriors who depended upon a readily available food surplus. Copper- and gold-bearing areas became pock-marked with small mineral workings. Widespread trade and the arrival of new settlers introduced new ideas to Ireland including, during the later Bronze Age, the securely hafted socketed axe which made forest clearance much easier, and the sickle which enabled the farmer to harvest his grain crops more effectively. Shallow shifting cultivation and soil exhaustion intensified and many abandoned tillage patches were invaded by heath and bog plants, notably after the climate worsened towards the close of the Bronze Age. The landscape became an untidy patchwork of tillage plots, pastures, homesteads, graves and trackways lying between abandoned clearings, virgin forest and secondary scrub dominated by hazel, ash, birch, elder and blackthorn.

Around 500 B.C., the pleasantly warm dry climate which had characterized Neolithic and Bronze Age Ireland gave way to the cooler, wetter and stormier conditions which are such a familiar part of the present environment. Early Iron Age influences also began reaching the country, heralds of the Celtic invasions whose peoples came to play such a significant role in fashioning the landscape. Henceforth, climatic and human factors combined to lower the tree-line on the uplands, accelerate the growth of bogs and heaths, and induce further changes in the vegetation generally. The widespread turmoil generated by the Celtic warrior-herdsmen at first produced a lull in agrarian activity but around A.D. 300, towards the close of Irish prehistory and paganism, more settled conditions allied with the introduction of the heavy iron plough led

5

farmers to turn their energies to the heavier clay soils whose dense oakwood cover had previously been little touched. Under the Celts, Ireland became a land of cattle: wealth was counted in heads of cattle and these animals formed the main source of meat, dairy produce and leather. From their isolated homesteads, Celtic cowlords directed their animal husbandry, which included short-range transhumance, and also organized their tillage requirements but, with self-sufficiency as the main aim, the tilled area was small, agricultural surpluses were rare and trade consequently limited. The pastoral, self-sufficient nature of their economy combined with their powerful sense of kinship and family to produce an essentially scattered pattern of settlement. Small farmers and chieftains alike dwelt in isolated raths and crannógs while the poorer tributary peoples occupied clusters of simple dwellings and tilled the surrounding open fields. Society had no need for towns and, until the Vikings introduced urban traditions, the only features in the Irish landscape approximating to towns were the large early Christian monastic settlements, but even these were economically self-sufficient and possessed no central-place functions other than in a religious or cultural sense.

After the Vikings had introduced urban life to Ireland in the ninth century, the growth of their fortified seaports engaged in extensive overseas trade did much to change the simple pastoralism and ancient political system of the Celts and shift the country's social and political focus for all time from the midlands to the east coast. Dublin, Wicklow, Arklow, Wexford, Waterford, Youghal, Cork and Limerick all owe their origin as towns to the Vikings. As Viking settlement remained strictly coastal, however, it was left to the Anglo-Norman invaders after 1169 to penetrate inland establishing new towns in the river valleys of the interior. These settlements were essentially colonizing instruments and, finding little favour among the existing rural population, several failed to acquire any lasting role while others collapsed during the subsequent Gaelic resurgence which effectively confined English control to the Dublin Pale and a few major towns. Because the Anglo-Norman colonization process was only partly successful, largely owing to the lack of sufficient colonists, the landscapes of the north and west emerged from the medieval period little altered since before the Viking era. In the south and east on the other hand, where the Anglo-Normans and their followers organized the conquered lands into feudal manors, built villages, castles and abbeys, exploited the forests and introduced estate management, crop rotations and grain production for sale overseas, the imprint of the medieval colonists is still clearly legible.

The most significant event of the sixteenth and seventeenth centuries was the plantation of English and Scots colonists loyal to the Crown and to the Protestant cause on lands confiscated from rebellious Gaelic and Anglo-Irish landowners. The plantation policy served as security for the English reconquest, as an outlet for England's expanding population, commercial interests and in-

6

vestment capital, and as a painless way of rewarding loyal servants of the Crown through grants of Irish land. The initial sixteenth-century plantations were soon acknowledged failures but, with the final collapse of Gaelic resistance in 1603, the way was opened for the remarkable plantation of Ulster and for less dramatic changes elsewhere. The large influx of new colonists initiated a century of sweeping changes. The remaining woodlands were felled, commercial livestock-rearing expanded, tillage revived, many fields were enclosed, industries were introduced, old towns broke free of their outmoded walls, and new planned towns and villages arose almost everywhere. The presence of Scots and English planters in Ulster served not only to transform the landscape but also to sow the seeds of Ireland's present political division. As Ireland succumbed to social and economic controls designed to suit England's needs, so the effect was transmitted to the Irish landscape. Furthermore, the plantation policy, the iniquitous land settlement under Cromwell's rule and the confiscations of William of Orange, effectively transferred the sources of wealth and power into the hands of a favoured minority of mainly Protestant landlords, good, bad and indifferent, who could thus remodel the landscape at will.

Under the 'improving' landlords of the eighteenth and early nineteenth centuries, much of the landscape acquired a more orderly and well-furnished appearance. New farming methods were adopted, lands drained, fields enclosed, crops and livestock improved, trade and industry fostered, and new roads, canals and harbours constructed. Tasteful demesnes planted with many exotic trees and shrubs provided idyllic settings for new country mansions. Existing towns were rebuilt or extended in accordance with Georgian planning concepts while newly created towns and villages completed Ireland's framework of nucleated settlements as it now exists. Nevertheless poor management, absenteeism and lack of capital among many landlords left the country's resources grossly under-developed while pernicious social and economic forces condemned the mass of their tenants to a state of abject poverty, wretchedness and squalor, dependent on agriculture for a livelihood and on potatoes for food. The landlord era witnessed a grim progression of rising population, increasing rents and diminishing holdings, tempered by high death rates, recurrent famines and emigration. Never had Ireland's two societies been so far apart. Some landlords attempted to solve the problem by reorganizing the traditional farm clusters and open fields of their tenants into scattered single farm units but their work could not avert the disastrous great famine of 1846–48 when, out of a population of 8·5 million, over a million persons died and a further million emigrated.

The great famine formed a watershed in the social and economic life of the country. In the decades that followed, emigration became so firmly established as a cure for rural distress, at least in the minds of the people, that by 1926 Ireland's population had fallen to half of its pre-famine total. For those who

7

did not starve to death or emigrate, new avenues of economic development and rural organization were sought. Tillage declined, flour mills and grain stores fell derelict, and the countryside reverted largely to pasture. From 1870 onwards, a series of land acts tackled the iniquitous land problem, dismantled landlordism and created a country of peasant proprietors. The small compact family farm engaged in livestock production, intensive haymaking and mixed tillage now emerged as Ireland's most typical farm unit. Under these stimuli, the traditional customs and practices of the rural population were doomed. As kin groups scattered, so community spirit decayed and the Gaelic language gradually vanished. Meanwhile, the industrial revolution transformed the landscape of northeast Ireland which now emerged as the most industrialized part of the country, with linen manufacturing and shipbuilding encouraging the rapid growth of Belfast in particular. Nevertheless, the industrial revolution remained an intrusive element in an agricultural country and did not advance far beyond its urban footholds in east Ulster. Elsewhere, many towns stagnated or decayed after the famine while the rural landscape frequently acquired a melancholy, half-deserted appearance – a countryside abandoned by the landlords who had shaped it and by the faceless masses who had dwelt there.

Although the proportion of the population living in towns has increased from less than one-fifth in 1841 to more than one-half today, the Irish landscape still remains overwhelmingly rural. The more active components of this rural scene – the dispersed settlement pattern and the extensive grasslands supporting large numbers of livestock – have acquired their present personality largely over the past hundred years. The growth of commercial livestock-farming at the expense of cereal cultivation, the nearness of an expanding British market, improved agrarian techniques, co-operation and government policies have all exerted an influence on agriculture while the state, notably through the re-settlement schemes of the Land Commission, has done much to rationalize the relationship between man and the land. The state has also been particularly active in afforestation and drainage projects, bringing into use lands which were previously of limited value. Nevertheless, the strong regional variations in the character of the present rural economy and settlement pattern express not only existing physical, social and economic factors but also reflect potent historical forces. The countryside abounds with relics of the past. Prehistoric tombs, ruined monasteries, deserted raths, castle ruins and derelict demesnes serve to evoke memories of the several colonizing forces that have shaped the landscape. Abandoned farm clusters and old spade ridges climbing high up the hillsides are reminders of the extreme pressures that faced much of pre-famine society, pressures that were so radically relieved by famine and emigration. Sufficient thatched cottages survive to show how the inherited customs and skills of their builders were blended to suit local conditions and contacts. The hedgerows and stone walls that were thrown up to rationalize agrarian development during the

8

2. *Inishmaan*
Limestone-walled and limestone-floored paddocks on Inishmaan in the exposed Aran Islands provide some indication of the remarkable lengths to which man may go to eke out a livelihood in an unpromising environment.

eighteenth and nineteenth centuries have carved the countryside into fields that diminish in size from east to west although, here and there, open fields survive to give a glimpse of the pre-enclosure landscape.

Urban landscapes also retain expressions of the past in their ground plans and fabric elements, some of which date back to medieval and plantation times. Nevertheless, because so many townscapes were either designed or extended during the eighteenth and early nineteenth centuries and then fossilized in the

9

depressed period that followed, formal Georgian fabric and town planning concepts commonly make striking contributions to the modern urban scene. If many Irish towns are today so remarkably uniform in plan and composition, it is because they were laid out more or less simultaneously during the prolonged Georgian era by landlords and architects imbued with the creative uniformity of their age. The majority have yet to experience renewal fitting to the era of the motor-car. The most common type of urban settlement in modern Ireland is the small service centre bearing a distinct functional relationship to its rural surroundings. The largest towns, however, are all ports which were designed initially for trade but have since become major regional centres. In terms of function, therefore, most Irish towns are expressions of a pre-industrial order which in most other west European countries was largely submerged by the industrial revolution. Towns whose main roles lie in manufacturing, mining or railway activity or which function solely as holiday resorts are the exception rather than the rule. Only in east Ulster has the industrial revolution left a striking impression on townscape personality. Even so, it is perhaps in the industrial sector that man is now doing most to change the face of Ireland. Opencast mineral workings, quarries and gravel pits are leaving the countryside pock-marked with devastation. The stripping of the vast peat bogs for fuel, the construction of large reservoirs for water supply and hydroelectric schemes, and the reclamations undertaken in such ports as Belfast and Dublin to provide more industrial and commercial space are even more dramatic. Furthermore, while old-established manufacturing landscapes are few and far between, the construction of new industrial estates outside most major towns is adding a new component to the landscape. As in the rural and urban spheres of activity, the state in its many guises is playing a leading role in these changes on both sides of the Border.

Finally, any study of Ireland's personality would be incomplete without mention of the country's subtle physical qualities. Throughout the year, clouds drift eastwards across the country from the Atlantic, discharging their moisture over the hills and plains and imparting a soft misty light to the countryside. Not all this moisture returns directly to the sea for much is locked up in the heavier soils and in lonely tracts of bog, to be released but slowly to the lakes and streams in which the country abounds. The abundant moisture also expresses itself in the frequency of rushes and sedges in the pastures, and of mosses on trees and walls. Ireland's pastoral economy is certainly in keeping with this climatic endowment for grass grows profusely while grain crops are slow to ripen and difficult to harvest, except perhaps in the east. In a physical sense, the country is something of a meeting place: its weather depends largely on the frontal depressions that form between conflicting polar and tropical airmasses over the nearby North Atlantic; its vegetation embraces, among other things, both tundra and Mediterranean species that come together in the exposed but

relatively warm west; and its structural framework owes much to the converg-
ence of the Caledonian and Armorican fold systems which are so vividly expressed in the relief. Within this physical framework major contrasts do exist,
notably between the stark grandeur of the mountains and the lush green character of the plains, and also between the physically more favoured southeast and
the harsher northwest. Everywhere the legacies of the glacial epoch are expressed in terms of minor landforms and soil-forming materials. A bountiful
nature has thus provided man with a challenging range of opportunities and
limitations which he has exploited according to his traditions, skills and needs.
Much of the fascination of the contemporary scene lies in the way in which successive colonists have changed and augmented the landscapes, both physical
and human, which they found on their arrival in Ireland.

Map legend (inset, structural zones):
- ...IAN
- ZONE OF FAULT BLOCKS
- ZONE OF OPEN FOLDS
- ZONE OF STEEPER FOLDS AND MINOR THRUSTS
- ARMORICAN FRONT
- ARMORICAN ANTICLINES
- ZONE OF CLEAVAGE FOLDING
- 100 Km
- 60 miles

Scale:
KILOMETRES
0 10 20 30 40 50 60 70 80 90 100

0 10 20 30 40 50 60
MILES

Place names and features:
Malin Head, Fair Head, Bloody Foreland, Bush, 554 [1817], The Rosses, 752 [2466], 468 [1535], ANTRIM PLATEAU, NORTH CHANNEL, 615 [2019], R. Foyle, 683 [2240], R. Bann, Lough Neagh, 676 [2219], Donegal Bay, Lower Lough Erne, R. Lagan, Slieve Croob, Slieve Gullion, 852 [2796], MOURNE MOUNTAINS, Mullet, Lough Conn, Ox Mountains, 644 [2113], 667 [2188], 807 [2646], R. Moy, Curlew hills, Lough Allen, Achill, R. Shannon, Slieve Bawn, R. Suck, IRISH SEA, Clew Bay, 819 [2688], Lough Mask, Connemara, Lough Corrib, Lough Ree, R. Boyne, Slyne Head, Galway Bay, R. Brosna, R. Liffey, Dublin Bay, Curragh, Aran Islands, Burren, Slieve Bloom, R. Barrow, WICKLOW MOUNTAINS, 927 [3039], Wicklow Head, Cliffs of Moher, Lough Derg, R. Nore, 532 [1746], R. Suir, 695 [2279], Castlecomer plateau, Loop Head, Golden Vale, 796 [2610], Cahore Point, ...rry Head, GALTEE MOUNTAINS, 920 [3015], 795 [2609], 792 [2597], Carnsore Point, R. Blackwater, Dungarvan Harbour, Hook Head, ...e Bay, 1041 [3414], 696 [2284], R. Lee, R. Bandon, Cork Harbour, R. Slaney, ...enmare River, 708 [2321], Bantry Bay, Old Head of Kinsale, ...zen Head, Cape Clear

Legend:
- MOUNTAINS — ABOVE 600 m [2000 ft]
- UPLANDS — 200–600 m [655–2000 ft]
- PLATEAUS — 200–600 m [655–2000 ft]
- LOWLANDS — BELOW 200 m [655 ft]
- ESCARPMENTS
- ABRUPT RISE FROM LOWLANDS
- GRADUAL RISE FROM LOWLANDS
- HEIGHTS IN METRES [AND FEET] ABOVE SEA LEVEL

...e principal landform, drainage and structural elements of the Irish landscape

Chapter 1
The physique of Ireland

Ireland is a lowlying country whose broad drift-mantled central lowla
which commonly lie between 200 and 400 feet about sea-level, are divers
by isolated hills and plateaux and surrounded by a discontinuous upland
which rarely exceeds 3,000 feet. The physique expresses a subtle interpla
tween the intensity and duration of the various earth-sculpturing proces
the one hand and the nature and disposition of the underlying rocks
other. Long before man began carving his own inimitable signature
countryside, mass wasting and running water had long been the do
physical processes moulding the landscape. As functions of climat
naturally varied in intensity with changes of temperature and precipita
only during the coldest phases of the Pleistocene epoch were they sup
by ice and frost, and then only temporarily. Nevertheless, despite th
paratively short duration, the Pleistocene glaciations have endowed the
side with a rich legacy of minor landforms and soil parent materials: th
which nurtured local glaciers display ice-dressed scenery of remarkal
while the lowlands exhibit one of the world's finest landscapes of g
position. Since the glacial interlude closed 10,000 years ago, mass w
running water have reasserted their former dominance. Today, Irel
wet climate exerts a profound influence on the country's persona
expressed physically in high water-tables, numerous lakes, close-text
age networks, frequent flooding and rapid decay of chemically weak r
the 2,000-mile coastline, wave action contributes to a rich variety of
scenery while, throughout Ireland, the changing base levels o
typical of the past few million years have left a vivid imprint on t
drainage generally.

Structure, drainage and landforms – their evolution

Structural framework
Beneath its Pleistocene deposits, Ireland is built up largely of P
which bear the firm imprint of two major mountain-building
older or Caledonian orogeny which began towards the close
period, and the younger or Armorican orogeny which began l
ferous times. Except in the extreme south, the crumpling of Pr

16

and Lower Palaeozoic geosynclinal sediments by Caledonian folding along predominantly northeast to southwest lines, together with the emplacement of granite bodies, set the main structural framework of the country. The Caledonian uplands of the northwest form a linear extension of the Scottish Highlands, the Newry axis continues the line of the Southern Uplands and the Leinster axis continues that of the Isle of Man and North Wales. South of a line from Dungarvan to Dingle Bay, later Armorican movements imposed a tectonic grain of east–west folds on Devonian and Carboniferous rocks, continuing the trend of similar structures found in South Wales and southwest England. As the Armorican folds died out in intensity northwards, structures of this episode within the central lowlands were progressively modified by the proximity of pre-existing Caledonian elements. Only in northeast Ireland do Mesozoic and Cainozoic rocks make any significant contribution to the landscape. There, vast sheets of early Cainozoic basalt lavas spilled out across the country burying Mesozoic sediments while granites and other intrusive rocks were emplaced beneath the surface. This igneous activity was a prelude to earth movements which later culminated beyond Ireland in the Alpine orogeny but which were confined locally to the warping and fracturing of the established framework. The Irish Sea basin, a region of sporadic subsidence since Armorican times, was further accentuated by these convulsions and by some marginal faulting – such as the strong strike faults which caused some Antrim basalt and underlying rocks to collapse into the North Channel.

Drainage and landforms

While the Caledonian and Armorican movements set Ireland's main structural framework, subsequent denudation shaped the country's present landforms. Following the Armorican orogeny, the Carboniferous rocks that once largely covered Ireland were subjected to tremendous erosion which soon exposed many older rocks and yielded fresh sediments for the New Red Sandstone deserts. Although Triassic and marine Liassic deposits may have covered much of Ireland, at least temporarily, the net erosional loss resulting from prolonged subaerial denudation had, by Lower Cretaceous times, moulded a broad rolling plain flanked by residual uplands. The only traces of this landscape that may still be identified lie buried beneath later rocks in northeast Ireland but one may reasonably assume that Ireland's rough outlines were blocked out by Mesozoic denudation. During Upper Cretaceous times, the sea spread across Ireland depositing chalk and other materials which now survive mainly beneath the protective Cainozoic basalts in the northeast. That the chalk was once more widespread is suggested by a chalk outlier near Killarney, by chalk and flint debris on the seabed offshore, and by numerous flints in certain beach and glacial deposits – notably in Wexford.

Around 70 million years ago, the Cretaceous sea withdrew from Ireland and the emergent sea floor soon attracted streams which showed scant respect for the buried Caledonian and Armorican structures. Some drainage systems were quite new; others were dominated by streams which had extended their courses across the emerging sea floor from uplands that had suffered only marginal incursion by the chalk sea. An important component of this early Cainozoic drainage pattern comprised south-flowing streams whose general direction is perhaps reflected in the present courses of the Slaney, Barrow and Nore and in the south-flowing sections of the Shannon, Suir, Blackwater, Lee and Bandon. Other important streams undoubtedly drained directly westwards to the Atlantic Ocean. These rivers soon began cutting through the soft Cretaceous cover and other surviving Mesozoic sediments onto the folded Caledonian and Armorican framework with little regard, at least initially, for the grain of the structures thus exhumed. This superimposition of the drainage may explain why such rivers as the Shannon and Barrow, after following seemingly undistinguished courses through the central lowlands, suddenly cut seawards through noteworthy water gaps excavated across resistant rocks. Since superimposition, drainage basins have adjusted in varying degrees to the underlying rock structures. Where competent tributaries have been favoured by these structures, river capture has vastly rearranged several drainage networks of which the trellis patterns of central southern Ireland, dominated by the eastward-flowing stretches of the Blackwater, Lee and Bandon, are spectacular instances.

The present drainage systems of northeast Ireland have developed from streams that arose initially on the early Cainozoic basalts and were later influenced by powerful postbasaltic flexures and faults and by the creation of the Lough Neagh basin. Lough Neagh may once have drained southwards along the Newry-Carlingford weakness zone but the Lower Bann, cutting back along the Bann fault, eventually carried the lake's drainage away northwards against the regional dip of the basalts. A few miles farther east, the Main still retains its southward flow with the dip. The Lagan, working back along the softer Triassic rocks beyond the southeast margins of the basalt, has also poached some of Lough Neagh's drainage.

As these drainage systems developed, so the landscape was gradually worn down at rates varying with the relative resistance of the rocks involved. The abrasive tools used by the rivers in this work were supplied by mass wasting which, under the favourably warm moist Cainozoic climate, was quite rapid. Selective decay and erosion soon produced a vivid contrast between uplands sustained in resistant quartzites and sandstones, and lowlands excavated in limestones and granites which, though mechanically strong, are chemically weak. The weaker formations undoubtedly yielded large quantities of rock waste but, excepting the Lough Neagh clays and tropical laterites derived from the basalts in the north and some pipeclays and lignites in Tipperary and Cork, the paucity of Cainozoic sediments that have survived greatly restricts our understanding of this significant era. Furthermore, because earlier Cainozoic landforms were locally warped and fractured by subsequent earth movements and because later erosion has levelled Ireland so efficiently – only small areas now exceed 1,200 feet while less than 0·25 per cent of the country tops 2,000 feet – few worthwhile suggestions can be made about the nature and origins of this early Cainozoic landscape. Nevertheless, it seems likely that following the late Cretaceous emergence the sea never again wholly engulfed Ireland, that landforms were subsequently shaped by mainly subaerial processes related to intermittently falling base levels of erosion, and that the highest planation surfaces, fragments of which survive on some marginal uplands, are remnants of earlier Cainozoic denudation.

At intermediate levels, notably in the south, extensive plateaux ranging from 600 to 1,200 feet above sea-level are apparently undeformed, and were probably shaped by rivers directly ancestral to the present drainage during later Cainozoic times. Two distinct planation surfaces occur at 600–820 feet and 920–1,080 feet, the lower of which was moulded by subaerial processes attuned to seas, not higher than 500 feet above the present, which completely surrounded Ireland. By this time, the sea had certainly occupied the Irish Sea basin, for derived Pliocene and early Pleistocene marine shells dredged from the basin occur in neighbouring glacial deposits. Undoubtedly, Ireland's location near the edge of the European continental shelf predestined it to be strongly affected by the worldwide changes of sea-level, so characteristic of the Quaternary era, and its coastal margins predictably display both raised and submerged shore features, attributable to these oscillations. For instance, the extensive late Cainozoic surface of Waterford and Cork falls away seaward across a stepped sequence of narrow rock benches – some fluvial, some marine – shaped relative to falling Quaternary sea-levels. Farther inland, the drainage responded to these falling base levels by rapid downcutting. In the wetter north and west, the Cainozoic landscape was soon devoured by Quaternary erosion, so that today modest residual hills, such as The Twelve Pins of Connemara, descend abruptly on to extensive lowlands. In the drier south and east, strongly convex valley sides and narrow river terraces suggest that downcutting was also relatively rapid but that, in resistant rocks, less valley widening was accomplished. Where soluble Carboniferous Limestone was exposed as its shale and grit cover was stripped off, the land was lowered exceptionally rapidly. In this way, the central lowlands came to assume their present shape.

In terms of evolution, therefore, Ireland contains three main relief categories: mountain remnants derived from earlier Cainozoic landscapes, broad intermediate plateaux shaped by later Cainozoic planation, and deep valleys and extensive lowlands produced by Quaternary denudation. This sequence is admirably illustrated in the south where the Knockmealdown mountains rear up to 2,609 feet from the drift-mantled Tipperary lowland, only to fall away equally abruptly southwards on to the 600–820-foot late Cainozoic surface, into which the Blackwater valley is deeply incised.

The Pleistocene legacy

The climactic variations of the Quaternary era culminated, as far as Ireland was concerned, in at least two major glaciations each characterized by components of diverse origins which have furnished the landscape with a varied microrelief of immense ecological significance. In view of the related contrasts in drainage, soil, vegetation and land use, one may distinguish simply between a composite Older Drift glaciation whose surviving deposits are commonly strongly weathered and rather featureless at the surface, and a less extensive Newer Drift or last glaciation whose fresh hummocky debris widely mantles the lowlands. Present evidence suggests that the complex Older Drift embraces, apart from its demonstrably very old deposits, certain components which may be equivalent to the main Würm/Weichsel glaciation of Europe, while the much fresher Newer Drift represents the last major Würm/Weichsel glacial episode. The preexisting relief strongly influenced the growth and movement of these glaciers. Early in each cold phase, the marginal uplands generated local glaciers which later pushed down preglacial valleys into the lowlands. As individual glaciers coalesced, a large ice sheet was built up over the central lowlands from which ice streams then radiated outwards, creating a pattern similar to that envisaged for the present Greenland ice cap. Meanwhile, powerful ice streams, originating partly in Scotland, travelled southwards through the Irish Sea basin. As these major ice sheets waned, so the local mountain glaciers temporarily reasserted themselves.

Following a warm phase whose climate and vegetation were not unlike those of today, the Older Drift glaciation was heralded by the establishment of tundra conditions throughout Ireland and by the birth of mountain glaciers. Frost action and solifluction masked this tundra with a crudely sorted sludge of rock waste, as ice from the mountains of Donegal, west Connacht, Wicklow and southwest Ireland began reaching the nearby lowlands. The sea fell away from just above its present level, as the increasing cold began locking up much of the world's ocean waters in expanding ice sheets. Soon, powerful Scottish ice streamed across the north coast and through the North Channel into the Irish Sea basin, restricting the glaciers emerging from the surrounding mountains. Erratics from Scotland and northeast Ireland show that this invading ice crossed Inishowen, reached the Sperrin mountains and Slieve Beagh, and rose 1,800 feet up the Mourne mountains. It dredged marine muds and shells from the Irish Sea floor and plastered them across Ireland's eastern margins as a brown or purple plastic calcareous till containing few stones. Farther south, the main ice stream broke free of the constricting mountains and fanned out into a

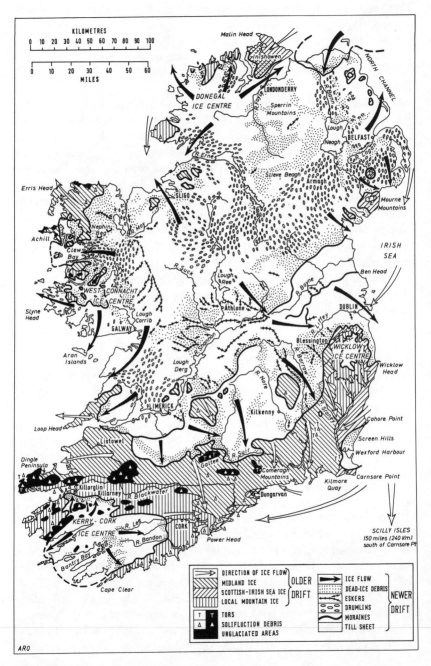

4. *Glaciation*

21

vast ice sheet over the Celtic Sea. Its most westerly component passed across Wexford to enter the limestone corridors of south Waterford and Cork, nearly reaching Power Head. Its most southerly component impinged on the north coast of Devon and Cornwall and just reached the Scilly Isles. As the Irish Sea ice decayed, its meltwaters cut spectacular marginal drainage channels such as the Glen of the Downs and the Scalp along the eastern flanks of the Wicklow mountains.

Meanwhile, indigenous glaciers had coalesced to form a midland ice sheet which spread south carrying Galway granite erratics into Kilkenny and Cork and later moved west across the Shannon estuary and north Kerry. Between Kilmore Quay and Dungarvan, this ice stream was powerful enough to push the waning Irish Sea ice away from the southeast coast. Another component passed across north Mayo going in a northwesterly direction. As this midland ice decayed, its meltwaters cut marginal and overflow channels around the Galtee mountains and near Listowel in north Kerry, while the local ice caps centred over Donegal, west Connacht, Wicklow and southwest Ireland temporarily expanded. Several higher mountains in the south and west projected as nunataks through these encircling glaciers. The interlude following the Older Drift glaciation saw weathering and erosion attack its various deposits.

During most of the Newer Drift or last glaciation, ice streams flowed from sources within Ireland. Although less extensive than the earlier episode, this glaciation has had greater influence on the present landscape because of its recency. As before, outflowing mountain glaciers coalesced to form a midland ice sheet which radiated from an iceshed stretching from Lough Neagh to east Galway. Its southern limits are still clearly defined by a hummocky end moraine that stretches in a broad arc across the south central lowlands. The ice wrapped around the northern flanks of the Wicklow mountains, reaching 1,250 feet due south of Dublin, and its meltwaters became impounded against the mountains to form proglacial lakes at Blessington and Glenasmole. Ice streams that passed across the east coast were deflected by south-flowing Irish Sea ice back onshore as far south as Wicklow Head and again near Wexford Harbour. As the ice was only 1,000 feet thick around Dublin and Limerick, the Castlecomer plateau and the uplands flanking the Shannon at Killaloe, as well as some marginal country in west Mayo and Donegal, remained unglaciated. Higher nunataks in the Mourne and Partry mountains carried separate corrie glaciers which survived the dissolution of the midland ice sheet and only finally melted around 10,000 years ago. Beyond the main ice front, fresh block moraines show that corrie glaciers also existed in the Comeragh, Galtee and Nephin Beg mountains, on Achill, and in the Dingle and Iveragh peninsulas. The Wicklow mountains carried separate valley glaciers, while a local ice cap centred over the Kenmare River spread north to Killarney and Killorglin and east down the Lee, Bride and Bandon valleys but failed to reach the south coast of Cork. Elsewhere, tundra

Part One
The landscape without man

Chapter 1
The physique of Ireland

Ireland is a lowlying country whose broad drift-mantled central lowlands, which commonly lie between 200 and 400 feet about sea-level, are diversified by isolated hills and plateaux and surrounded by a discontinuous upland rim which rarely exceeds 3,000 feet. The physique expresses a subtle interplay between the intensity and duration of the various earth-sculpturing processes on the one hand and the nature and disposition of the underlying rocks on the other. Long before man began carving his own inimitable signature on the countryside, mass wasting and running water had long been the dominant physical processes moulding the landscape. As functions of climate, they naturally varied in intensity with changes of temperature and precipitation but only during the coldest phases of the Pleistocene epoch were they superseded by ice and frost, and then only temporarily. Nevertheless, despite their comparatively short duration, the Pleistocene glaciations have endowed the countryside with a rich legacy of minor landforms and soil parent materials: the uplands which nurtured local glaciers display ice-dressed scenery of remarkable beauty while the lowlands exhibit one of the world's finest landscapes of glacial deposition. Since the glacial interlude closed 10,000 years ago, mass wasting and running water have reasserted their former dominance. Today, Ireland's mild wet climate exerts a profound influence on the country's personality and is expressed physically in high water-tables, numerous lakes, close-textured drainage networks, frequent flooding and rapid decay of chemically weak rocks. Along the 2,000-mile coastline, wave action contributes to a rich variety of shore-zone scenery while, throughout Ireland, the changing base levels of erosion so typical of the past few million years have left a vivid imprint on the relief and drainage generally.

Structure, drainage and landforms – their evolution

Structural framework
Beneath its Pleistocene deposits, Ireland is built up largely of Palaeozoic rocks which bear the firm imprint of two major mountain-building episodes: the older or Caledonian orogeny which began towards the close of the Silurian period, and the younger or Armorican orogeny which began late in Carboniferous times. Except in the extreme south, the crumpling of Precambrian rocks

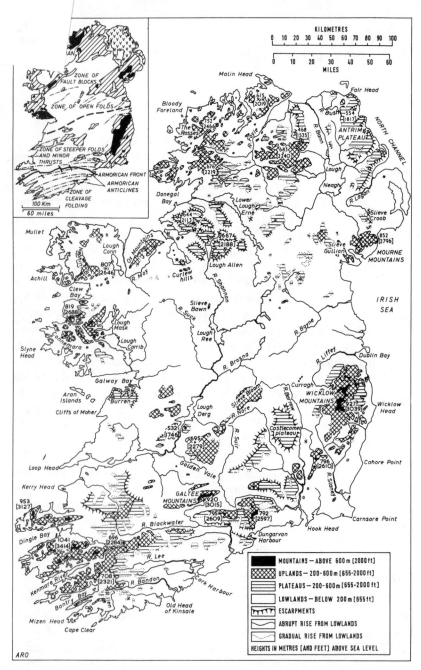

3. The principal landform, drainage and structural elements of the Irish landscape

and Lower Palaeozoic geosynclinal sediments by Caledonian folding along predominantly northeast to southwest lines, together with the emplacement of granite bodies, set the main structural framework of the country. The Caledonian uplands of the northwest form a linear extension of the Scottish Highlands, the Newry axis continues the line of the Southern Uplands and the Leinster axis continues that of the Isle of Man and North Wales. South of a line from Dungarvan to Dingle Bay, later Armorican movements imposed a tectonic grain of east–west folds on Devonian and Carboniferous rocks, continuing the trend of similar structures found in South Wales and southwest England. As the Armorican folds died out in intensity northwards, structures of this episode within the central lowlands were progressively modified by the proximity of pre-existing Caledonian elements. Only in northeast Ireland do Mesozoic and Cainozoic rocks make any significant contribution to the landscape. There, vast sheets of early Cainozoic basalt lavas spilled out across the country burying Mesozoic sediments while granites and other intrusive rocks were emplaced beneath the surface. This igneous activity was a prelude to earth movements which later culminated beyond Ireland in the Alpine orogeny but which were confined locally to the warping and fracturing of the established framework. The Irish Sea basin, a region of sporadic subsidence since Armorican times, was further accentuated by these convulsions and by some marginal faulting – such as the strong strike faults which caused some Antrim basalt and underlying rocks to collapse into the North Channel.

Drainage and landforms

While the Caledonian and Armorican movements set Ireland's main structural framework, subsequent denudation shaped the country's present landforms. Following the Armorican orogeny, the Carboniferous rocks that once largely covered Ireland were subjected to tremendous erosion which soon exposed many older rocks and yielded fresh sediments for the New Red Sandstone deserts. Although Triassic and marine Liassic deposits may have covered much of Ireland, at least temporarily, the net erosional loss resulting from prolonged subaerial denudation had, by Lower Cretaceous times, moulded a broad rolling plain flanked by residual uplands. The only traces of this landscape that may still be identified lie buried beneath later rocks in northeast Ireland but one may reasonably assume that Ireland's rough outlines were blocked out by Mesozoic denudation. During Upper Cretaceous times, the sea spread across Ireland depositing chalk and other materials which now survive mainly beneath the protective Cainozoic basalts in the northeast. That the chalk was once more widespread is suggested by a chalk outlier near Killarney, by chalk and flint debris on the seabed offshore, and by numerous flints in certain beach and glacial deposits – notably in Wexford.

Around 70 million years ago, the Cretaceous sea withdrew from Ireland and the emergent sea floor soon attracted streams which showed scant respect for the buried Caledonian and Armorican structures. Some drainage systems were quite new; others were dominated by streams which had extended their courses across the emerging sea floor from uplands that had suffered only marginal incursion by the chalk sea. An important component of this early Cainozoic drainage pattern comprised south-flowing streams whose general direction is perhaps reflected in the present courses of the Slaney, Barrow and Nore and in the south-flowing sections of the Shannon, Suir, Blackwater, Lee and Bandon. Other important streams undoubtedly drained directly westwards to the Atlantic Ocean. These rivers soon began cutting through the soft Cretaceous cover and other surviving Mesozoic sediments onto the folded Caledonian and Armorican framework with little regard, at least initially, for the grain of the structures thus exhumed. This superimposition of the drainage may explain why such rivers as the Shannon and Barrow, after following seemingly undistinguished courses through the central lowlands, suddenly cut seawards through noteworthy water gaps excavated across resistant rocks. Since superimposition, drainage basins have adjusted in varying degrees to the underlying rock structures. Where competent tributaries have been favoured by these structures, river capture has vastly rearranged several drainage networks of which the trellis patterns of central southern Ireland, dominated by the eastward-flowing stretches of the Blackwater, Lee and Bandon, are spectacular instances.

The present drainage systems of northeast Ireland have developed from streams that arose initially on the early Cainozoic basalts and were later influenced by powerful postbasaltic flexures and faults and by the creation of the Lough Neagh basin. Lough Neagh may once have drained southwards along the Newry-Carlingford weakness zone but the Lower Bann, cutting back along the Bann fault, eventually carried the lake's drainage away northwards against the regional dip of the basalts. A few miles farther east, the Main still retains its southward flow with the dip. The Lagan, working back along the softer Triassic rocks beyond the southeast margins of the basalt, has also poached some of Lough Neagh's drainage.

As these drainage systems developed, so the landscape was gradually worn down at rates varying with the relative resistance of the rocks involved. The abrasive tools used by the rivers in this work were supplied by mass wasting which, under the favourably warm moist Cainozoic climate, was quite rapid. Selective decay and erosion soon produced a vivid contrast between uplands sustained in resistant quartzites and sandstones, and lowlands excavated in limestones and granites which, though mechanically strong, are chemically weak. The weaker formations undoubtedly yielded large quantities of rock waste but, excepting the Lough Neagh clays and tropical laterites derived from the basalts in the north and some pipeclays and lignites in Tipperary and Cork, the paucity of Cainozoic sediments that have survived greatly restricts our understanding of this significant era. Furthermore, because earlier Cainozoic landforms were locally warped and fractured by subsequent earth movements and because later erosion has levelled Ireland so efficiently – only small areas now exceed 1,200 feet while less than 0·25 per cent of the country tops 2,000 feet – few worthwhile suggestions can be made about the nature and origins of this early Cainozoic landscape. Nevertheless, it seems likely that following the late Cretaceous emergence the sea never again wholly engulfed Ireland, that landforms were subsequently shaped by mainly subaerial processes related to intermittently falling base levels of erosion, and that the highest planation surfaces, fragments of which survive on some marginal uplands, are remnants of earlier Cainozoic denudation.

At intermediate levels, notably in the south, extensive plateaux ranging from 600 to 1,200 feet above sea-level are apparently undeformed, and were probably shaped by rivers directly ancestral to the present drainage during later Cainozoic times. Two distinct planation surfaces occur at 600–820 feet and 920–1,080 feet, the lower of which was moulded by subaerial processes attuned to seas, not higher than 500 feet above the present, which completely surrounded Ireland. By this time, the sea had certainly occupied the Irish Sea basin, for derived Pliocene and early Pleistocene marine shells dredged from the basin occur in neighbouring glacial deposits. Undoubtedly, Ireland's location near the edge of the European continental shelf predestined it to be strongly affected by the worldwide changes of sea-level, so characteristic of the Quaternary era, and its coastal margins predictably display both raised and submerged shore features, attributable to these oscillations. For instance, the extensive late Cainozoic surface of Waterford and Cork falls away seaward across a stepped sequence of narrow rock benches – some fluvial, some marine – shaped relative to falling Quaternary sea-levels. Farther inland, the drainage responded to these falling base levels by rapid downcutting. In the wetter north and west, the Cainozoic landscape was soon devoured by Quaternary erosion, so that today modest residual hills, such as The Twelve Pins of Connemara, descend abruptly on to extensive lowlands. In the drier south and east, strongly convex valley sides and narrow river terraces suggest that downcutting was also relatively rapid but that, in resistant rocks, less valley widening was accomplished. Where soluble Carboniferous Limestone was exposed as its shale and grit cover was stripped off, the land was lowered exceptionally rapidly. In this way, the central lowlands came to assume their present shape.

In terms of evolution, therefore, Ireland contains three main relief categories: mountain remnants derived from earlier Cainozoic landscapes, broad intermediate plateaux shaped by later Cainozoic planation, and deep valleys and extensive lowlands produced by Quaternary denudation. This sequence is admirably illustrated in the south where the Knockmealdown mountains rear up to 2,609 feet from the drift-mantled Tipperary lowland, only to fall away equally abruptly southwards on to the 600–820-foot late Cainozoic surface, into which the Blackwater valley is deeply incised.

The Pleistocene legacy

The climactic variations of the Quaternary era culminated, as far as Ireland was concerned, in at least two major glaciations each characterized by components of diverse origins which have furnished the landscape with a varied microrelief of immense ecological significance. In view of the related contrasts in drainage, soil, vegetation and land use, one may distinguish simply between a composite Older Drift glaciation whose surviving deposits are commonly strongly weathered and rather featureless at the surface, and a less extensive Newer Drift or last glaciation whose fresh hummocky debris widely mantles the lowlands. Present evidence suggests that the complex Older Drift embraces, apart from its demonstrably very old deposits, certain components which may be equivalent to the main Würm/Weichsel glaciation of Europe, while the much fresher Newer Drift represents the last major Würm/Weichsel glacial episode. The pre-existing relief strongly influenced the growth and movement of these glaciers. Early in each cold phase, the marginal uplands generated local glaciers which later pushed down preglacial valleys into the lowlands. As individual glaciers coalesced, a large ice sheet was built up over the central lowlands from which ice streams then radiated outwards, creating a pattern similar to that envisaged for the present Greenland ice cap. Meanwhile, powerful ice streams, originating partly in Scotland, travelled southwards through the Irish Sea basin. As these major ice sheets waned, so the local mountain glaciers temporarily reasserted themselves.

Following a warm phase whose climate and vegetation were not unlike those of today, the Older Drift glaciation was heralded by the establishment of tundra conditions throughout Ireland and by the birth of mountain glaciers. Frost action and solifluction masked this tundra with a crudely sorted sludge of rock waste, as ice from the mountains of Donegal, west Connacht, Wicklow and southwest Ireland began reaching the nearby lowlands. The sea fell away from just above its present level, as the increasing cold began locking up much of the world's ocean waters in expanding ice sheets. Soon, powerful Scottish ice streamed across the north coast and through the North Channel into the Irish Sea basin, restricting the glaciers emerging from the surrounding mountains. Erratics from Scotland and northeast Ireland show that this invading ice crossed Inishowen, reached the Sperrin mountains and Slieve Beagh, and rose 1,800 feet up the Mourne mountains. It dredged marine muds and shells from the Irish Sea floor and plastered them across Ireland's eastern margins as a brown or purple plastic calcareous till containing few stones. Farther south, the main ice stream broke free of the constricting mountains and fanned out into a

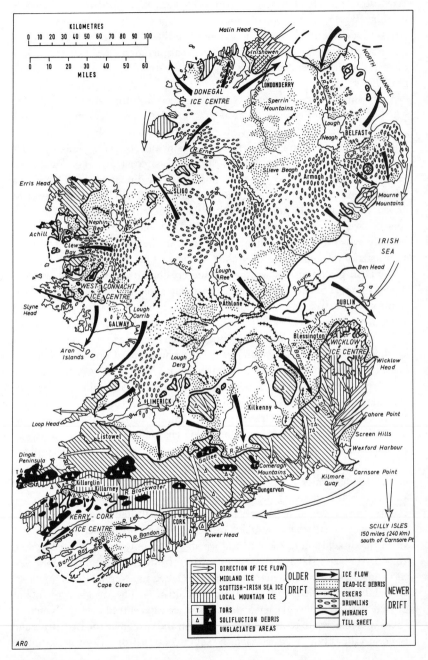

4. Glaciation

vast ice sheet over the Celtic Sea. Its most westerly component passed across Wexford to enter the limestone corridors of south Waterford and Cork, nearly reaching Power Head. Its most southerly component impinged on the north coast of Devon and Cornwall and just reached the Scilly Isles. As the Irish Sea ice decayed, its meltwaters cut spectacular marginal drainage channels such as the Glen of the Downs and the Scalp along the eastern flanks of the Wicklow mountains.

Meanwhile, indigenous glaciers had coalesced to form a midland ice sheet which spread south carrying Galway granite erratics into Kilkenny and Cork and later moved west across the Shannon estuary and north Kerry. Between Kilmore Quay and Dungarvan, this ice stream was powerful enough to push the waning Irish Sea ice away from the southeast coast. Another component passed across north Mayo going in a northwesterly direction. As this midland ice decayed, its meltwaters cut marginal and overflow channels around the Galtee mountains and near Listowel in north Kerry, while the local ice caps centred over Donegal, west Connacht, Wicklow and southwest Ireland temporarily expanded. Several higher mountains in the south and west projected as nunataks through these encircling glaciers. The interlude following the Older Drift glaciation saw weathering and erosion attack its various deposits.

During most of the Newer Drift or last glaciation, ice streams flowed from sources within Ireland. Although less extensive than the earlier episode, this glaciation has had greater influence on the present landscape because of its recency. As before, outflowing mountain glaciers coalesced to form a midland ice sheet which radiated from an iceshed stretching from Lough Neagh to east Galway. Its southern limits are still clearly defined by a hummocky end moraine that stretches in a broad arc across the south central lowlands. The ice wrapped around the northern flanks of the Wicklow mountains, reaching 1,250 feet due south of Dublin, and its meltwaters became impounded against the mountains to form proglacial lakes at Blessington and Glenasmole. Ice streams that passed across the east coast were deflected by south-flowing Irish Sea ice back onshore as far south as Wicklow Head and again near Wexford Harbour. As the ice was only 1,000 feet thick around Dublin and Limerick, the Castlecomer plateau and the uplands flanking the Shannon at Killaloe, as well as some marginal country in west Mayo and Donegal, remained unglaciated. Higher nunataks in the Mourne and Partry mountains carried separate corrie glaciers which survived the dissolution of the midland ice sheet and only finally melted around 10,000 years ago. Beyond the main ice front, fresh block moraines show that corrie glaciers also existed in the Comeragh, Galtee and Nephin Beg mountains, on Achill, and in the Dingle and Iveragh peninsulas. The Wicklow mountains carried separate valley glaciers, while a local ice cap centred over the Kenmare River spread north to Killarney and Killorglin and east down the Lee, Bride and Bandon valleys but failed to reach the south coast of Cork. Elsewhere, tundra mantled with soliflual rock waste stretched across the south and reappeared at intervals along the Atlantic seaboard.

The dissolution of the ice was characterized partly by the decay of large wads of dead ice *in situ* and partly by an orderly retreat of the ice margin, punctuated by stillstands and brief readvances. The former dumped sands and gravels over wide areas to create, after the stranded ice blocks had melted, hummocky kame and kettle-hole moraines interspersed with eskers and crevasse infillings. Such country occupies much of southeast Galway and mid-Ulster and forms the Screen Hills north of Wexford Harbour. The latter produced prominent morainal ridges with feeding eskers formed by the infilling of subglacial river channels leading to the ice margin. The conspicuous esker chains of central Ireland were associated with the steady shrinkage of a sluggish ice cap from east to west. The esker system in the plains of Mayo was related to ice retreating towards Lough Corrib. Several thousand drumlins, streamlined hillocks of

5. A corrie notched into the north slope of Slieve Corragh in the Mourne mountains

6. *Glengesh*

A remote glaciated valley in Donegal whose slopes have been much modified by mass movement since the last glacier disappeared. As the glen opens out northwards small farms growing oats and potatoes amid pastures and rough grazings come to occupy the valley floor and lower hillslopes.

glacial till, cross north central Ireland from Down to Sligo and also occur north of Lough Neagh, in Donegal, in east Mayo passing seawards into Clew Bay, in east Clare and around Bantry Bay. Drumlin country altogether covers 4,000 square miles of Ireland, but although drumlins may provide relatively better land in the otherwise harsh west, poor drainage conditions everywhere restrict their fertility.

In short, the Pleistocene glaciers generally scoured the uplands of rock waste, deepened existing valleys and provided enhanced scenery of vast recreational value. The ice and its meltwaters also plastered variable thicknesses of boulder clay, sand and gravel across the lowlands and mountain glens thereby providing a wide range of parent materials for soil development. Nearly everywhere, post-glacial streams have had to adapt to vastly different physical circumstances from those to which their ancestors were accustomed. Although the main pre-glacial drainage pattern has re-emerged little modified by the glacial interlude, some quite large rivers have been locally deflected from their buried preglacial channels by wads of Pleistocene debris: the Bush and the Bann in the extreme northeast, the Shannon between Killaloe and Limerick, the Erne above Bally-shannon, and the Liffey beneath Dublin are cases in point. Many minor streams have arisen on and still flow across extensive till sheets while sections of the Boyne, Slaney, Suir and Bandon are entrenched in thick outwash deposits fed into their valleys by glacial meltwaters.

The fluctuations of sea-level caused by the growth and decay of the world's ice sheets have left their mark on Ireland's coastal margins. Sometime before the Irish Sea glaciers arrived, the Slaney and the Blackwater had each cut deep channels in response to a base level 150 feet lower than today while, during the last glaciation, sea-level probably fell 400 feet or more below the present. As the ice melted, the sea began drowning the lower portions of the more deeply exca-vated valleys, eventually producing a highly indented coastline. Since the sea rose to its present level around 3400 B.C., only the lesser irregularities have been smoothed out by wave action. Headlands have been cliffed and beach materials have been thrown across minor inlets but the majestic rias of the south and west

7. Glenree
A former glacial drainage channel in the Ox mountains.

coasts survive little impaired. Meanwhile, the slow uplift of the land that had been depressed beneath the ice, and which raised and tilted beaches formed during the transgression, has ceased.

Physique – regional contrasts

The Caledonian country of the north and west

This discontinuous region contains much spectacular scenery but frequent strong winds, drenching rains, widespread blanket bog and poor soils combine to produce some of the least hospitable country in Ireland. Fortunately, its rugged mountain clusters and barren uplands are commonly fringed by coastal lowlands, dissected by deep glens and interrupted by drift-mantled corridors from the central lowlands which provide man with space for agriculture and settlement and allow access between the interior and the coast. The legacies of prolonged denudation and intense glaciation are to be seen everywhere. The wild but picturesque Atlantic coast comprises an alternation of shallow island-studded bays, deeper fiords like Killary Harbour and Lough Swilly, bold head-lands and impressive quartzite cliffs such as Slieve League (1,972 feet), Slieve Tooey (1,515 feet) and Horn Head (626 feet) in Donegal, and Croaghaun (2,192 feet) and Minaun (1,530 feet) on Achill Island.

In Donegal, the Caledonian trend is clearly expressed in the northeast-southwest grain of the relief which is dominated by quartzite ridges culminating in stark conical peaks like Errigal (2,466 feet) and Muckish (2,197 feet), by rounded granite uplands such as the Derryveagh mountains (2,240 feet), and by desolate schist country as in the Sperrin mountains (2,240 feet). At inter-mediate levels, bleak dissected moorlands occur around 1,000–1,400 feet in Gweedore and southeast of the Blue Stack mountains (2,219 feet) and at 600–800 feet elsewhere. Apart from the quartzite cliffs, high ground rarely reaches the coast which is more often fringed by rugged glaciated lowlands such as the lake-studded granite country in The Rosses. Although temporarily interrupted by glaciation, prolonged fluvial erosion has been mainly responsible for excavat-ing weak structures to form, for example, the Gweebarra corridor, the wide Foyle lowland, and Glenelly and Glenlark in the Sperrin mountains.

After plunging beneath Carboniferous rocks around Lower Lough Erne and Donegal Bay, Caledonian structures re-emerge near Manorhamilton to define a narrow 60-mile-long ridge culminating in the Ox mountains (1,786 feet). This ridge is breached by noteworthy water gaps where the Owenmore and Moy rivers cut seawards at Collooney and Foxford respectively. The Caledonian country of west Connacht is divided by the Clew Bay lowland into the desolate moorlands of northwest Mayo and the dissected mountain clusters of southwest Mayo and west Galway. Quartzites again form prominent ridges, such as the Nephin Beg range (2,369 feet) and the Maumturk mountains (2,307 feet), and

8. *Errigal (751 m, 2,466 ft)*
A prominent quartzite mountain in Donegal.

scree-mantled conical peaks such as The Twelve Pins (2,395 feet), Croagh
Patrick (2,510 feet) and solitary Nephin (2,646 feet). Equally spectacular mountains, deeply sapped by glaciation, are carved from Ordovician rocks north and
east of Killary Harbour, namely Mweelrea (2,688 feet), the Sheeffry hills
(2,504 feet) and the Partry mountains (2,239 feet). Some plateau country lies
west of Galway city and around the Nephin Beg mountains but, more commonly, rapid destruction of the comparatively weak schists and granites has
caused most residual mountains to descend abruptly on to extensive glaciated
lowlands. In the ice-scoured, lake-studded Connemara lowland, as elsewhere
along the Atlantic seaboard, man's activities are now normally confined to
farming scattered patches of drift, cutting the blanket bog for turf, and using
the remaining country as rough grazing. The eastern margins of west Connacht
are bounded by lakes, such as Loughs Conn, Carra, Mask and Corrib, which
occupy basins where streams from the less permeable Caledonian structures
flow on to soluble limestones.

The Caledonian country of the east

Underlain by Lower Palaeozoic rocks and igneous intrusions, this region is divided into two dissimilar areas by the central lowlands which reach the coast along a 50-mile-wide front north of Dublin. To the north lies the Newry axis, to the south the Leinster axis. The Newry axis dominates a roughly triangular area stretching from Belfast Lough southwest to Longford and then east to the coast near Drogheda. Prolonged denudation has reduced the contorted Ordovician and Silurian shales and grits to low rolling country, 200–600 feet above sea-level, with some higher land reaching 800–1,200 feet in south Armagh and east Cavan. Most bedrock, however, is masked by glacial deposits including several thousand drumlins which, with their intervening peat bogs, marshes and lakes, impart a distinctive personality to the region. Low drift cliffs form most of the coastline with partly submerged drumlins appearing in Strangford Lough. Major uplands occur only where igneous intrusions have been recently exposed along the Newry axis. Caledonian granite forms some hills between Slieve Croob (1,755 feet) and the Louth border but underlies lowland at Crossdoney near Cavan town. Cainozoic granite outcropping over 53 square miles forms the prominent Mourne mountains which sweep down to the sea from Slieve Donard (2,796 feet). During the glacial epoch, these deeply dissected mountains were sufficiently high to generate local glaciers, intense frost action and strong solifluction which have mantled their lower slopes with thick rock waste while exposing bare crags and pinnacles at higher elevations. Slieve Gullion (1,894 feet) and the Carlingford peninsula are both dominated by dissected Cainozoic ring dykes, the low central portion of the Carlingford complex being encircled by a gabbro rim which reaches 1,935 feet in Slieve Foye. Many northwest-trending Cainozoic dykes provide minor relief in Down and Armagh, some as rough ridges, others as trenches.

Farther south, the Leinster axis may be traced for 120 miles from Rockabill off Skerries to the east Waterford coast. The axis is dominated by a Caledonian granite batholith intruded into strongly folded Ordovician shales that have been altered to mica-schists along the contact zone. Although temporarily exposed during the Upper Palaeozoic, the granite has been mainly revealed piecemeal during and since Cainozoic times and now covers 625 square miles. Its outcrop extends from Dun Laoghaire southwest for 70 miles to Brandon Hill (1,703 feet), but is never wider than 18 miles. Wherever the granite has just lost or is still losing its protective mica-schist roof, it forms bold uplands such as the Wicklow mountains and Blackstairs ridge (2,610 feet) whose rough asymmetry clearly reflects the steep western face and the gentler eastern flanks of the batholith. The Wicklow mountains, reaching 3,039 feet in schist-capped Lugnaquillia, form Ireland's most extensive upland above 1,000 feet. Their rounded summits and subdued convex slopes stand out in strong contrast to the ragged mica-schist hills such as Djouce (2,385 feet), and to the scenic glens like

Glenmacnass, Glendalough and Glenmalure that become deeply incised as they cross the granite–mica-schist junction farther east. Where the granite was exposed some time ago, as around Tullow, it has been reduced to broad lowlands. Lower hills, bold quartzite peaks like the Great Sugar Loaf (1,654 feet), fragmentary upland plains such as the Calary plateau, entrenched valleys and narrow drift-mantled coastal lowlands typify east Wicklow. Southwards, Wexford is mainly lowland, thickly plastered with drift through which a few isolated steepsided hills such as the Tara Hill volcanics (833 feet) and the Forth mountain quartzites (779 feet) protrude. The low rocky headlands of the smoothly curving coast are linked by broad bays backed by sand dunes or low drift cliffs, and by lengthy sand and shingle spits thrown across shallow inlets. The drainage of southeast Ireland has three main components: trunk streams like the Slaney, Barrow and Nore which probably owe their anomalous courses across the Caledonian country to superimposition; other mainstreams which drain either northwest or southeast away from the central waterparting of the Wicklow and Blackstairs mountains; and major tributaries which have excavated strike vales and effected several river captures, notably along the eastern margins of the Wicklow mountains. The uplands and the Wicklow glens have been strongly modified by glacial erosion while lowland drainage patterns have been frequently deranged or impeded by glacial deposits. Thus the Liffey often departs from its preglacial course while most of Wexford's small streams flow across drift.

The Armorican ridges and valleys of the south

Structural controls are clearly expressed in the parallel ridges and valleys of the south where the Armorican movements created broad anticlines and synclines that trend due west across Waterford and east Cork but turn westsouthwest in west Cork and Kerry. Denudation has since shaped linear uplands from the anticlinal Devonian sandstones, confining the less durable Carboniferous limestones and shales that once covered the Devonian sediments to synclinal valleys. In south Cork, the Carboniferous facies changes to slates and grits, thus lessening the topographic contrast with Devonian rocks. As the fold axes rise westwards across Cork, the synclinal valleys narrow and the anticlinal ridges broaden, reaching mountainous proportions in Kerry. The Armorican front, the northern limit to this main fold zone, finds surface expression in sandstone uplands which plunge into a 100-mile-long corridor between Dungarvan and Dingle Bay.

South of the Armorican front, the country is separated by the Derrynasaggart mountains (2,133 feet) and the Shehy ridge (1,797 feet) into two contrasting parts. East of this watershed, the Blackwater, Lee, Bandon and Argideen rivers occupy east-pitching synclines and drain the dissected plateaux of Cork and Waterford. The latter are enclosed by a broken upland arc formed by the Ilen–

Bandon watershed and the bleak Shehy and Derrynasaggart moorlands to the west, the Boggeragh (2,118 feet) and Nagles (1,406 feet) mountains to the north and, beyond the Blackwater–Dungarvan corridor, the bold Knockmealdown mountains (2,609 feet) and the Comeragh–Monavullagh massif (2,597 feet). Two later Cainozoic land surfaces and several narrower Quaternary benches, ranging in all from over 1,000 feet down to abrupt 200-foot-high coastal cliffs,

9. West Cork landscape
Near Skibbereen, looking east. The grain of the Devonian sandstones is clearly expressed in the trend of the ridges. Small scattered farmsteads exploit the intervening patchwork of better land which is commonly underlain by glacial debris or alluvium.

compose the often poorly drained plateaux. The country drains towards trunk streams arranged in an unusual trellis pattern for which an explanation has already been suggested. For most of their length, the main rivers flow east but, rather than pursue easy courses through broad synclinal lowlands to the sea, they turn suddenly south through magnificent water gaps cut through successive sandstone ridges to reach the sea in picturesque drowned estuaries. At Cappoquin, the Blackwater turns away from an obvious outlet through the Dungarvan corridor and cuts seawards for 15 miles across the Drum Hills, Clashmore and Youghal anticlines. The Lee breaches the Great Island and Ballycotton anticlines, and the Bandon, Argideen and lesser inlets cut through coastal ridges farther west.

West of the above area, the mountainous sandstone peninsulas of Kerry and west Cork are separated by impressive rias that occupy west-pitching downfolds, largely floored by partly submerged Carboniferous rocks. The dissected pre-glacial landscape was profoundly modified by local ice caps which, at their maximum, radiated from an iceshed over the Kenmare River and spilled over the mountains into mid-Cork and mid-Kerry. Most higher summits, such as massive Mangerton (2,756 feet), Stoompa (2,281 feet), Purple mountain (2,739 feet), the sharp Macgillycuddy's Reeks (3,414 feet), and several peaks in the Iveragh peninsula, escaped regional glaciation but were deeply gutted by corrie glaciers and mantled with frost-shattered debris. In the Dingle peninsula, the crests of Brandon mountain (3,127 feet), Beenoskee (2,713 feet) and Slieve Mish (2,798 feet) also remained unglaciated. At lower levels, however, outflowing glaciers scoured the mountain slopes, deepened existing valleys, breached watershed cols such as the Gap of Dunloe, deposited thick drift on the lowlands and then, as the ice withdrew, meltwaters cut such impressive channels as the Pass of Keimaneigh. The Upper Lake, the Long Range and Muckross Lake near Killarney each occupy ice-gouged rock basins, while Loughs Leane and Caragh are impounded behind crescentic moraines dumped at the mouths of mountain glens.

The central lowlands

Drift-mantled lowlands dominate central Ireland and frequently penetrate the upland rim to reach the coast. The most extensive lowlands overlie almost horizontal but sometimes strongly folded Carboniferous Limestone which usually rests conformably upon a platform of Devonian rocks but often overlaps directly onto the Caledonian framework. Likewise, the lowlands frequently transgress beyond the limestones on to Lower Palaeozoic rocks while their rivers often cut seawards across Caledonian structures. The levelling processes, however, have yet to complete their work. Large residual plateaux survive wherever Carboniferous shales and grits either still protect or have only just been stripped from the underlying limestones. Furthermore, linear uplands occur where sharp Armorican upfolds have caused resistant older rocks to be exposed by erosion. Typically, the central lowlands average 200–400 feet above sea-level, harbour assorted Pleistocene debris, numerous raised bogs and some large lakes like Lough Corrib (65 square miles), Lower Lough Erne (53 square miles) and Lough Ree (39 square miles), and are further diversified by low hills of reef limestone and volcanic rocks. In Fermanagh, Sligo, Clare and elsewhere the limestone underground is riddled with caves while, west of the Shannon, the drift cover thins and bare limestone pavements often occupy the surface. The lowlands drain mainly to the 230-mile-long Shannon which, after flowing for much of its course at about 120 feet, cuts deeply into the Slieve Bernagh-Arra massif at Killaloe and reaches sea level at Limerick only 12 miles away. Broad middle reaches that give way suddenly to steeper narrower channels towards their mouths are in fact common to many Irish rivers. The Barrow (119 miles long), Nore (72 miles), Suir (114 miles), Erne (84 miles) and Boyne (70 miles) are other important rivers draining the lowlands.

Several remnants of later Cainozoic planation survive as plateaux around the lowlands. Some are composed of shales, sandstones, grits and thin coal seams overlying the Carboniferous Limestone, and are sometimes optimistically termed coalfields. The sandstones and grits often form prominent marginal escarpments around otherwise poorly drained moorlands. Thus the desolate country south of the Shannon estuary is flanked by an abrupt escarpment (1,189 feet) overlooking the west Limerick lowlands and, farther west, by the bold Stacks mountains (1,170 feet) above Tralee. North of the Shannon, a similarly ill-drained, rush-infested plateau reaches 1,284 feet on Slieve Callan. The Castlecomer plateau occupies a broad synclinal basin whose rim rises abruptly from the Nore and Barrow valleys to over 1,100 feet. Farther south-west, similar structures form the Slieve Ardagh escarpment (1,132 feet). Bleak, inhospitable moorlands also enclose the upper Shannon and middle Erne basins, reaching 2,188 feet in Cuilcagh and 1,927 feet in Slieve Anierin.

Other marginal plateaux are formed of Carboniferous Limestone that has more or less just lost its protective cover rock but has not yet had time to be reduced to lowland. Well-jointed, gently dipping limestones form the spectacular Burren, a karst landscape in northwest Clare characterized by bare limestone pavements, terraces and cliffs, by underground drainage systems, and by enclosed basins as at Carran which are occupied in wet weather by turloughs or seasonal lakes. The Burren limestones culminate in Slievecarran (1,073 feet). Wherever the drainage passes from impervious shales on to the underlying limestones, notably along the eastern margins of Slieve Elva (1,134 feet), streams commonly disappear underground through swallow holes. Similar bare limestone topography occurs in the Aran Islands offshore and at lower levels in Galway. Massive limestones also form the imposing tabular hills of the Yeats Country, notably the Dartry mountains (2,113 feet) whose sheer cliffs are so finely displayed in Ben Bulben (1,730 feet) and above picturesque Glencar and Glenade.

The posthumous Caledonian influence on the Armorican folds is clearly expressed in the northeast–southwest trend of Slieve Bloom (1,734 feet) and other isolated uplands which protrude through the Carboniferous Limestone. Many such inliers contain bowls of Silurian shale exposed, for example between the Galtee (3,015 feet) and Ballyhoura (1,696 feet) mountains, in the Silvermines mountains (2,279 feet) and east of Slievenamon (2,368 feet), along anticlinal axes partly ringed by Devonian sandstone escarpments. The Curlew Hills (863 feet), Slieve Bawn (864 feet) and Mount Mary (537 feet) are low inliers in the north central lowlands.

The Cainozoic basalt country of the northeast

Cainozoic volcanic activity has profoundly influenced the scenery of this small but distinct physical region. The basalt lavas were once thicker and more wide-spread than today but, although they are still 2,600 feet thick beneath Lough Neagh, fracturing and denudation have now restricted them to 1,550 square miles, mainly in Antrim and east Derry. The surviving lavas form a synclinal basin centred along the wide, drift-mantled lower Bann valley. Lough Neagh (153 square miles) occupies a warped and downfaulted basin farther south where Cainozoic lake clays and lignites, up to 1,148 feet thick, underlie ill-drained lowlands. The syncline's eastern limb forms the dreary peat-covered Antrim plateau (800–1,500 feet) which culminates in Trostan (1,817 feet). Its outer margins form a striking escarpment of black basalt resting upon thin white chalk, which overlooks the North Channel and is dissected by the secluded Glens of Antrim. Farther south, a similar escarpment towers over the Lagan valley and Belfast Lough, both partly floored with Triassic sandstones and marls. The dipslope is drained by the Six Mile Water and left bank tributaries of the Main to Lough Neagh and by the Bush directly to the north coast, where successive lava flows characterized by columnar joints are well displayed in the remarkable Giant's Causeway. The syncline's western limb forms another bold escarpment, overlooking the Roe valley in mid-Derry, which culminates in Benbradagh (1,535 feet) above Dungiven and in Binevenagh (1,260 feet), with its chaotic landslips, towering above Lough Foyle. Elsewhere, volcanic plugs exposed by erosion of the lava often form prominent dolerite hills, such as Slemish (1,437 feet) on the plateau and Tievebulliagh (1,346 feet) and Carn-money Hill (766 feet) along its margins. Dolerite sills compose Scrabo Hill near Newtownards and bold Fair Head at Antrim's northeast tip. Generally, as the protective basalts have been removed so the soft Mesozoic sediments beneath have also been eroded and thus only very locally do the latter influence scenery, notably in the narrow chalk downs behind White Park and Murlough Bays in north Antrim.

33

10. The Giant's Causeway, County Antrim
Cainozoic basalt lava fractured by hexagonal joints.

Chapter 2
Weather and climate

Some 2,500 years ago, the relatively warm dry sub-Boreal climate of Bronze Age Ireland gave way to the wetter, more stormy sub-Atlantic climate which, with minor fluctuations, has persisted ever since. Summers became cooler and cloudier and evaporation diminished. This change was but one of several climatic variations that postglacial Ireland experienced and which had such impact on the vegetation. For man it was very significant. The deterioration set in just before the arrival in Ireland of the Gaelic-speaking peoples who were to play such an important role in shaping the landscape. These and later colonizers thus enacted their various parts beneath a similar canopy of mild, moist and changeable weather. Generally speaking, the weather pattern established some 2,500 years ago has bestowed a distinctive quality on the landscape and upon human activity although woodland clearance, drainage schemes, agricultural practices and urban growth have, by altering the climate near the ground, influenced the habitability of some areas.

Ireland's weather reflects its mid-latitude oceanic position which places it in the path of the relatively warm North Atlantic Drift and of moisture-laden airstreams, depressions and fronts throughout the year. Some rain may fall on two days in every three but, in reality, two consecutive days are rarely alike. Irish people talk of the weather with quiet resignation and gratitude. When, as often happens, warm clinging air and persistent drizzle invade the country from the Atlantic they speak of 'a soft day, thanks be to God'. With frequent winds, the sky is ever changing. Sullen threatening sheets of grey cloud, enshrouding mist, drizzle and heavier rain commonly alternate with glittering beams of sunlight and patches of blue sky that penetrate broken clouds driven before the wind. The contrast of delicate light and menacing shade adds further tone to the green, brown and purple patchwork of the landscape.

Ireland extends through only 4° of latitude and no point is more than 70 miles from the encircling seas which modify the thermal and moisture characteristics of all approaching airstreams. Thus, as a statistical mean of daily weather conditions throughout the year, the climate reveals a more even rhythm than elsewhere in Europe. Seasons merge imperceptibly into each other. Compared even with Britain, Ireland commonly experiences less warmth in summer, less cold in winter, more cloud, more days of rain but less snow. Nevertheless, whilst mild winters, cool summers, cloudiness, persistent rainfall and frequent winds typify the Irish climate, they can all be equalled or exceeded somewhere in Britain.

General circulation and the weather

Ireland's notoriously variable weather is dominated at all seasons by frontal depressions that form between unlike airmasses over the North Atlantic and then move east towards the British Isles. Cool moist maritime polar and warm moist maritime tropical airmasses are of paramount importance in this conflict but the former, in its many varieties, is the most common type to reach Ireland. Maritime polar air originates over the icy wastes of the Arctic but as it passes south across the comparatively warm North Atlantic, it is warmed from below, absorbs moisture, becomes unstable and develops cumulus and thundery cumulonimbus cloud through the intermittent ascent of warm moist air into the cold airstream. Such air reaches Ireland as a strong westerly or northwesterly airstream accompanied by cold blustery winds and heavy rain, followed by bright cool weather with showers. Its leading edge often forms the cold front of a mature depression. When a deep depression forms southwest of Ireland, maritime polar air may penetrate far south into the Atlantic before approaching the country from the southwest as a warmer airstream that is relatively stable at the surface and provides much low stratus cloud and drizzle in winter, and clearer weather in summer. Many depressions may in fact have warm sectors of maritime polar air from this direction whenever cyclogenesis occurs between two differing maritime polar airmasses over the Atlantic. In winter maritime Arctic air may reach Ireland directly from the north as a strong, bitterly cold, highly unstable airstream whose gale force winds and sharp snow and hail showers are felt fully along exposed north-facing coasts and mountains. To leeward the air becomes drier, and cold but sunny weather may spread across the country. Such outbreaks may bring cold spells as late as May. Depressions that form wholly within unstable polar air provide cold, showery and unsettled weather. When such 'polar air depressions' are large and deep they sometimes bring the heaviest winter snowfalls to the north and west of Ireland.

Maritime tropical air forms over the Azores–Bermuda anticyclone and as it moves north its lower layers are cooled by the underlying sea, its relative humidity rises towards saturation point and very little uplift of this moist surface air is normally required to form extensive sheets of low cloud. Such uplift usually occurs along the North Atlantic Polar Front where warm moist maritime tropical air is forced to rise over a shallow wedge of colder denser surface air from the north and thereby initiate a depression. Maritime tropical air commonly reaches Ireland as a humid southwesterly airstream in the warm sector of a travelling depression whose centre lies well north of the country. The warm front along its leading edge is characterized by gentle to moderate rainfall and rising temperature. If the airstream's motion is slight, widespread sea fog will mantle the coast. Generally, however, it moves briskly and with much turbulence over the cool Atlantic so that saturated air is carried up to form extensive low stratus or stratocumulus cloud. In winter the cloud thickens on passing across the still cooler coast to form a dull grey canopy associated with poor visibility, drizzle and mild weather. In summer the cloudbase may rise and break into detached cumulus over the warmer land beyond the coast to bring fine weather with average temperatures. Sometimes maritime tropical air may reach Ireland as a broad flow deflected around the west and north margins of an anticyclone centred over France or Spain.

Airmasses from other sources are less frequent visitors to Ireland than to Britain and are less prolonged when they do arrive. In summer, persistent cool air off the Irish coast soon wards off any warm airstreams that may venture across from Europe whilst shallow depressions easily disperse brief warm dry spells. In winter, the one or two outbreaks of continental polar air from Siberia or Scandinavia, that give Britain its most severe weather, reach Ireland less often. Thus whilst continental polar air wrought prolonged havoc throughout the British Isles during the 1947 winter, a similar outbreak in the 1963 winter, that caused extremely cold weather and a heavy snow cover to persist over southern England, had little effect on an Ireland wrapped in an oceanic airstream. More commonly brief outbursts of such cold air across the relatively warm Irish Sea bring instability and snow showers to eastern Ireland.

The persistence of various airstreams over Ireland is closely related to the position of the North Atlantic Polar Front and to the passage of depressions along that front. Cyclonic activity is more marked in winter when the main storm track passes from eastern North America towards the Norwegian Sea along a course just north of the British Isles. Travelling at some 30–40 m.p.h., depressions develop rapidly and commonly reach Ireland as occlusions wherein the warm sector has been lifted off the surface by the swiftly advancing front of a maritime polar airstream. The latter will then cover the country exclusively with bright showery weather. When the following airstream is relatively warm, a warm occlusion will give stratiform rain clouds and weather similar to a warm front. When the following airstream is cold, a cold occlusion will give more localized cumuliform rain clouds and weather not unlike a cold front. In summer the main storm track lies farther north across the Atlantic so that intense primary depressions affect Ireland less frequently. At all seasons, however, depressions may take any number of paths south of the Polar Front while secondary depressions, forming along fronts well south of the primary depressions, may give cloud and precipitation at any time. Prolonged summer rainfall is commonly associated with depressions moving at less than 20 m.p.h.

Occasionally anticyclones may give more settled weather. In summer warm anticyclones, detached masses of deep subsiding air up to 1,500 miles across, may spread northeastwards from the Azores to give bright sunny weather with flat-based cumulus and light easterly or southerly winds. Such weather commonly occurs in May and June when the paucity of rainfall may retard crop growth. Even so, the movement of such air over the surrounding seas often generates much stratiform cloud near the coast. Whilst the fine weather that accompanies the expanding Azores anticyclone is eagerly awaited by most Irish people each year, they are as often as not poorly rewarded for their patience. In autumn and winter following a rainy spell, warm anticyclonic conditions associated with damp ground, clear skies and quiet stagnant air may cause radiation fog to develop over land and drift out to sea. Such fogs may persist until dispersed by increasing winds. Otherwise warm anticyclones tend to give gloomy overcast weather inland in winter and along the coasts at all seasons. In winter expanding cold anticyclones from Europe may bring clear skies and low temperatures to eastern Ireland but these conditions rarely reach the west. Short-lived cold anticyclones may also form in maritime polar air and reach Ireland behind intense depressions moving off the Atlantic. More commonly, persistent anticyclones well south and east of Ireland are reflected in the general circulation of the atmosphere over the country.

Elements of the Irish climate

Temperature, frost and sunshine

Ireland's oceanic situation and airstream circulation are clearly reflected in its equable temperatures. The annual range at Valentia is only 8° C (14° F) and at Dublin only 10° C (18° F). Extreme heat and cold are virtually unknown. Ireland shares with Britain rather higher winter temperatures than other countries in similar latitudes. Mean January temperatures vary from 6·5–7° C (44–45° F) in the southwest to 4·5–6° C (40–43° F) elsewhere. The warming effect of the sea is reflected in the isotherms which parallel the coast so that the coldest parts of the country lie in the north centre. During the period 1921–50, the mean January temperature at Armagh was 4·5° C (40·2° F) and at Aldergrove 4·3° C (39·7° F). In February the coldest month for the encircling seas, surface waters vary from 6·5–7° C (44–45° F) along the east coast to 8·5–9° C (47–48° F) along the west coast. In summer the sea exerts less influence so that mean July temperatures vary latitudinally from 14° C (57° F) in north Donegal to 15·5° C (60° F) over southeast Ireland. July is the warmest month at most inland localities such as Armagh which averages 15° C (59·3° F). However, the surrounding seas are warmest during August with 13·3° C (56° F) off Antrim and Down and 16° C (61° F) off west Cork so that Valentia reaches its maximum temperature at that time.

Frost, while common in winter throughout east and central Ireland, is rare in the west. At Markree in inland Sligo frost has been recorded in every month

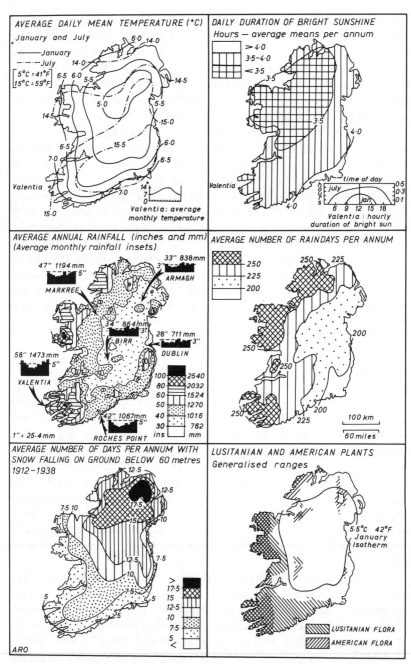

11. *Elements of Irish climate and vegetation*

Climatic data based on the *Climatological Atlas of the British Isles*, H.M.S.O., 1952; averages are for the period 1901–30 adopted by the World Meteorological Organization, unless otherwise stated.

except July while at Armagh and Dublin only June, July and August are frost free. In contrast Roches Point in Cork and Cahersiveen in Kerry are frost free from May to September inclusive. Indeed, mild winters, adequate moisture and relatively few frosts help to explain the luxuriance with which Mediterranean evergreen plants can flourish in the southwest whilst there is a marked check to plant growth farther east. Spring spreads across Ireland from the southwest to reach the northeast three weeks later.

Owing to the frequent cloud cover, Ireland receives only 27–35 per cent of the bright sunshine possible throughout the year. Only southeast Wexford receives more than 35 per cent but this compares reasonably well with most resorts of southern England that obtain about 40 per cent. The coastal zone from Arklow to Cork Harbour receives on average 4 hours of sunshine daily throughout the year but this varies from less than 2 hours in January to more than $6\frac{1}{2}$ hours in June when even northwest Ireland has more than 5 hours daily. Armagh receives 1,265 hours of bright sunshine or 28 per cent of the 4,490 hours possible in a year. Birr and Claremorris receive similar amounts to Armagh but Dublin and Cork receive some 1,390 hours and Carrick-on-Suir 1,430 hours of bright sunshine per annum. May and June are commonly the sunniest months so that insufficient sunshine later in the summer frequently hinders the ripening of the harvest.

Precipitation, humidity and evaporation

Rainfall in Ireland is not as great as is often suggested although drought rarely occurs. It is the frequency and persistence of the rain rather than its volume, combined with high relative humidity and feeble evaporation that give the Irish climate its distinctive quality. The average relative humidity at Valentia is 84 per cent ranging from 81·2 per cent in May to 87·2 per cent in December when humidity is fairly uniform over the British Isles. In May, however, when relative humidity averages less than 60 per cent over central England, western Ireland still shows values exceeding 75 per cent. The mean annual saturation deficit, the difference between the actual vapour pressure and the saturation vapour pressure, even in the driest parts of Ireland is smaller than that of most of England and Wales and large areas of Scotland. It thus takes little frontal or orographic uplift to condense this moist air into cloud and eventually to cause rain.

Most rainfall is associated with frontal activity but falls increase as moist airstreams pass inland from the Atlantic and are forced to rise and cool over mountains. Areas of heavier rainfall and higher relief thus closely correspond. The lowlands generally experience between 30 and 50 inches of rainfall annually while west Offaly and a small coastal area between Dublin Bay and Clogher Head have less than 30 inches. Dublin experienced only 28·25 inches per annum between 1901 and 1930 but only 8 miles farther south Glenasmole in the

Wicklow mountains had 53 inches. In the north, the recording period 1916–50, when Armagh averaged 33 inches, Belfast 38 inches, Derry 42 inches and Belleek 48 inches of annual rainfall, was slightly wetter than the preceding period 1881–1915. Larger uplands all receive more than 50 inches, with 80–100 inches falling in the mountains of west Connacht and Kerry where some localities may have 150 inches annually. Lowland stations nestling beneath these mountains also experience moderately heavy rainfall. Thus Valentia receives 58 inches, Kenmare 65 inches and Garinish Island 70 inches. Secondary maxima occur in the eastern uplands where the Antrim plateau receives 50 inches, the Sperrin mountains 61 inches and the Wicklow and Mourne mountains well over 60 inches. Rainfall variability, deviation from the mean average, ranges from only 6 per cent in Donegal to 12 per cent along the southeast coast and is thus generally less than in Britain.

The number of days on which rain (0·01 inch or more rainfall in 24 hours) falls in an average year is exceedingly high, ranging from 180 in the comparatively sunny southeast to over 250 in the west. Half Ireland can expect rain on two days in every three and the western mountains three days in every four. There is a marked winter rainfall maximum in the west but throughout central and eastern Ireland August is the wettest month of the year, a feature that retards the harvesting of wheat and barley. Everywhere there is a rainfall minimum in late spring, with April, May or June as the driest month, and a second minimum in September. Armagh averages 3·4 inches in August but only 2·0 inches in March. In winter, snow may cover the mountains of the north and east for several weeks but at lower levels it rarely persists for more than a few days. Thus while snow falls on Armagh on an average of seventeen days in a year it only lies on the surface for about half that period. Snow or sleet may be observed to fall on Dublin, Birr and Malin Head over twelve days in a year but only on about three mornings will it be found lying on the surface. The south and southwest coasts rarely experience falling snow.

Persistent, frequent and well-distributed rainfall from abundant cloud and often totally overcast skies combines with only moderate temperatures to restrict evaporation from damp surfaces and transpiration from plants. Thus Aldergrove near Lough Neagh has an annual average potential evaporation of only 16·3 inches which thereby renders its 33 inches of rainfall highly effective. Even during the comparatively warm six months between April and September, rainfall exceeds evaporation by 4 inches. Whilst water is undoubtedly a valuable resource its superabundance from time to time poses many vexing problems for agriculture. Not surprisingly grass is the one crop well suited to the climate whilst most farmers speak only of 'saving the harvest'. Indeed, were climatic factors allowed to prevail over economic considerations, wheat might not be grown. Frequent rainfall and low evaporation are also reflected in the luxuriance of ferns, mosses, liverworts and other moisture-loving plants, in the spread of aquatic plants well beyond lakes and streams, in widespread peat bogs, and in generally poor drainage. With low winter evaporation values, discharge from Irish rivers is predictably at its highest from October through March. Nevertheless at other times of the year, the generation of hydro-electric power and other means of using the water resource more efficiently are sometimes beset with problems arising from abnormal fluctuations of rainfall and stream discharge.

Wind

Because depressions move generally eastwards across Ireland while higher pressure occurs to the south and east, moderate to strong westerly winds are common at all seasons. At Blacksod Bay, in Mayo, 75 per cent of the wind has a westerly component; at Dublin the figure is 65 per cent, and at Valentia 62 per cent. Such winds frequently reach gale force and winds of 90-100 m.p.h. are not uncommon along the exposed west coast. Many former light railways in Donegal, Clare and Kerry would cease operations when winds reached 80 m.p.h. However, while prevailing westerly winds are a statistical reality, the passage of numerous secondary depressions, troughs and fronts across Ireland generates wind from all other quarters. Thus, although most fishing harbours along the east coast are located with a view to protection from prevailing westerlies, dominant northeasterly winds cause much erosion of soft boulder clay cliffs and a net southward transport of beach materials north of Dublin.

The effect of the persistent westerly winds is vividly expressed in the vegetation, particularly in the west. Trees and shrubs are stunted and, owing to the killing of all twigs that face west, weirdly streamlined in sympathy with the prevailing wind. Halophytic plants, adapted to salt spray, often grow at heights of 200 to 300 feet above sea-level on exposed cliffs while a *Plantago* sward, an association of dwarf herbs dominated by two shore-zone plantains, is widespread on the west coast. The extent to which the wind determines the upper limit of tree growth in the mountains is disputed. As D. A. Webb (in Meenan and Webb, 1957) has suggested, grazing by sheep and other animals with concomitant periodic burning doubtless prevents the growth of woodland or scrub over large areas of mountain on which it would climatically be possible. However, in many such situations exposure and low summer temperatures combine to retard tree growth so that only a very low intensity of grazing is needed to stop it completely. It should also be remembered that man has introduced his grazing animals at the expense of the native fauna. There are some western localities where a thousand years ago red deer probably caused as much damage to seedling trees as sheep and rabbits do today. Probably the nearest approach to a natural climax vegetation in the windy western seaboard may be found in the low dense scrub that occurs on some islands in lakes notably in Connemara, islands that are too small to warrant grazing, felling or some other human interference.

Chapter 3
The biotic resources

Few native plants and animals have escaped man's influence since he first arrived in Ireland some 8,000 years ago. Not only have they provided him with food, clothing, tools, weapons and building materials, but they have also yielded ground to new plants and animals introduced by man. Yet, although the countryside now contains few native species whose distribution has not been modified by human agencies, reconstruction of the original biota is essential if man's impact on the landscape throughout time is to be assessed accurately. Literary and historical records provide some indications of the changing flora and fauna over the past 1,500 years but, for this and earlier episodes which lack written records, the surviving field evidence provides an invaluable tool for reconstructing the past. Much of the plant pollen that has rained down on the Irish landscape ever since it was vacated by ice has been trapped and preserved, along with some larger plant and animal remains, in the peat deposits which cover so much of the country. The painstaking pollen analyses conducted by K. Jessen (1949) and G. F. Mitchell (1956) into these deposits have, with the aid of radiocarbon dating techniques, revealed a fascinating record of landscape change dating back over 12,000 years. Other field material is less useful: archaeological evidence should begin with the advent of man but in fact reveals little about the pre-Neolithic landscape; and cave deposits containing remains of extinct and living animal species have been often so disturbed by later intruders that they can be interpreted only with considerable caution.

Flora

Most plants found in Irish interglacial deposits were driven from the country during the last glaciation, leaving only a few arctic-alpine and boreal species to colonize the tundra that lay beyond the ice front. It is conceivable that a few temperate plants whose light and moisture needs were satisfied by the mid-latitude oceanic situation may also have survived the cold, particularly as lowered sea-level extended the icefree area well beyond the present south and west coasts. Considerable mass movement on those hillslopes lying beyond the ice front clearly shows that Ireland received appreciably more moisture, at least seasonally, than the tundra of continental Europe. Nevertheless, most temperate plants undoubtedly reached Ireland with the increasing warmth of postglacial times when, in response to milder, wetter climatic conditions, the vegetation soon acquired a strikingly oceanic personality.

Development of the vegetation cover

The changing environment of late glacial and postglacial Ireland is shown in the table on pp. 46 and 47. (The vegetation is based largely on the published works of K. Jessen and G. F. Mitchell; recognizing that the effects of climatic changes on the pollen rain during the Neolithic, Bronze and early Iron Ages are partly concealed by the grosser effects of human activity, many Irish workers include pollen zone VIIb with an extended zone VIII lasting from around 3000 B.C. to A.D. 300. Zone VIIa thus becomes zone VII.)

ZONE I: OPEN TUNDRA, before 10,000 B.C. As ice withdrew from the low-lands, so open tundra spread northwards across a virgin late-glacial landscape of boulder clay, sand, gravel, bare rock and deranged drainage – the legacy of glaciation. Small glaciers survived in the surrounding mountains and a Scottish ice lobe invaded north Antrim and Derry but elsewhere mass movement was common and mainly inorganic clays began filling lake basins. The vegetation was poor in species and dominated by the arctic-alpine shrub, dwarf willow (*Salix herbacea*). Oceanic and sub-Arctic species, such as crowberry (*Empetrum nigrum*) and certain lake plants, also existed but many areas carried only mosses and lichens. Mountain avens (*Dryas octopetala*), an undershrub typical of contemporary European tundras, was less common in oceanic Ireland.

ZONE II: SUB-ARCTIC BIRCH TUNDRA, 10,000 to 8,800 B.C. As the climate became warmer, running water replaced mass movement as the dominant geomorphic process, organic muds were carried into lake basins, and numerous sub-Arctic plants spread into Ireland. Prominent among these were tree birch (*Betula pubescens*), shrubs like juniper (*Juniperus communis*), dwarf birch (*Betula nana*) and tea-leaved willow (*Salix phylicifolia*), and marsh plants such as spike rush (*Eleocharis multicaulis*), greater spearwort (*Ranunculus lingua*) and shoreweed (*Littorella*). Ireland became covered by birch copses, which rose 750 feet above present sea-level up the Wicklow mountains, alternating with stretches of open country which in the oceanic north and west carried broad crowberry heaths similar to those in modern Iceland and northern Norway. Grasses and herbs supported a growing animal population.

ZONE III: OPEN TUNDRA, 8,800 to 8,300 B.C. Climatic deterioration led to the decline of the park tundra and to the renewal of small corrie glaciers in the mountains, strong mass movement and inorganic sedimentation in lakes. Tree growth was restricted and birch copses survived only in sheltered places. Once again the country was mostly open herbaceous tundra with arctic and sub-

Arctic plants such as dwarf willow, dwarf birch, mountain avens, mountain sorrel (*Oxyria digyna*) and Irish sandwort (*Arenaria ciliata*) forming extensive heaths. Strongly oceanic crowberry heaths persisted in the northwest.

ZONE IV: PRE-BOREAL BIRCH WOODLAND, 8,300 to 7,500 B.C. The onset of a markedly warmer climate, introducing the postglacial period, caused lowland vegetation to lose its arctic qualities and allowed birch, aspen (*Populus tremulus*) and other temperate plants to spread into Ireland. Running water resumed dominance, organic muds were deposited, swamp plants became more common and peat began to form. Initially, the birch woods were open, willows grew vigorously, and crowberry heaths survived in Connemara. Later, dense birch woods spread rapidly through the lowlands and on to lower mountain slopes suppressing their competitors, crowberry heaths almost died out and heather (*Calluna vulgaris*) became notable.

ZONE V: BOREAL HAZEL AND BIRCH WOODLAND, 7,500 to 6,900 B.C. The sudden expansion of hazel (*Corylus avellana*) through the existing birch woods heralded a change in forest composition which was to reach its full development later. Birch woods now reached their greatest extent and then began a gradual decline. Aspen was less common but silver birch (*Betula pendula*) and Scots pine (*Pinus sylvestris*) appeared locally, and a few oak and elm reached Ireland. The arrival and spread of temperate swamp plants like sedge (*Cladium mariscus*), pondweed (*Potamogeton polygonifolius*) and the aquatics *Naias flexilis* and *Naias marina*, together with oceanic heath plants like bell heather (*Erica cinerea*), cross-leaved heath (*Erica tetralix*) and royal fern (*Osmunda regalis*) suggest that the climate was similar to that of the present.

ZONE VI: BOREAL HAZEL AND PINE WOODLAND, 6,900 to 5,200 B.C. At first, hazel copses were better developed in Ireland than anywhere else in Europe but later, as pine, elm (*Ulmus glabra*) and oak (*Quercus*) spread through the declining birch woods, two broad regions evolved: a northeastern mixed woodland of hazel, elm and oak that only yielded to pine towards the close of the period; and a southwestern woodland where hazel, elm and oak were less common and pine soon became dominant. A warm oceanic climate was indicated by holly (*Ilex aquifolium*), ivy (*Hedera helix*) and the heaths which now included *Erica mackaiana*. Although dense woodlands spread to the western seaboard suggesting that conditions were less stormy than later, Ireland did not experience the dry climate characteristic of Boreal Europe because peats continued to form and the moisture-loving alder appeared. Into these woodlands a new imponderable force arrived – man – at first hesitant but later purposeful and, so far as native plants and animals were concerned, generally destructive.

TIME	PERIOD	ZONE	CLIMATE	VEGETATION	TREES	SHRUBS
2000	POSTGLACIAL — SUBATLANTIC	X			Partial Afforestation	
1000	POSTGLACIAL — SUBATLANTIC	IX	Oscillating Oceanic: cool, wet, cloudy, windy	ALDER, OAK and BIRCH WOODLAND	Widespread Deforestation	
A.D. / B.C.	POSTGLACIAL — SUBATLANTIC	VIII	Falling summer temperature		Birch expands	
1000	POSTGLACIAL — SUBBOREAL	VIIb	Rather dry Summer temperature reaching postglacial maximum	ALDER and OAK WOODLAND	Pine almost disappears Oak maximum Holly maximum Ash expands Elm declines	Blackthorn Elder
2000						
3000						
4000	POSTGLACIAL — ATLANTIC	VIIa	Warm, moist, oceanic Moister than Boreal (Rather warm and oceanic)	ALDER, OAK and PINE WOODLAND	Mountain ash common Alder expands	Hazel minimum
5000						
6000	POSTGLACIAL — BOREAL	VI	Warm, moist, less stormy Sea warmer than today (Rather warm and oceanic)	HAZEL and PINE WOODLAND	Pine maximum in northeast Sporadic alder Pine maximum in southwest Elm maximum Hazel maximum Oak and elm expand	Erica mackaiana Holly Guelder rose Dogwood
7000	POSTGLACIAL — BOREAL	V	Climate similar to present	HAZEL and BIRCH WOODS	Silver birch Scots pine Hazel expands widely	Bell heather Bog heather
8000	POSTGLACIAL — PRE-BOREAL	IV	Rising temperature	BIRCH WOODLAND	Goat willow Aspen Common sallow Birch expands	Heather
	LATE GLACIAL — ARCTIC	III	Subarctic oceanic	OPEN TUNDRA		Dwarf birch Mountain avens Dwarf willow
9000	LATE GLACIAL — SUBARCTIC	II	Mild, subarctic oceanic	BIRCH TUNDRA with crowberry heaths	Birch Juniper	Eared sallow Tea-leaved willow Dwarf birch
10000						
	LATE GLACIAL — ARCTIC	I	Arctic oceanic	OPEN TUNDRA		Crowberry Dwarf willow
11000						

OTHER PLANTS	LAND DEPOSITS	SEA-LEVEL	HUMAN CULTURES
Alien plants widely introduced			
	Sphagnum peats, slightly decayed		Plantations
			Anglo-Norman invasion
Hornwort (*C. submersum*)			Viking invasion
Corn spurrey and other weeds			Christianity arrives
Hulled barley			Arrival of Celts
Flax			
	Pine migrates onto bogs: stumps entombed in peat		
Ivy maximum		Land uplift virtually ceases	
Small spelt	Diatomite		Metal working introduced
Emmer	Chara marls		
Naked barley	Wood peat and well-decayed *Sphagnum* peat	Land in the northeast continues to rise gently	
Ribwort plantain			
Bog myrtle			
	Well-decayed *Sphagnum* peat	Sea reaches present level	Agriculture introduced
Pipewort	Wood peat and swamp peat common		
	Tufa		
Raised and blanket bog species expand	First records of raised and blanket bog peat	Donegal–Islay land link submerged	
Ivy	Wood, swamp and fen peat common	Britain cut off from continent	Man arrives in Ireland
Royal fern Sedge	Limnic deposits prevailing Wood peat	Leinster–Wales land link submerged	
Naias aquatics			
Hornwort (*C. demersum*)	Limnic deposits prevailing Wood, swamp and fen peat		
Mountain sorrel / Irish sandwort	Solifluction / Corrie ice Inorganic clays	Sea-level still over 200 feet below present	
Many-stemmed spike rush	Abundant running water		
Shoreweed	Organic and calcareous muds		
Great spearwort			
Quillwort	Inorganic clays / Solifluction		
Water milfoil	Extensive snow patches / Mountain glaciers	Parts of Irish Sea floor exposed	

LAND DEPOSITS (margin): Normal weathering and running water dominant with periodic mass movement (bog-flows) and much almost still water

SEA-LEVEL (margin): Static sea level with minor fluctuations periodically — Rising sea-level—the Flandrian or postglacial marine transgression

HUMAN CULTURES (margin, top to bottom): HISTORIC — IRON — BRONZE — NEOLITHIC — MESOLITHIC

47

Although vegetation continued to respond to climatic changes, the relationship was never again quite the same or quite so simple.

ZONE VIIa: ATLANTIC ALDER, OAK AND PINE WOODLAND, 5,200 to 3,000 B.C. The onset of Atlantic times saw the mixed woodlands enriched by the rapid spread of alder (*Alnus glutinosa*), holly and ivy in response to moister, even more oceanic conditions. Pine survived but the regional contrast between northeast and southwest Ireland became blurred. Mountain ash (*Sorbus aucuparia*) also existed, but the tree probably arrived much earlier. Higher water-tables encouraged the widespread growth of raised and blanket bogs while the wider distribution of holly and ivy, the displacement of pine by broad-leaved trees, and the contemporary marine fauna each indicate a climate warmer than today. Hazel and, later, elm, declined throughout the British Isles. The sea, which had begun rising soon after the world's glaciers commenced melting, reached its present level around 3,400 B.C., drowning the woodlands along the earlier coast to create the so-called submerged forests. Mesolithic man was nibbling ineffectually at the biota.

ZONE VIIb: SUB-BOREAL ALDER AND OAK WOODLAND, 3,000 to 500 B.C. The climate became drier and summer temperatures reached their postglacial maximum, perhaps 2·5° C (4·5° F) warmer than today. Birch and pine spread to about 1,000 feet above their present mountain limits, flourished in the west and, towards the close of the period, migrated to the bogs where pine virtually disappeared. Alder and hazel again expanded, ash (*Fraxinus excelsior*) began spreading, while oak, holly and ivy all reached their greatest postglacial extent. Elder (*Sambucus nigra*) and blackthorn (*Prunus spinosa*) shrubs, indicating warmer conditions combined with early woodland clearance, appeared for the first time. The continued decline of elm and the appearance of ribwort plantain (*Plantago lanceolata*) and cereal crops shows that Neolithic and Bronze Age farmers were extending their pastures and croplands at the expense of the native woodlands. As woodland clearances exposed the earth to increased leaching and podsolization, iron pans formed locally and drainage became impeded. With the ecological balance thus upset, many abandoned clearings were invaded by blanket bogs rather than by secondary woodlands.

ZONE VIII–X: SUB-ATLANTIC ALDER, BIRCH AND OAK WOODLAND, after 500 B.C. The climate now became generally wetter and more windy and the summers cooler so that oak, holly and ivy yielded some ground to birch. Tree growth and, more significantly, the establishment of young trees were restricted in their areal and altitudinal range, and bog growth was accelerated. Although climate now turned against certain species, the general reduction of the woodlands was due undoubtedly to timber cutting and the expansion of tillage, stock-rearing and settlement, each controlled by man, who now became the dominant ecological factor. The corn spurrey (*Spergula arvensis*) and other troublesome weeds of arable land spread as tillage expanded. The sub-Atlantic climate has persisted with minor fluctuations to the present day but G. F. Mitchell has correctly emphasized man's dominance over the vegetation by recognizing a *Zone IX* of general deforestation from around A.D. 300 to 1700 and a *Zone X* of partial afforestation, dominated by the introduction of numerous alien species, from 1700 to the present.

Nature and distribution of sub-Atlantic vegetation

Only a few shreds of the once widespread sub-Atlantic woodlands, covering less than 1 per cent of the country, have survived man's assault on the native vegetation. Likewise, few other plant communities have escaped man's attentions. No study of the present vegetation cover can thus exclude man as a dominant ecological agent nor can any reconstruction of past vegetation be compiled simply from surviving distributions. For instance, some plants may have been prevented by the continued presence of man and his grazing animals from adapting properly to the sub-Atlantic climatic deterioration. The lack of woodland over parts of western Ireland may be due in large measure to the inhibiting influence of man rather than climate.

Woodlands of durmast oak (*Quercus petraea*) must once have covered most non-calcareous soils that were neither waterlogged nor fully exposed to strong Atlantic winds. These oak woods probably had co-dominants or lower canopies of birch, mountain ash, yew, hazel, alder, holly and willow, and together rose much higher up hillsides than their present upper limits, virtually sea-level in northwest Ireland, suggest. The surviving Killarney oakwoods contain a lower canopy of shade-tolerant holly with some birch, hazel, willow and arbutus. These in turn shelter a luxuriant growth of ferns, mosses and liverworts. Similar woods occur around Glengarriff and Kenmare farther south, around Lough Gill near Sligo and near Lough Conn in Mayo. Yew (*Taxus baccata*) is often found in these woods and, like the juniper shrubs which are prominent in Connemara, is markedly western in its present distribution. Less spectacular durmast oak woods with holly and hazel shrubs, all strongly modified by man, survive in some Wicklow glens. Of the climax woodland that once occupied the calcareous soils of the central lowlands, no trace remains. It probably consisted of pedunculate oak (*Quercus robur*), which still reaches nearly 1,500 feet in the north, together with ash, alder and hazel. Today, these trees are mainly found singly in hedgerows, pastures and farm windbreaks. Ash trees and shrubs like hazel, blackthorn, hawthorn (*Crataegus monogyna*), honeysuckle (*Lonicera periclymenum*) and buckthorn (*Rhamnus catharticus*) owe much of their dominance in Ireland to the elimination of the oakwoods and to the creation of quickset hedgerows for enclosure purposes during the landlord era.

12. The Upper Lake and the Long Range near Killarney, County Kerry
This valley provided one of the principal outlets for glacier ice forming in the mountainous country to the south and the picturesque lakes occupy ice-excavated rock basins. The starkness of the ice-moulded sandstone topography is relieved by shreds of semi-indigenous mixed woodlands dominated by durmast oak and by such evergreens as holly, arbutus, yew and ivy.

Originally, the woodlands probably gave way reluctantly to lesser plant communities only under strongly localized ecological conditions but, because grassland, heath, bog and scrub have replaced the native woodlands so completely as a result of man's activities, the original nature and extent of these lesser communities are difficult to assess. The poor residue of arctic-alpine plants that survives on exposed hillsides in the north and west suggests that the woodlands once gave way at around 1,000 feet to montane shrubs such as mountain avens, dwarf willow, bilberry and bearberry (*Arctostaphylos uva-ursi*). Today, some of these plants extend down to sea-level in the Burren, happily coexisting with Mediterranean plants in response to the exposed but equable situation. Elsewhere, the native woodlands often passed laterally into hazel thickets or, with increasing dampness, into alder and willow scrub and ultimately into marsh, fen, bog and aquatic communities. On strongly siliceous soils and in exposed situations, heath plants are often prominent today but their status among the native vegetation is difficult to ascertain. Most probably the heaths have expanded their range as man has cut and burned the original woodlands, and then grazing by domestic and wild animals has prevented the trees from regenerating. In some instances, drainage improvements initiated by man have restricted the range of marsh, fen and aquatic plants. The wide variety of coastal and maritime habitats has long provided a wealth of shore zone vegetation but even here the establishment of sand dune, shingle beach and saltmarsh communities has not gone unhindered by man.

Fauna

Pleistocene legacy

During maximum glaciation, Ireland was largely devoid of animals which had been either exterminated or driven out by the advancing ice. The nearby Atlantic undoubtedly harboured a largely migratory marine and bird fauna while some land animals may have survived, at least temporarily, on nunataks and in areas marginal to the ice front beyond the present southwest coast. The ice sheet lying between Ireland and southwest England may also have allowed some arctic and tundra species to filter back and forth occasionally but little is yet known about the nature and direction of these movements. During the less extensive last glaciation, some tundra mammals undoubtedly occupied the ice-free south, spreading northwards as the glaciers retreated. Owing to oceanic influences and to more intensive summer radiation, plant growth and thus animal-carrying capacity in this tundra was probably greater than in modern high-latitude tundras. Cave deposits show that, at one time or another, the ecological balance was maintained by herbivorous tundra reindeer (*Rangifer tarandus*) and woolly mammoth (*Elephas primigenius*), by rodents such as Arctic lemming (*Dicrostonyx torquatus*) and Scandinavian lemming (*Lemmus lemmus*), and by migratory bird life, which in turn supported carnivores like the spotted cave hyaena (*Crocuta spelaea*) and Arctic fox (*Vulpes lagopus*). As the ice waned and open tundra was replaced by tree tundra, so wider-ranging carnivores from the expanding European forests like brown bear (*Ursus arctos*), wolf (*Canis lupus*) and an occasional lynx (*Felis lynx*) immigrated in increasing numbers, particularly during summer. The contemporaneity of these animals is difficult to assess for while some, such as the mammoth, were dying out, others, such as reindeer, were expanding their range and being preyed upon by carnivores who brought their remains into long-occupied caves.

The decay of the local mountain glaciers saw the extinction of most tundra animals as the ecological impact of the late-glacial climatic oscillations on animal life became reflected in changing habitats and food resources and in greater competition from new animal immigrants. Woolly mammoth and cave hyaena soon died out and are nowhere associated with human remains. Tundra reindeer and occasional woodland reindeer were prominent during late-glacial times but died out soon afterwards. Although specialized reindeer hunting allowed late Palaeolithic man to achieve a comparatively high population density elsewhere in Europe, there is yet no certain evidence that Palaeolithic hunters ever reached Ireland. In Scotland, reindeer survived alongside man well into post-glacial times. The giant Irish deer (*Cervus giganteus*) was the most conspicuous arrival during late-glacial times. It wandered widely through the park tundra during the Zone II warm interval and its remains, together with those of reindeer, have frequently been recovered from peat deposits of this phase around the central lowlands, notably from Limerick where the herbaceous flora was unusually rich. The giant Irish deer preferred open habitats for practical reasons, but found little attraction in the crowberry heaths of the north and west or the bleak upland tundras. It did not long survive the expansion of the postglacial woodlands and their carnivores, and became extinct about 10,000 years ago. Bear and Arctic lemming scarcely survived man's arrival although in Keshcorran cave in Sligo their remains were allegedly associated with charcoal layers. A few bears may conceivably have survived into the Neolithic.

Postglacial fauna

The expansion of the Boreal woodlands saw the arrival of most modern wild animals, but Ireland's present fauna, like its flora, is numerically poor in species compared with Britain. Ireland contains only 33 per cent of the reptiles and amphibia, 48 per cent of the land mammals and 85 per cent of the land birds found in Britain. The twenty-four surviving wild mammals which immigrated naturally comprise seven carnivores, namely fox (*Vulpes vulpes*), badger (*Meles meles*), otter (*Lutra lutra*), pine marten (*Martes martes*), Irish stoat (*Mustela hibernica*), grey seal (*Halichoerus grypus*) and common seal (*Phoca vitulina*); seven rodents, namely red squirrel (*Sciurus vulgaris*), Irish hare (*Lepus hibernicus*), black rat (*Rattus rattus*), brown rat (*Rattus norvegicus*), eastern house mouse (*Mus musculus orientalis*), common house mouse (*Mus musculus musculus*) and field mouse (*Apodemus sylvaticus*); two insectivores, namely hedgehog (*Erinaceus europaeus*) and pigmy shrew (*Sorex minutus*); seven species of Chiroptera or bats; and one representative of the Artiodactyla, namely red deer (*Cervus elaphus*). Three further species of seal and nineteen species of whale are occasional visitors.

Ireland has only one reptile resident, the widespread lizard *Lacerta vivipara*. Three species of turtle visit the coast, namely the common loggerhead (*Caretta caretta*), Kemp's loggerhead (*Colpochelys kempi*) and the leathery turtle (*Dermochelys coriacea*). Three species of Amphibia occur under suitable conditions: the frog (*Rana temporaria*), which is common everywhere, though its status as a native is uncertain and some authorities believe that it was introduced in 1696, the natterjack toad (*Bufo calamita*), which is restricted to Kerry, and the newt (*Triturus vulgaris*). Owing to continuing migrations, 370 species and subspecies of birds have been recognized in Ireland, including four endemic subspecies: Irish jay, Irish coal tit, Irish dipper and Irish red grouse. The varied freshwater and marine fish faunas have changed considerably over recent years because of their commercial significance.

Unusual aspects of the biota

Poverty of species

With 907 distinct native species, Ireland contains only two-thirds of the total native British flora while Britain contains less than half the native flora of France. Of the 460 species native to Britain and not to Ireland, only fifty-one have become naturalized in Ireland. Such British trees as beech (*Fagus sylvatica*), hornbeam (*Carpinus betulus*) and lime (*Tilia*), and widespread plants such as black bryony (*Tamus communis*) and even the markedly oceanic needle furze (*Genista anglica*) have never reached Ireland naturally. Ireland contains only one-third of Britain's arctic-alpine plants, only two-thirds of its liverworts and only three-quarters of its mosses. The resident Irish fauna is equally scanty, its differentiation into species has been slight and, excepting red deer, the country's surviving mammals are small and insignificant. The Irish hare and Irish stoat are endemic and widely distributed but, though the latter is often referred to as a weasel, *Mustela vulgaris* itself is unknown. Other notable absentees from Ireland include all species of vole, the common shrew (*Sorex araneus*) and the mole (*Talpa europaea*), although a small colony of the last-mentioned was recently found in the south. Ireland has no snakes but St Patrick cannot be held responsible for banishing them. Of the sixteen species of strictly freshwater British fish, only eight reached Ireland.

Why should Ireland lack such large proportions of the British biota? The answer is part historical and part ecological, but has little to do with man. As most Irish plants and animals are postglacial immigrants from continental Europe, their route lay through Britain, but the majority could only reach Ireland if a more or less continuous land connection was provided. As sea-level rose, the link between Wales and southeast Ireland was soon drowned and could have been used only by a few early immigrants. The remaining land bridge, between Islay and Donegal, remained open until after Britain's link with the Continent had been severed and probably persisted into early Atlantic times. Owing to the location of this bridge, however, even species ecologically well suited to Ireland had to pass through the greater part of Britain before they gained access to Ireland. Among the flora, beech, lime, traveller's joy (*Clematis vitalba*) and white dead-nettle (*Lamium album*) arrived in Britain too late to travel so far north before the connection was severed. Of the fauna, the bank vole and dormouse also arrived too late, the adder may have extended its range north through Britain only recently, while the smooth snake and sand lizard and some quite early arrivals have never spread far north through Britain for ecological reasons.

Ecologically, Ireland offers much less variety than Britain, less in fact than its smaller size alone merits. For reasons of climate, relief or soil, some British species such as the Breckland steppe plants are just not suited to Ireland and have never become established. To those immigrants that were eligible for and accomplished the journey to Ireland, however, the conditions they found in their new home were just as important as the means by which they arrived. Some species entered Ireland successfully but were unable to survive either because of unsuitable ecological factors, including overcrowding by more vigorous native species, or because of their small numbers (incidentally, this feature also forms a recurrent theme in the human colonization of Ireland). Irish mountains are rarely high or cool enough to support an arctic–alpine flora comparable in species with highland Britain; indeed, many uplands bear vegetation of markedly lowland composition. Thus only those species best suited to their new home have become well established: moisture-loving plants are quite happy in Ireland, xerophytes and succulents are not. Ecological conditions are against moles, which like burrowing in well-drained soil, and grass snakes. Even snakes introduced artificially to Ireland have never established themselves. Newts and toads may have been successful initially but have been unable to maintain large colonies. Changing ecological conditions of postglacial times have extinguished such early immigrants as dwarf birch, spiked woodrush (*Luzula spicata*), certain aquatic plants and those animals already noted. Scots pine and sea buckthorn (*Hippophae rhamnoides*) also colonized early postglacial Ireland, later died out but have since been reintroduced by man and naturalized. Apparently climate at one time turned against them and, although conditions later returned to within their range of tolerance, these plants were prevented from returning naturally because Ireland meantime had been severed from Britain.

Irish biota absent from Britain

Eighteen plant species occur in Ireland but not in Britain. Of these, greatest interest attaches to the so-called Lusitanian flora more characteristic of southwest Europe. Six species display a markedly Atlantic distribution in Europe, namely three heaths (*Erica mackaiana*, *Erica mediterranea* and *Daboecia cantabrica*), kidney saxifrage (*Saxifraga hirsuta*), St Patrick's cabbage (*Saxifraga spathularis*) and greater butterwort (*Pinguicula grandiflora*). The strawberry tree (*Arbutus unedo*) and orchid (*Neotinea intacta*) have strong Mediterranean affinities. The Irish invertebrate fauna also contains species from southwest Europe, namely the spotted slug (*Geomalacus maculosus*) of Kerry, three land snails, six insects, four woodlice and several earthworms. Although these species are ecologically well suited to their habitats in western Ireland, there is equally no climatic obstacle to their living in southwest England, but if they reached Ireland through Britain then they have become extinct in that part of their range and have left no trace of their passage. This marked discontinuity in the present Lusitanian range may have been accentuated by rising postglacial seas, climatic worsening or extermination by hardier species, but the means by which these plants and animals reached Ireland is still unknown.

Speculation on this issue has crystallized into two opposing beliefs – survival or extinction during the last glaciation. Praeger (1950) and others have argued that the Lusitanian biota reached Ireland during Pleistocene times and survived the last glaciation in comparatively warm humid refuges just beyond the ice front. Certainly *Erica mackaiana* and *Daboecia cantabrica* occur in some Irish interglacial deposits while some 400 species of flowering plants still survive along the narrow ice-free margins of the Greenland ice cap. Other authorities have envisaged the extinction of all but a few arctic–alpine species during the last glaciation and the introduction of the present biota during postglacial times. Although a land bridge connecting Ireland with Iberia is untenable on geological grounds, the narrowed water barrier produced by the lower sea-levels of early postglacial times probably facilitated migration. Floating rafts of vegetation, carriage by birds and accidental import by early man – each bypassing Britain – may also have helped.

Of the other distinctive species, a Mediterranean cottonweed (*Otanthus maritimus*) and a montane saxifrage (*Saxifraga rosacea*) have only just died out in Britain. Two American species (*Hypericum canadense* and *Sisyrhincium angustifolium*) represent the last stages in the retreat of plants that once straddled the Atlantic, across which they may have been carried by the Greenland white-fronted goose (*Anser albifrons flavirostris*). The continental willow-leaved inula (*Inula salicina*) and a herb (*Euphrasia salisburgensis*) are less easily explained. Postglacial time is very short in terms of evolution and the 6,500 years of Ireland's isolation is short in terms of speciation. The poverty of endemics is thus to be expected. Of the plants, only fringed rock cress (*Arabis brownii*), Irish sandwort (*Arenaria ciliata*), a saxifrage (*Saxifraga hartii*) and six liverworts can rank with the four birds and two mammals already noted as endemic species.

Man's impact on the native biota

Man's impact on native plants and animals has been broadly threefold: he has totally destroyed a few species, he has restricted the distribution of many others, and he has encouraged yet others. Hunting, fishing and food-collecting have long contributed to these changes but man's most violent assault on wild life really accompanied the expansion of agriculture, industry and settlement.

Frequently, as in clearing the woodlands, his actions were quite intentional and reflected the needs and technical facilities of the society in which he lived. Whether intentional or not, however, he created new habitats which upset the pre-existing natural balance and established new ecosystems in which some native plants and animals found difficulty in surviving, particularly where they were brought into competition with alien species introduced by man.

Few native plants have been utterly and intentionally destroyed by man although the drainage operations that reduced the flood hazard around Lough Neagh in 1855 led ultimately to the disappearance of a marsh fern and three sedges of which one, *Carex fusca*, is now found in the British Isles only in west Inverness. Of the fauna, early immigrants such as wild boar (*Sus scrofa*) and wolf had a prolonged existence owing to the protection of the forests. Boar tusks and bones are often found in early dwelling sites and boar-hunting figures frequently in early Christian literature. From persistent hunting and systematic forest clearance, however, the native boar died out in the twelfth century. Once a widespread scourge, the last wolf was killed by wolfhounds in Carlow in 1786. The native red squirrel was exterminated in the seventeenth century but was later reintroduced and is now widespread. Among the native birds, the abundant remains of capercaillie, great auk and crane in early dwelling sites testify to their former importance as food and suggest that their disappearance was due in large measure to man's insatiable appetite. The capercaillie became extinct about 1860 while the great auk, last seen alive in 1834 off the Waterford coast, had disappeared throughout the world some ten years later. Traps, poison and shooting also destroyed the golden eagle and white-tailed eagle as common breeding species and, like the bittern and marsh harrier, they are now only occasional visitors. The Lough Neagh charr was exterminated by overfishing.

The clearance of the woodlands, a classic illustration of how man has restricted certain plant distributions, has so profoundly changed the face of Ireland that it forms a recurrent theme of subsequent chapters. Of the fauna, the once widespread red deer is now confined as a native to Kerry where it survives only owing to strict protection. Wild red deer still inhabited the Knockmealdown mountains in 1745 while they lingered still longer in northwest Mayo, before finally perishing during the great famine of the 1840s at the hands of starving peasants. Herds have frequently been introduced to private estates throughout Ireland and one such herd that escaped from the Powerscourt demesne now lives wild in the nearby Wicklow mountains. The pine marten, now found mainly in the south, has suffered owing to its status as vermin among gamekeepers and to its commercially valuable coat. Birds such as marsh harrier, hen harrier and common buzzard have been similarly decimated by zealous gamekeepers although, following the breakup of the large estates over the past hundred years, this threat to the native fauna has substantially decreased. Overfishing has reduced the number or size of such freshwater fish as salmon, trout and pollan while the disappearance of submarine meadows of eelgrass (*Zostera marina*) during the 1930s restricted the range of many sea fish. Haddock and hake are now less plentiful in the Irish sea than formerly; sea bream and sand smelt have virtually disappeared from the Dublin area.

Illustrating the encouragement that man has given to certain native plants, woodland clearances deliberately increased the range of grassland species and, less deliberately, encouraged heath, scrub and bog plants to colonize exhausted pastures and croplands. The fox, which was becoming rare during the mid-nineteenth century but was later protected locally for hunting purposes, is now a serious pest throughout Ireland. The widespread badger has also multiplied as trapping disappeared following the collapse of estates. This increase in the fox and badger population probably explains the recent marked decrease in hedgehogs. Of the rats and mice, only the field mouse reached Ireland before man; the remainder immigrated accidentally as a result of human movements, including commerce, and now rank as residents. Of these, the long-established black rat was largely replaced during the eighteenth century by the more aggressive brown rat, although the former is still a frequent visitor from ships.

The introduction of alien plants and animals by man

With or without man's continued assistance, the introduction of domestic and wild species by man has severely restricted the native plants and animals and in the new habitats thus created yet other alien species have become established. For example, ever since Neolithic farmers first cultivated barley, small spelt and emmer in Ireland some 5,000 years ago, a wide variety of domesticated crops has been introduced to the country's farmlands but cultivation has also encouraged the spread of numerous alien weeds. The past 300 years have seen a remarkable acceleration in the importation of exotic trees, shrubs and plants for use in planted woodlands, parks and gardens. Even the fuchsia hedges so common in the west were introduced to Ireland, in fact to southwest Donegal, only seventy years ago. Some introduced species have long since escaped from controlled woodlands, gardens and fields and have become naturalized. The sycamore (*Acer pseudoplatanus*), introduced in the sixteenth century, low-latitude evergreen shrubs like *Cotoneaster microphyllus* and *Erica stricta* (naturalized on the Magilligan dunes in Derry), North American herbs such as yellow monkey flower (introduced 1830), Canadian pondweed (1836) and pitcher plant (1906), and several Michaelmas daisies have all extended their range among native species. Introduced medicinal plants such as comfrey, still used in rural areas as a poultice, and culinary herbs such as fennel, catmint, groutweed, alexanders and bistort have frequently escaped from gardens but, failing to fight their way into the native vegetation, are generally confined to waysides and fields. The wall rocket, fine-leaved sandwort and small toadflax have spread across Ireland along railway tracks while Canadian pondweed has long threatened to choke the country's canals. Other alien plants frequently spring up around docks, breweries, distilleries and corn mills handling imported grain but mostly vanish again within the year. Many alien fungi have been introduced with foreign plants and as parasites have done much damage to fruit trees and other crops. Significantly, around one-quarter of the flowering plants found in County Dublin are alien imports: Dublin is among the longest settled and most highly tilled of Irish counties and also contains the largest port. In remote, less-populated Kerry, the corresponding ratio is one-seventh.

Most domestic animals were imported to Ireland before the close of the Neolithic. Their remains from dwelling sites, bogs and caves show that early forms were generally smaller than modern breeds: early horses were no larger than ponies, cows resembled the present Kerry breed, and sheep were similar to present mountain sheep. Dogs and cats also arrived early. Strangely, in view of its importance as a transport animal in rural Ireland in recent times, no record of the use of the ass (*Equus asinus*) in a domestic capacity has been traced before 1780 (Praeger, 1950). Wild animals introduced by man include rabbit (*Oryctolagus cuniculus*), imported by the Anglo-Normans in the thirteenth century, fallow deer (*Dama dama*), brought to Glencree in 1224 but more widely introduced around 1600, and the destructive North American grey squirrel (*Sciurus carolinensis*), introduced in 1911 to Longford from which it has since spread. A pair of North American muskrats (*Ondatra zibethica*) escaped from captivity in Nenagh in 1927, multiplied and spread through Tipperary and Clare before the trapping of the 487th specimen in 1934 rid Ireland of this formidable pest. The pheasant and the mute swan are two notable bird imports that have become resident aliens. Of the freshwater fish, roach (which probably originated in Ireland from anglers discarding livebait), carp (which may have escaped from monastery ponds), tench, dace, rainbow trout and perhaps pike were all intentionally introduced.

Chapter 4
Resources of the earth

The mineral resources

Ireland's structural framework encloses a variety of metallic and non-metallic minerals whose exploitation by man has often changed the face of the local countryside. The impact of mining on the landscape, however, has been limited by the relative poverty of rich metallic mineral resources upon which indigenous heavy industry could develop, and has varied according to whether those minerals that were available have been quarried opencast or recovered by shaft-mining methods. Means of exploitation have in turn varied with the technical equipment of a given period and with the nature and disposition of the resources now outlined.

Underground mining in Ireland has been concerned mainly with the recovery of metallic minerals generated by the Caledonian and Armorican orogenies, although shaft mining for coal, salt and gypsum has been important locally. The Caledonian movements and associated igneous activity gave rise in southeast Ireland to complex sulphide ores in the Vale of Avoca, near Arklow, containing iron pyrites, copper, lead and zinc, and to copper pyrites in east Waterford. The Armorican movements generated minerals in many areas, notably copper at Allihies and elsewhere in west Cork, near Killarney, at Hollyford in Tipperary and Beauparc in Meath; lead and zinc sulphide ores in Glendasan, Glendalough and Glenmalure in the Wicklow mountains; manganese and iron near Ross Carbery in Cork; and barytes as fissure fillings in Ben Bulben, near Sligo, and throughout the south. Ascending magmatic solutions of this age also brought lead, zinc and some silver and copper as veins or replacement deposits into the Carboniferous Limestone and nearby rocks around the central lowlands. Notable deposits occur at Abbeytown and Ballysadare in Sligo, at Silvermines in Tipperary, at Oughterard in Galway, near Tulla and Ballyvergin in east Clare, and locally in Monaghan, Armagh and Down. Cainozoic lead and zinc occur in the Mourne mountains. Valuable deposits of lead, zinc, silver and copper also occur at Tynagh in east Galway. The veins from which the gold-bearing gravels of some south Wicklow streams were eroded have never been found and are thus of uncertain age.

Coal and gypsum are among rarer sedimentary minerals that have been recovered by both surface and underground mining from time to time. Coal lies within Upper Carboniferous sandstones, shales and fireclays that were flexed by

Armorican movements and, owing to later widespread erosion, now survive mainly as residual plateaux around the central lowlands. In fact, while two-thirds of Ireland are underlain by Carboniferous rocks, mainly limestones, less than 5 per cent of the country now has coal-bearing sediments beneath it. Added to this cruel blow dealt by erosion, the surviving coal seams are generally thin, impersistent, broken and, after several score years' of desultory working, of little economic value today. Some anthracite survives in the Castlecomer plateau and nearby Slieve Ardagh in Leinster, and at Kanturk and Crataloe in Munster. Farther north, beyond the strongest Armorican flexures, soft friable bituminous coals suitable for steam-raising and household use occur around Lough Allen in the upper Shannon basin, near Carrickmacross in Monaghan, in the downfaulted and part-protected Coalisland field southwest of Lough Neagh and, slightly older, at Ballycastle in Antrim.

Gypsum and anhydrite occur in small New Red Sandstone deposits at Kingscourt in Cavan and, with thick rock salt, around Belfast Lough. The basalt of northeast Ireland contains much low-grade bauxite and lateritic iron ore, products of Cainozoic tropical weathering. Like so many dolerite intrusions throughout Ireland, however, basalt is now quarried largely for road metal. Carboniferous Limestone and Pleistocene sands and gravels are also important sources of road metal.

Ireland is studded with numerous abandoned quarries that once, notably during the urban growth of the eighteenth and nineteenth centuries, produced building stones from granite, Carboniferous Limestone and sandstone, and Old and New Red Sandstone, roofing slates from Lower Palaeozoic outcrops, and brick clays from Carboniferous shale, Triassic marl and glacial clays. Few such quarries remain open. Carboniferous Limestone and, in northeast Ireland, chalk have long been used for agricultural lime and more recently for cement. Indeed the abundance of such limestone and of Pleistocene sands and gravels strewn across Ireland is fortunate in view of current demands for concrete by the building industry and the scarcity of good brick clays. Of the remaining minerals, peat is commercially valuable and diatomite occurs in the Bann valley north of Lough Neagh. In vivid contrast to other countries, it is the surface exploitation of Ireland's geologically most recent mineral resources – its Pleistocene sands and gravels, and its Holocene peat – that is today doing most, in terms of extractive industry, to change the face of the landscape.

Soils

Formative factors
Parent material, climate, vegetation, relief, time and man have all played significant roles in forming Ireland's valued soil resources. Consequently, the

nature and distribution of these soils can only be understood when viewed against the legacy of Pleistocene glaciation and against the changing physical, biotic and cultural scene of postglacial times. The influence of parent material upon soil has long been recognized but, owing to varied site characteristics and to the chemical, physical and biological changes involved in soil formation, many soils developed from uniform parent materials display wide differences. Most Irish soils have formed from the variable drift deposits left by the glaciers and are thus inherently complex in both chemical and physical constitution and in distribution. The frequent occurrence of glacial till with a high proportion of clay combines with the levelness of much agricultural land to maintain high water-tables. The direct impact of solid bedrock upon the soil has been limited to small driftless areas, mainly on uplands where peat does not blanket the landscape.

The climatic factor is expressed both in the chemical and physical weathering of the parent material and in the development of a layered soil profile under freely drained conditions. Both processes require time and aeration to reach maturity and in Ireland neither demand is well satisfied. The limited temperature range retards mineral weathering while poor drainage conditions confine climatically induced zonal soils to a few areas and encourage the extensive development of intrazonal gleys. As may be expected in an environment whose rainfall-evaporation ratio strongly favours rainfall, most soils have been leached and podzolized to varying degrees. Leaching, the downward movement of chemical and physical constituents from the upper to the lower soil horizons, is a dominant process in all better-drained soils, such as those developed from coarse-grained sandy tills and from outwash sands and gravels, which tend therefore to have well-developed A/B/C profile characteristics. Such mature soils fall clearly into the pedalfer group of zonal soils or more specifically into the zone of medium to light-coloured podzolized soils so typical of cool temperate humid climates.

Persistent humidity, poor natural drainage, the limited permeability of many parent materials, and inefficient or non-existent artificial drainage works commonly render soil environments extremely wet. Extensive poorly drained gley soils commonly occur either where water movement is retarded in the profile, giving surface-water gleys, or where high water-tables give ground-water gleys. The former may reflect the physical constitution of the profile, inherited mainly from the parent material, as in drumlin soils. The latter is often found in depressions and areas of low relief where the relief factor asserts its influence over all others in the soil profile. Gleys are mineral soils whose iron oxide has been reduced to ferrous iron oxide by the anaerobic conditions of waterlogging. Both rusty oxidized ferric iron and blue-grey ferrous iron occur in mottled combination and partial mottling of the profile is a widespread feature in Irish soils. Extreme instances of site wetness have led, as will be shown, to the growth of extensive peat bogs. Conversely, with steeper slopes and better drainage the tendency towards increased leaching and podzolization becomes evident.

Owing to the profound changes in the landscape wrought by man over the past 5,000 years, the impact of vegetation and time on soil development is not easily deciphered. Clearly, most soils developed initially in accordance with the changing climatic and biotic patterns of the early postglacial environment and are thus relatively young in age. Most alluvial soils are extremely young. Immediately prior to man's first onslaught on the native vegetation sometime before 3000 B.C., soils were maturing beneath a deciduous woodland canopy but, as a result of human activity, this was in most areas later superseded by a grassland cover with consequent modification of the soil profile. Changing agricultural practices, various land drainage and reclamation projects and other cultural factors have since predominated.

Classification and distribution
As early as 1848, Sir Robert Kane described a system of land classification, based upon detailed chemical and physical analyses and the agricultural capabilities of Irish soils, but his maps and reports were unfortunately lost. A century later, in the emergency of the 1940s, scientific interest in soils was renewed, but before the creation of a National Soil Survey by the Agricultural Institute in 1959 little attempt had been made to survey, classify and map the soils of Ireland in a systematic manner (Ryan, 1963). The National Soil Survey instigated a systematic study of Irish soils on a county basis and, while it is still too early to provide an accurate overall picture, detailed soil maps and memoirs have been published for Wexford (1964), Limerick (1966) and Carlow (1967), other counties have been completed, and resource surveys have been carried out in such critical areas as west Cork and west Donegal. Other reconnaissance soil surveys elsewhere have been completed independently. The more significant features of the major soils recognized are summarized below.

BROWN EARTHS. These well-drained, medium textured, relatively mature soils have a uniform brownish profile in which weathering more or less keeps pace with leaching so that the B horizon is not very pronounced. Their humus is normally of the mull or mild variety although a moder humus occurs in the sandier types. Brown Earths may represent the natural soil climax under deciduous woodland, particularly on the lighter textured parent materials of the lowlands, with podzols forming where the woods were removed and reversion to heath took place. Acid Brown Earths occur mainly on more acid parent materials such as non-calcareous shales, sandstones, granites, schists and glacial drift derived from these sources but may also be found on drifts, formerly base-rich, that have been decalcified and base-depleted through weathering and leaching. Brown Earths of medium to high base status are associated with parent materials such as limestone and calcareous drifts th have undergone less leaching. Brown Earths are extensively cultivated owing to their desirable drainage conditions and well-developed structure. Together with podzolized Brown Earths, they extend discontinuously through the eastern counties wherever sloping ground or permeable parent material provide good drainage. Over highly basic parent materials, such as the Antrim basalts, they are well supplied with weathered minerals but although of low to moderately high base status and of relatively low natural fertility elsewhere, they respond well to manurial treatment.

RENDZINA-LIKE SOILS. These shallow, free-draining, superficially dark brown to black soils are similar to both the shallower Brown Earths of high base status and to continental Rendzina soils. Their A horizon rests directly on the parent material – generally Carboniferous Limestone or limestone drift – to the exclusion of a B horizon. Despite decalcification under the prevailing climate, their base status is mostly high. The surface content of organic matter is high relative to other mineral soils and humus is of a mull variety. Rendzina-like soils are common around Roscommon, Galway, Ennis and Rathkeale where, in the prevailing rainfall régime, they are productive especially under grassland. In some areas, notably south of Galway Bay, the parent rocks come too near the surface to allow cultivation, hazel scrub is common, and frequent rocks break the ground.

GREY-BROWN PODZOLICS. These soils form where, as a result of leaching, the B horizon acquires a significantly larger clay content than the A or C horizons. They are generally well-drained soils of medium base status, moderate to neutral reaction, and of heavier texture than the Brown Earths. The organic matter content in the surface is moderately high and the humus is a mull variety. The lighter textured soils are good for all agricultural purposes when adequately manured and well managed but the heavier textured members compare less favourably in this respect with the Brown Earths, although they can be highly productive as grassland soils under correct manurial and management practices. With Brown Earths, they form the most common agricultural soils over the east and central lowlands although gleying increases towards the north and west. Soils intermediate between Brown Earths and Grey-Brown Podzolics characterize vast areas of deep limestone drift throughout the central lowlands.

MODIFIED GREY-BROWN PODZOLICS. This unusual mixed group of soils has formed, probably owing to human interference, on the limestone-bearing outwash sands and gravels of the Newer Drift across the lowlands. They frequently show podzol characteristics under rather strange conditions for pod-

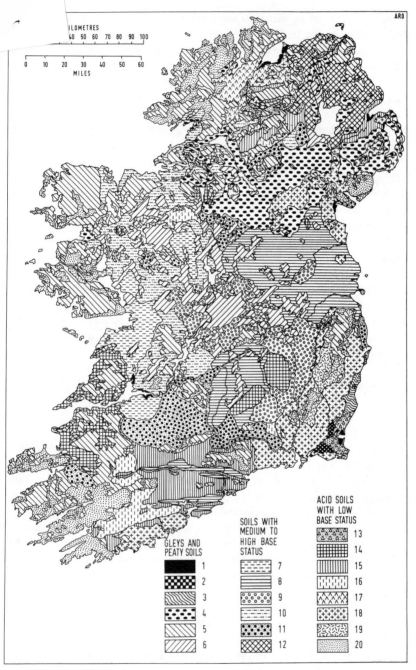

KILOMETRES
40 50 60 70 80 90 100

0 10 20 30 40 50 60
MILES

ACID SOILS
WITH LOW
BASE STATUS

13

14

SOILS WITH
MEDIUM TO
HIGH BASE
STATUS

GLEYS AND   7   15
PEATY SOILS
                   8   16
1
                   9   17
2
                   10   18
3
                   11   19
4
                   12   20
5

6

13. The soils of Ireland

64

GLEYS AND PEATY SOILS

1 Deep ground-water gleys developed on silts and slobs of alluvial and estuarine origin.
2 Surface-water gleys and slightly gleyed acid Brown Earths developed on clayey Lower Palaeozoic parent materials mainly in the form of dense glacial drift.
3 Deep surface-water gleys and slightly gleyed Brown Earths developed on dense plastic glacial till derived originally from marine clays.
4 Extensive drumlin gleys with some acid Brown Earths and Grey-Brown Podzolics (with or without gleying) developed on dense, mainly clayey, glacial till associated with drumlins.
5 Organic soils associated with blanket peats.
6 Organic soils associated with raised-bog peats, valley bogs and fens.

SOILS WITH MEDIUM TO HIGH BASE STATUS

7 Brown Earths of high base status and rendzina-like soils developed on Carboniferous Limestone with or without a thin veneer of limestone-bearing glacial till.
8 Deep Brown Earths of medium and high base status and Grey-Brown Podzolics developed on mixed but mostly limestone-bearing glacial till. Some gleying locally.
9 Brown Earths of high base status, Grey-Brown Podzolics and some podzolized Grey-Brown Podzolics developed on coarse mixed, mainly limestone-bearing, fluvio-glacial outwash deposits.
10 Brown Earths of medium to high base status and Grey-Brown Podzolics developed on impure limestones and mixed, mainly limestone-bearing, glacial drift.
11 Brown Earths of mixed but mainly medium base status and Grey-Brown Podzolics developed on coarse-textured glacial drift containing a mixture of limestone, sandstone and igneous rock debris. Some gleying locally.
12 Brown Earths of high base status and Grey-Brown Podzolics developed on Cainozoic basalts and glacial drift rich in basalt debris.

SOILS WITH LOW BASE STATUS

13 Acid Brown Earths, Brown Podzolics and some Podzols developed on coarse-textured glacial morainic deposits.
14 Acid Brown Earths, Brown Podzolics, gleys and some podzolized gleys developed on Upper Palaeozoic shales and mixed glacial drift containing abundant shale debris.
15 Acid Brown Earths, Brown Podzolics and gley-Podzols developed on mixed glacial drift containing abundant sandstone debris.
16 Acid Brown Earths, Brown Podzolics, Podzols, gley-Podzols and gleys developed on Devonian sandstones and siltstones with patches of glacial drift containing similar debris.
17 Acid Brown Earths and Brown Podzolics developed on metamorphic parent materials, mainly mica-schists and gneisses, and on mixed glacial drift containing similar debris.
18 Acid Brown Earths and related Brown Podzolics developed on Palaeozoic slates and shales, with local igneous influences, and on thin mixed glacial drift containing similar materials.
19 Acid Brown Earths and Brown Podzolics developed on granite and on mixed, mainly granite-bearing, glacial drift. Some gleying locally.
20 Podzols, Brown Podzolics, gley-Podzols and skeletal soils developed on highly acid parent materials—mainly sandstones and acid igneous and metamorphic rocks and glacial drift containing similar debris.

zolization. These soils are apparently polygenetic, having developed where the native woodlands have been replaced by heath or grassland and the original profiles modified accordingly. They vary considerably in profile depth, degree of development and extent of modification but, being well drained, relatively light textured and favourably structured, are widely cultivated. They most commonly retain a high base status with low or normal amounts of organic matter and a mull-type humus although numerous exceptions occur. Manured and well-managed pastures may be highly productive on these soils but in drier seasons the water deficit, particularly on lighter, shallower varieties, can be a major problem. Where developed upon eskers, cultivation is naturally difficult.

BROWN PODZOLICS. Owing to more intense leaching, these soils are more acid and degraded than the Brown Earths although they still retain an acid mull or, in the more degraded forms, a moder-type humus. Their upper horizons are more base-depleted and their lower levels strongly stained by iron enrichment. Brown Podzolics predominate in better drained areas at moderate elevations above 500 feet on acid parent materials such as granite, sandstone, quartzite, non-calcareous shales, mica-schists and glacial drifts from such sources. As such they are often transitional between the acid Brown Earths of the lowlands and the more intensely leached podzols of the uplands. This altitudinal sequence is well shown on the better drained slopes of the Wicklow, Mourne and Sperrin mountains. Brown Podzolics are less naturally fertile than Brown Earths but, being well drained and favourably structured, offer useful tillage and mixed farming soils when adequately limed, manured and well managed, resembling the Brown Earths in behaviour. They once carried extensive oak woodlands throughout southeast Ireland and are today considered excellent forestry soils.

PODZOLS. These intensely leached soils usually occur on parent materials of very low base resources or under conditions that deplete the base reserves to this low level. Thus uplands formed of acid shales, sandstones, granites, quartzites or mica-schists, and experiencing high rainfall with low evapotranspiration losses on steep hillsides are ideally suited to podzolization. Mineral bases, iron and aluminium oxides, humus and other soil constituents are leached rapidly downward, easy percolation being aided by the coarse texture and open structure of the developing podzol. If deterioration continues, conditions for decay by micro-organisms become unfavourable so that a peatlike raw humus accumulates near the surface which carries a typical heath vegetation. Podzols thus develop a distinct A/B/C profile and, in more extreme cases, the B horizon will contain a thin iron pan which hinders root penetration (important in forestry as well as in the agricultural use of these soils) and water percolation. For the latter reason, surface horizons in these soils may become poorly drained and encourage peat growth. Podzols are poor soils, deficient in the major nutrients and trace elements so vital to plants and animals, and needing abundant lime to be of any use. Some strongly leached podzols, that occur in the moranic and outwash sands and gravels strewn throughout the lowlands from Tipperary to Tyrone and Sligo, have been reclaimed for cultivation. The podzols that are so typical of those upland areas not mantled by peat are, for reasons of terrain, rarely capable of mechanical reclamation and cultivation. They are often best used for forestry.

GLEYS. Owing to intermittent or permanent waterlogging, gleys and partly gleyed soils occur extensively throughout lowland Ireland, notably where the soil has been derived from glacial till with high proportions of clay and silt. The drab blue-grey colours and ochreous mottling of the gley profile clearly reveal the poor drainage-aeration conditions prevailing. The clay subsoil is often so impermeable that internal drainage is almost impossible. Gleys are commonly characterized by heavy textures, very weak structures, shallow rooting areas, and slowly decaying organic matter that may lead to undesirable surface accumulations of raw humus. Most gleys are not very friable and when wet become very sticky. Some gleying can usually be seen in soil profiles throughout central and western Ireland and, farther north, is notable on the lower slopes of drumlins, in the clay-silt soils of the Bann valley, and around Lough Neagh, Lough Erne and other poorly drained areas. Owing to poor physical qualities, these soils are difficult to cultivate well and are very susceptible to overgrazing, a feature accentuated by their poor drainage which retards early season growth and shortens the grazing season on them. Nevertheless, with effective drainage and correct manurial and management practices, their potential for pasture production is often very high. However, until weeds such as rushes and sedges are eradicated and general soil fertility improved, most gleys will continue to support poor-quality pastures.

OTHER SOILS. Throughout the lowlands, azonal or immature *Alluvial soils* with weakly developed A/C profiles and extremely variable texture and drainage qualities are scattered along river valleys. These, together with soils from lacustrine, marine and postglacial raised beach deposits, are potentially productive but poor drainage and temporary flooding often restrict their use. In the uplands, thin poor *Skeletal soils*, namely *Rankers* and *Lithosols*, occur around outcropping rocks and are of strictly limited value.

Owing to the widely varying factors that have influenced soil development, both past and present, any small-scale map such as Fig. 13 purporting to show the distribution of Irish soils does nothing more than grossly simplify a complex variation of soil profiles. Associations of dominant great soil groups together with their most common parent materials are shown for each area, minor subgroups are ignored and soil boundaries are only approximate. Furthermore, prolonged human activity has deeply modified the nature of many soils, sometimes blurring, sometimes emphasizing local variations.

Peat

The growth of 3 million acres of peat covering one-seventh of Ireland has been a distinctive feature of the postglacial environment. Frequent rainfall, cool temperatures, low evaporation, gentle slopes and impervious subsoils all combined to impede drainage and to produce many lakes and other waterlogged habitats where, under anaerobic conditions, the principal bacteria normally responsible for decomposing dead plant matter could not survive. In such localities bogs arose and peat accumulated. As we shall see, man may have encouraged this process.

The nature of peat depends largely on the plant association which has created it, which in turn reflects the nature and amount of mineral nutrients in the bog waters in which the plants were growing. Thus eutrophic peats accumulate in groundwaters rich in mineral bases whilst oligotrophic peats develop in downward percolating rainwaters and become acid. There are many intermediary situations. Bogs may be classified into topogenous bogs, controlled by the groundwater table and thus only indirectly related to climate, and into climatic bogs which occur where precipitation is high and evaporation is low. Topogenous bogs form in lakes and rivers where peat builds up to water level, in depressions waterlogged by a rise of the water-table, and around springs. Climatic bogs are either of the soligenous type, where peat formation is controlled by the movement of surface water on sloping ground, or of the ombrogenous type, where the only water available for plant growth is rainfall precipitated directly onto the bog surface. Despite their varied origins, the blanket and raised bogs of Ireland have grown in recent times under ombrogenous conditions.

Irish peats have been classified according to their plant remains into two main groups. The first group comprises swamp peats containing poorly decayed reeds and sedges, well-humified fen peats that accumulated in the alkaline waters of some lakes and rivers, and wood peats where alder and birch woods had a field vegetation of swamp or fen plants. This group generally develops under eutrophic conditions rich in organic matter. The second group consists of bog moss peats composed of numerous *Sphagnum* species and other plants that have grown under either topogenous or ombrogenous conditions where oligotrophic waters reduced the amount of organic matter available. Owing to the changing environment of postglacial times, most Irish bogs are composed of a variety of peat types when viewed in section.

Once freed of glaciers, Ireland's drift-mantled lowlands were littered with lakes. Following the late-glacial interlude, rapid bog growth began about 8300 B.C. with the arrival of temperate plants along lake and river margins. From then until the close of Boreal times, swamp, fen and wood peats accumulated. Many lakes were soon filled in with fen peats or covered by a mat of floating bog moss vegetation, thereby forming topogenous basin bogs. Around 5200 B.C. extensive fens probably occupied the central lowlands. Thereafter, the increased moisture and higher water-tables of Atlantic times caused the fens to encroach on the surrounding woodlands and further peats to accumulate in newly waterlogged depressions. Soon, however, the fens and the floating mats of lake vegetation became more oligotrophic and ombrogenous bog moss peats began concealing them and the stumps of former woodland trees. Thus under typical Atlantic and sub-Atlantic conditions, acid ombrogenous raised and blanket bogs became self-perpetuating and in many localities continued to expand until man became aware of their value as a fuel resource. Thereafter, as man made inroads into the bogs so he unknowingly improved their drainage so that colonization by heath plants and birch trees became possible. Few bogs have escaped man's influence.

Blanket bogs spread indiscriminately across the uplands and lowlands of the Atlantic seaboard, west of a line joining the Foyle estuary through Galway Bay to Courtmacsherry Bay, and also occur in the Wicklow mountains and the Antrim plateau. They are finely developed in Kerry, west Galway, northwest Mayo and Donegal, varying from a few inches to over 20 feet in depth but commonly averaging 5 to 8 feet deep. Although occurring in areas with more than 40 inches of rainfall per annum, the blanket bogs reflect the quality rather than the quantity of rainfall. Persistent drenching rains and low evaporation throughout the year maintain a downward flow in the groundwater system so that organic acids forming in the peat are never neutralized by mineral bases derived from underlying sources. Thus in parts of the west, highly acid peat may even be found on limestone. The extensive blanket bog around Glenamoy in northwest Mayo has 270 raindays per annum. The colourful flora of the blanket bogs is commonly dominated by bog mosses, cotton grass (*Eriophorum vaginatum*), purple moor grass (*Molinia caerulea*), deer's hair grass (*Scirpus caespitosus*), bog myrtle (*Myrica gale*) and some heath plants.

Because trees failed to regenerate over large areas of the Atlantic seaboard during sub-Atlantic times and because persistent wetness, rapid leaching and increasing soil and groundwater acidity have come to typify the physical environment, some authorities believe that blanket bogs may form the natural climax vegetation of much of the west, as well as of uplands farther east. Alternatively, man's role in changing the biotic environment may have triggered off the processes of peat formation, with or without the help of climatic deterioration. While the removal of forests from Neolithic times onwards has created valuable arable and grazing lands throughout Ireland, the loss of the woodland

14. Traditional turf-cutting with a slane on the Wicklow mountain blanket bog

cover has had at least one unforeseen result. During sub-Atlantic times, persistent rainfall and low evaporation accompanied by agricultural malpractices have undoubtedly stimulated soil deterioration once the protective forest cover was removed. Such deterioration was marked among the poorer soils of the uplands and in the higher rainfall areas generally. Increased intensity of grazing prevented the regrowth of trees and shrubs, poor cultivation methods exhausted the soil, and continued leaching and podzolization of the topsoil was frequently followed by the formation of an iron pan which impeded drainage and promoted peat formation. Many blanket peats may thus have an anthropogenic origin for it can be shown that they have originated during the human period and have frequently engulfed Neolithic and Bronze Age dwellings, tombs and field boundaries.

Although blanket bogs may occur on slopes of up to 15°, many bogs exceeding 6 feet thick become unstable on shallower slopes after heavy rains and consequent overloading, and also after peat cutting. Spectacular bog bursts may then cause much water and plant debris to cascade downslope, engulfing farmlands and roads in their path. Such bog flows have been prominent in Donegal, the Glens of Antrim, and the Wicklow mountains. Fortunately, they generally occur far from human activity so that, excepting the loss of occasional sheep, some gullying and telltale paths of destruction, they are of little consequence. On many exposed hillsides, notably in the Wicklow and Mourne mountains and at low levels on Achill Island and the Curraun peninsula along the west coast, blanket bogs have been dissected by rills and the resultant gashes deepened and widened by wind deflation until isolated peat haggs are left standing on bare rock. The relative importance of changing climate, overgrazing by sheep and peat cutting by man in this erosion is difficult to ascertain.

Raised bogs are magnificently developed in central Ireland, mainly east of the Shannon and Suck rivers, and in the north. They originated mainly as topogenous bogs in poorly drained lowlands but, regardless of original differences in groundwater chemistry and vegetation, all were tenanted ultimately by acid bog plants and covered thickly with ombrogenous peat, namely the fresh Upper *Sphagnum* peat which has given the characteristic humped profile to the bogs. Some raised bogs occupy small basins of a few acres, others may cover many square miles, notably in the country stretching westwards from the so-called Bog of Allen in north Kildare to the Shannon. They average 18 to 20 feet in depth and sometimes reach 30 feet. Their surface is today colonized by numerous bog mosses, deer's hair grass, bog heather, purple moor grass, two species of cotton grass and, where their drainage has been improved, by heather and birch trees. Owing to their economic significance few raised bogs now survive in their natural state.

Although natural fens were once common in Ireland, most have either been buried by acid ombrogenous peats of Atlantic and sub-Atlantic age or drained by man to provide good farmland. Drainage schemes have taken in much fen south of Lough Neagh, around Lower Lough Erne and along river margins, but some natural fens still survive alongside the Shannon, Barrow and Suir rivers and between drumlins farther north.

Part Two
The evolving landscape moulded by man

Chapter 5
Prehistoric Ireland

For all practical purposes Ireland was virtually uninhabitable for modern types of man until the glaciers had receded and the harsh Pleistocene tundra was invaded by new immigrant plants and animals. Even so there is yet no certain evidence that late Palaeolithic hunters from the European mainland ever pursued reindeer or any other animal into the country.

Mesolithic

The earliest inhabitants of Ireland were primitive Mesolithic hunters and food-collectors who probably travelled across the then narrower North Channel by dugout canoe around 6000 B.C. They soon became established along the shores and river banks of Antrim and Down where abundant Cretaceous flint was readily available for making tools. They later filtered south along the shore to Dublin Bay, and inland to Carlow, southwest to Lough Gara near Boyle, and west to Magilligan Point in Derry, and Dunaff in Donegal. Beyond northeast Ireland their activities were hampered by a scarcity of flints so that their implements, though of the same type, were much smaller. They also made tools of pine and hazel but this had little effect on the woodland.

The warm moist Boreal environment into which they intruded was characterized in northeast Ireland by a dense mixed woodland of hazel, elm, oak, pine, holly and ivy. With the onset of still moister Atlantic conditions after 5200 B.C., this woodland was further enriched by alder while higher water-tables encouraged the widespread growth of peat bogs. Game was plentiful and red deer, wild boar, wild fowl and possibly wild ox (*Bos primigenius*) were important sources of food. Only the wolf and brown bear were dangerous. In seas slightly warmer than today, fish and molluscs abounded and formed the staple diet for many small coastal communities. With an almost inexhaustible flint supply, a warm equable climate, a long vegetative season and consequently rich biotic resources, life was comparatively easy for Mesolithic man. The population was numerically very small and there was little competition among the scattered inhabitants for the abundant food resources which they exploited by hunting, trapping, fowling, fishing, sealing and gathering of edible seeds, fruits and molluscs. The nature of their food quest entailed some mobility and semi-permanent camps were common. On coasts and estuaries, however, the slowly rising seas which first reached their present level around 3400 B.C. ultimately drowned many such campsites. Only the resistant flint tools, rather battered and wave-worn, have survived to reveal anything of the Mesolithic way of life. Such tools are commonly found in postglacial beach deposits, raised above present sea-level by the slow but prolonged recoil that northeast Ireland, once freed of its weighty glaciers, experienced and which continued after the main marine transgression, caused by the addition of meltwaters from the world's glaciers, had closed.

From an analysis of these implements, a distinctive Mesolithic culture, apparently derived from Upper Palaeolithic strains in Britain, has been labelled Larnian because of the abundant worked flints found in raised beach gravels at Curran Point, Larne, in Antrim. H. L. Movius (1942) has recognized an Early Larnian culture of Boreal age in which numerous flint blades used as cutting tools, scrapers and spear heads, together with other scrapers, awls, adzes and picks testify to skilled toolmakers who depended on a hunting economy. Isolation in an easy environment later caused workmanship to degenerate so that Late Larnian tools are coarser and more generalized. Flakes and blades for use as scrapers are common while choppers, axes and picks are also characteristic. Apparently Late Larnian peoples lived largely on fish and edible molluscs but as rising seas encroached upon the Atlantic woodlands so heavier tools were needed for clearing small campsites and making dugout canoes.

Mesolithic peoples pursued their uneventful, unprogressive way of life for some 3,000 years before Neolithic farmers invaded their rather stagnant cultural pool. Despite their lengthy tenure of the country, however, the small Mesolithic population had little impact on the landscape. They formed one but by no means dominant element in the ecosystem. Cultural groups living from hunting, fishing and food-collecting persisted in some areas of Ireland for a further 3,000 years after the arrival of the Neolithic colonists but even then their impact was slight.

Neolithic

At the onset of the relatively warm dry sub-Boreal climatic phase about 3000 B.C., Neolithic farming folk were already colonizing Ireland. They introduced crop cultivation, stock-rearing and permanent settlements, space for which was inevitably cleared from the mixed oak and alder woodlands. These early farmers thus initiated revolutionary changes in the landscape. From their introduction of distinctive tombs and pottery making, much is known about the origins and distribution of successive waves of colonists and of the Neolithic way of death. Their way of life and their precise impact on the landscape are less well understood but archaeological and pollen evidence have revealed something of Neolithic society and economy.

Origins and distribution

The most dramatic legacies of Neolithic Ireland are the widely distributed great stone or megalithic tombs covered by large cairns that served usually, but not exclusively, for collective cremation burials. Apart from their bold appearance, their distribution and style together with their grave goods have told much about their builders. Despite the basic unity of western European megalithic culture, a dramatic regionalism clearly arose when colonists of differing origins converged on Ireland. They probably arrived in skin boats.

Early Neolithic settlers built a specialized form of segmented gallery grave for collective cremation and inhumation burials, known as the court cairn or horned cairn. Some 300 court cairns survive, largely in north and northwest Ireland, commonly sited on the margins of uplands where lightly wooded, easily cultivated soils presumably attracted primitive farmers. Almost continuous settlement stretched from north Mayo to Carlingford Lough and, with similar concentrations around the Firth of Clyde, archaeologists have recognized a distinct Clyde–Carlingford culture tracing its origins to the Bay of Biscay and Mediterranean area. Some believe that these people spread westwards across Ireland from the northeast coast while others have argued for initial settlement in Mayo and Sligo followed by an eastward spread across Ireland into southwest Scotland. The 150 portal dolmens scattered through the north, east and west of Ireland may be single-chamber relatives of the court cairns.

Five centuries after the arrival of the first farmers, a fresh group of sophisticated Neolithic colonists sailed up the Irish Sea, landed near the Liffey and Boyne estuaries, spread purposefully northwestwards to Sligo Bay and also wandered into Ulster and the south-central lowlands. They had come from Brittany; before that their ancestors had voyaged across the Bay of Biscay from Iberia and all along the Atlantic coast of Europe they left behind impressive megalithic monuments. In Ireland they built large collective passage graves, such as the elaborately decorated tombs at Newgrange, Knowth and Dowth in the Boyne valley, that rank among Europe's most spectacular prehistoric monuments. Unlike other builders of prehistoric chamber tombs, they favoured hilltop sites, notably around the Wicklow mountains, and often grouped their tombs into cemeteries, notably in the Boyne valley and at Loughcrew in Meath, and at Carrowkeel and Carrowmore in Sligo. Passage graves continued to be used well into the Bronze Age.

The elusive Beaker folk who settled in Late Neolithic Ireland heralded the approaching Bronze Age. They commonly built widely distributed wedge-shaped gallery graves for collective burial, as at Labbacallee in Cork and in Derry and Tyrone, and also erected ritual stone circles. The wedge-shaped gallery graves are most evident on the lighter soils and in those areas of the southwest, west and north that today offer good winter pasture. Beside megalith builders, numerous other farming communities that buried their dead in single graves or beneath their dwellings also strongly colonized south and central Ireland. Finally with the arrival of the above 'primary' Neolithic settlers, the native Mesolithic communities commonly adopted new equipment, penetrated deeper into the heavily wooded interior, and generated 'secondary' Neolithic cultures, notably among the indigenous flint workers and axe makers of the northeast. The occurrence of Neolithic pottery with Mesolithic-style flint implements in the Bann valley indicates a cultural overlap on sites where fishing and fish-curing were still practised, at least seasonally, by people who became farmers. Among coastal sandhills, isolated and impoverished Mesolithic communities, dependent on fishing and food-gathering but also making pottery, persisted into early Christian times. Despite contact with more advanced cultures, the Sandhills people, unlike other 'secondary' Neolithic elements, exerted little influence on the landscape or on new colonists.

Society, economy and landscape

Neolithic Ireland was thus occupied by many varied peoples who imported a wide range of European cultures and also absorbed some native Mesolithic traditions. What effect did this cultural amalgam have on the landscape? Scanty evidence suggests that most Neolithic settlements were individual self-sufficient farmsteads, often accompanied by a burial place, that occupied woodland clearings along the coast, in river valleys and on upland margins wherever initially less wooded country and lighter well-drained soils favoured primitive agriculture. Villages and hamlets were less common. However, at Lough Gur in Limerick, several round and rectangular houses built largely of timber, reeds and rushes coexisted to indicate a small village community dependent mainly on cattle-raising but also growing grain. The first settlers used round-based undecorated western Neolithic pottery, leaf and lozenge arrowheads and polished stone axes. Later, as 'primary' Neolithic traditions slackened and native styles emerged, coarse flat-based ware was used while Beaker pottery shows continuity of settlement well into the Bronze Age. The passage grave cemeteries indicate a cohesive social organization in which important persons were buried in traditional well-furnished mausolea.

Despite their varied origins, several recurring elements in the economy of all Neolithic peoples justify viewing their impact on landscape as a whole. Mesolithic peoples may have herded wild game but the new colonists were essentially stockbreeders. Imports of animals for breeding and of seed grain came with the first Neolithic settlers as an essential part of their material culture. Domestic animals are attested from many sites. The wedge-shaped gallery grave at Labbacallee, Cork, yielded charred bones of domestic ox (*Bos longifrons*), pig and sheep; the court cairn at Ballyalton, Down, yielded ox, sheep, pig and dog. Ox also occurred in the Carrowkeel and Loughcrew passage graves. Ox, deer and bear bones and deer antlers also provided awls, pins and needles. Whorls of bone and stone were used in spinning wool. Grain cultivation is also well attested. Indeed the sub-Boreal environment was probably more conducive to wheat-growing than is the present climate. Sherds from the Dunloy court cairn in Antrim contained impressions of Emmer wheat and small spelt. The passage grave on Baltinglass Hill (1,258 feet), Wicklow, yielded carbonized wheat grains, hazel nuts and oak charcoal, and many other sites have yielded naked barley and wheat. 'Secondary' Neolithic peoples grew little grain but, although hunting continued, their association with domestic animals shows an essential break with tradition, the beginnings of a new economy.

By definition, the Neolithic peoples of Ireland used stone for tools and weapons, the best sources of which lay in Antrim. Flint was worked at Glenarm and Cushendun into polished axes, leaf-shaped arrowheads and scrapers by native workers responding to Neolithic techniques and requirements. At Tievebulliagh near Cushendall and on Rathlin Island, a hard finegrained bluish rock called porcellanite gave rise to large axe factories whose products, the Antrim bluestone polished axes, have been found as far afield as northeast Scotland and southern England. Although these industries were strictly localized, the accompanying trade exposed Ireland to many outside influences.

By combining the archaeological material with pollen evidence revealed by the earlier sub-Boreal peats, notably by G. F. Mitchell (1956), the landscape changes effected by Neolithic peoples are more clearly evinced. Controlled use of fire and the stone axe cut inroads into the woodland for purposes of stock-rearing, cultivation and settlement. The gradual decline of elm, the rise of hazel and the appearance of ribwort plantain and bracken in the pollen record at the onset of sub-Boreal times all suggest human interference. Ribwort thrives on open pastures where it is widely spread by cattle, while grazing may be fatal to woodland regeneration. Apparently with abundant land available for the new colonists, shifting cultivation was practised. Initially, high forest on well-drained ground was cleared for tillage and pasture and alder expanded, but as the soils became impoverished these clearings were abandoned and immediately invaded by hazel and birch scrub, which at first dominated the secondary wood-land. The farmers did not abandon the region but simply moved to newly cleared areas. Gradually the landscape became a mosaic of virgin forest, tillage patches, rough pastures and secondary woodlands in various stages of regeneration until elm, oak and alder once again predominated. During mid-Neolithic times, around 2400 B.C., ash, which could not flourish in the virgin forests and had been restricted to thin limestone soils, began expanding through the un-stable secondary woodlands. About 2200 B.C., as elm began a renewed decline generally, probably because the soils of the secondary woodlands had been exhausted by poor farming practices, oak, for which the summer warmth of sub-Boreal times was ideal, increased in importance. Neolithic farmers thus initiated changes in the vegetation cover of far-reaching significance but at the close of the period Ireland, if less tidy, was still a well-forested country.

The Bronze Age

The dawn of the Bronze Age about 1800 B.C. saw the sporadic adoption of metal tools by pre-existing farming folk. There was no sudden economic or cultural revolution nor any immediate large-scale influx of new settlers but, with better tools becoming available, landscape changes assumed a fresh quality. At first Neolithic settlements, pottery and burial traditions continued in use as metal-working spread through the country. Soon, however, a flourishing Bronze Age culture developed. Mining, metal-working and farming made increasing demands on resources while the needs of a growing population, supplemented notably by Late Bronze Age immigrants, for more space led almost inevitably to turmoil. Under such varied stimuli, the woodlands were further reduced. New metallurgical, pottery and jewellery techniques and styles were acquired through trade, while Irish bronze and gold manufactures were widely exported.

Mining, metallurgy and trade

By definition, the Bronze Age was distinguished by the use of copper and tin for making bronze objects. Successful farmers made available the food surplus necessary for the support of miners and craftsmen who could exploit Ireland's mineral resources and apply the newly acquired metal-working techniques. Copper is widely scattered through Ireland but Bronze Age miners soon recognized the importance of the copper-bearing rocks of west Cork and Kerry, where Galician rock-scribings indicate that Iberia was a significant source of early Irish metallurgy. The earliest metal types and some Early Bronze Age pottery support this belief although other metal-workers arrived from central Europe. Gold and some tin were probably extracted from some south Wicklow stream gravels, but large quantities of tin were of necessity imported from Iberia and Cornwall.

During the earlier Bronze Age (1800–1200 B.C.), the metallurgical industry was greatly stimulated by both home and overseas demands for Irish metal goods and owing to this trade new styles and techniques constantly reached Ireland. Simultaneously, itinerant traders and craftsmen were diffusing their wares and their knowledge throughout Europe. Irish and Irish-style products such as lunulae and sundiscs of sheet gold, bronze knives, daggers and axes, and copper halberds have been found throughout western and central Europe and some as far afield as Scandinavia, Crete and Iberia. In return Ireland imported Portuguese daggers and axes, Baltic amber, and glass and faience beads from the eastern Mediterranean. The later Bronze Age (1200–200 B.C.) saw metal-working revolutionized as craftsmen developed a wider range of tools and used clay moulds for casting. Torques of twisted bar gold and other jewellery, tools and weapons were made that clearly reveal contacts with Scandinavia, Mycenae, Cyprus and Egypt. Indeed the manufacture of personal gold ornaments and of flanged and later socketed axes suggests that certain echelons of society were achieving both power and wealth. Eastern Mediterranean beads and Mycenaean weapons reached Ireland, probably through southern England.

While the Neolithic record has yielded no weapons designed specifically for warfare, no fortifications and no defended farms, the Bronze Age was characterized by increasing turbulence, resulting probably from growing competition for the better land. The halberd appeared in the Early Bronze Age (1800–1400 B.C.) and was joined by the rapier, dirk and several new spears during the Middle Bronze Age (1400–1200 B.C.). The armament industry reached a prehistoric climax during the Late Bronze Age (1200–200 B.C.) when leaf-shaped slashing swords, finely worked spears and ornate shields of bronze, leather and wood, together with the abundance of gold bracelets, gorgets and bullae, suggest the presence of a warrior aristocracy. Simultaneously, the increased number of hoards buried for safety in the earth by metal craftsmen and merchants suggests that life was less secure. Late Bronze Age metallurgy was influenced strongly by new industrial techniques and by immigrant bronzesmiths from many parts of Europe. Spectacular bronze cauldrons and buckets were modelled after Mediterranean art styles; some metal types reveal contacts with Denmark; while after 700 B.C. there appear metal wares showing connections with the Final Bronze (Late Urnfield) and Initial Iron (Hallstatt) Ages of central and Mediterranean Europe. Jet and amber imports increase in amount.

Society, economy and landscape

Following the Beaker folk and the first metal-workers, the only notable earlier Bronze Age immigrants were the late collective tomb-builders and copper-seekers from the European mainland who built V-shaped passage graves in Waterford, and peoples from Britain in whom the European single grave tradition had been fused with insular late Neolithic cults. The latter invaded Ulster in two waves and later spread through Ireland. First came the Food Vessel folk from northern Britain who strongly influenced Middle Bronze Age pottery styles. Secondly, Cinerary Urn peoples, originating from southern England, reached Ireland and introduced cordoned and encrusted varieties of cinerary urn. After them came Late Bronze Age immigrants of ultimately continental origin who had already been affected by Late Urnfield and Hallstatt peoples in Europe and who brought Knocknalappa and Flat-rimmed wares to Ireland. The appearance of new European metal techniques, equipment and pottery during the first millennium B.C. suggests that Ireland experienced a series of invasions that were to culminate with the arrival of the Celts.

Apart from the appearance of miners and metal craftsmen among the people,

Early Bronze Age society altered but gradually. Farmers and herdsmen at Lough Gur continued to occupy round and rectangular dwellings, some of which were built around free-standing timber and wattle frames while others were enclosed by low stone kerbs. At Carrigillihy near Glandore, Cork, an oval drystone house with timber posts, associated with Early Bronze Age pottery, stood inside a small ringfort-style enclosure bounded by massive drystone walling. At Rathjordan near Lough Gur and at Lough Gara near Boyle, small circular crannógs – dwellings on artificial island and lake shore sites – of suggested Neolithic and Early Bronze Age have been found. While simple undefended homes were occupied throughout the Middle Bronze Age, the need for defence for man and his animals soon dawned upon many inhabitants and quite early in the Bronze Age the custom of enclosing dwellings with a protective wall or wooden palisade arose. Nevertheless, the Bronze Age dates assigned to the Carrigillihy house, the Rathjordan crannóg and similar dwellings still occasion controversy. Likewise, some small ringforts enclosed by ditches and ramparts at Cush in Limerick have been assigned to the Late Bronze Age, but are more probably Celtic. Inside stood oval and rectangular houses up to 26 feet long while similar dwellings stood in nearby fields. Known dwellings of the Late Bronze Age include crannógs without enclosing palisades. A crannóg at Ballinderry, Offaly, had a large 45-by-40-foot rectangular dwelling supported by a strong frame of excellent joinery work. One Lough Gara crannóg probably held ten small houses, each with a central hearth. Bronze Age settlements were generally scattered through the countryside, connected by paths such as the Corlona trackway, dated at about 1440 B.C.

Cattle-rearing and tillage expanded to meet the needs of the growing farming population and of the miners, craftsmen and warriors who depended upon a readily available food surplus. The metallurgical advances of the later Bronze Age had important practical repercussions on the landscape. The introduction of the securely hafted socketed axe made forest clearance much easier while the sickle enabled the farmer to harvest his grain crops more effectively. Shallow and shifting cultivation and attendant soil exhaustion intensified. On thin, light-textured soils along many upland fringes, cultivation exposed the earth to increased leaching, podzolization and local erosion. As iron-pans induced by man impeded drainage and altered the ecological balance, many abandoned tillage patches were invaded by blanket bogs. Early field banks, of stones and sods designed to protect cultivated land from damage by deer and straying domestic animals, have been recognized from Neolithic sites in Down and Tyrone, and became more common during the Bronze Age. At Ballygroll, Derry, irregular fields varying from 3 to 12 acres in extent were enclosed by distinct banks but, together with nearby dwellings and burial sites, were abandoned before the overlying peat began to form about the middle of the first millennium B.C.

Pollen analysis reveals a continued shrinkage of the virgin woodlands and suggests that Bronze Age farmers were attacking not only elm trees but also the dense oak woods. Elm was probably used by early farmers to indicate soils that suited their purpose while its leaves and twigs probably provided fodder for their animals. The expanding secondary woodland was dominated by hazel and birch scrub and by elder and blackthorn shrubs. The pollen record also shows a continued expansion of the ribwort plantain, the appearance of nettles, bracken and gorse in abandoned clearings, and the development of heaths on some exhausted soils. By the close of the warm dry sub-Boreal climatic phase during the Late Bronze Age, the Irish landscape had been transformed by man into an untidy patchwork of tillage patches, pastures, dwellings with perhaps a local smithy, and trackways lying among abandoned clearings, secondary scrub and virgin woodland. Lastly, Bronze Age folk built a wide variety of funerary and ritual monuments, many of which still litter the landscape. During the Early and Middle Bronze Age degenerate chamber tombs, multiple cist cairns, single cist barrows, pit burials, open-air temples, pillar stones and stone alignments were erected. Late Bronze Age burials were commonly by single grave crema-tion in flat cemeteries though cemetery cairns and ring barrows continued in use.

Early Iron Age

During the Late Bronze Age two events occurred that were to have major repercussions on the Irish landscape. First, the warm dry sub-Boreal climate gave way to cooler, wetter, stormier sub-Atlantic conditions, notably after 500 B.C. Secondly, Early Iron Age influences began reaching the country, heralds of the forthcoming Celtic invasions. Consequently, climatic deterioration com-bined with human factors to lower the treeline on the uplands, accelerate bog growth, induce further changes in the woodlands generally, and see the virtual disappearance of Scots pine. Oak was the dominant species. Durmast oak and birch shared the siliceous soils of the hill country, the latter flourishing at higher elevations, while pedunculate oak dominated the deep calcareous drift soils of the lowlands. Ash, with wych elm in lesser numbers, also grew on lime-rich soils and probably became dominant on shallow limestone soils in the west. Alder abounded in the lowland fens and marshes and in the west, and probably shared poorly drained shale soils with ash. From 400 B.C. to about A.D. 300, a lull in agrarian activity, probably indicative of the widespread turmoil of the times, caused elm and ash to expand temporarily at the expense of hazel scrub. Later, a dramatic fall in elm pollen, dated by radioactive carbon to about A.D. 300, suggests an intensified onslaught on the virgin woodlands. Hazel scrub again spread through abandoned clearings. Evergreen shrubs were represented by holly and yew, with arbutus in the west.

15. Staigue fort
A fine univallate dry-stone ringfort or cashel on the slopes of Eagles Hill, west of Sneem, County Kerry. An elaborate system of stairways leads to the terraces of its 4 m (13 ft) thick ramparts. The fort may trace its origins to the pagan Iron Age.

The arrival of the Celts

Although the earliest Iron Age influences reached Ireland about the middle of the first millennium B.C. and were later followed by Hallstatt adventurers and craftsmen, Late Bronze Age culture persisted for some considerable time. The Early Iron Age proper began about 250 B.C. with the arrival of the Celts, whose social organization and strongly pastoral economy subsequently played such an important role in shaping the Irish landscape. The Early Iron Age and Irish pre-history generally closed with the firm establishment of Christianity and a documentary record among the Celtic peoples in the fifth century A.D., but the distinctly Celtic contribution to the rural landscape persisted well into modern times, frequently disturbed by later intrusive elements but never wholly quenched.

The Celtic invasions, stemming ultimately from the loosely knit barbaric peoples that had evolved in central Europe during the first millennium B.C., were proclaimed in Ireland by the appearance of sophisticated La Tène metal-work, stone carvings, weapons and horse trappings in an otherwise meagre Early Iron Age archaeological record. Judging from the decorated cult stones and metal objects found throughout western Ireland, most Celts probably arrived direct from the European mainland. Some martial Iron Age B chariot warriors may have entered Ulster from northern Britain in the first century B.C. Celtic society was strongly patriarchal and led by a warrior aristocracy whose wealth was counted in cattle, whose heroic exploits centred on cattle-raiding, and whose power was only finally overthrown by the English conquests of the seventeenth century.

Stemming from the Celtic invasions, the dispersed population of Early Iron Age Ireland increased, fortified settlements became common, but, significantly, the people never gathered into towns. Scattered ringforts or raths were occupied by warrior-herdsmen who became overlords of the poorer cultivating peasantry, derived in part from native Bronze Age folk. Raths served as ranches from which animal husbandry and short-range transhumance could be directed. Festivals among the pagan Celts belonged essentially to a pastoral rather than to an arable cycle. While raths, crannógs, isolated huts and farm clusters characterized the settlement landscape, large fortifications were less common. There were some 200 promontory forts defended by palisaded earthworks thrown across the necks of upland spurs and sea-girt headlands, notably at Dunseverick in Antrim and on the Old Head of Kinsale, Cork. With the growth of regional consciousness among the Gaelic-speaking peoples, several tribal centres domi-nated by great hill forts arose, associated with Celtic royal houses. Notable examples of such royal sites, whose earthworks still feature in the landscape, occur at Tara in Meath, Emain Macha or Navan fort near Armagh, Dún Ailinne near Kilcullen in Kildare, and Cruachain in Roscommon. Indeed as Celtic settlement and land-use practices spread through the country, man's impact on the landscape became more uniform.

Chapter 6
The Celts and the rural landscape

Following their arrival around 250 B.C. the Celts had a thousand years in which to shape the landscape according to their traditions and desires, unimpeded by any major invasion by alien peoples. Ireland was never brought under the power of Rome and, alone among the countries of Europe, was spared the fury of the barbarian invaders who swept across the Continent during the years immediately following the decline of Rome. The Roman occupation of Britain had little effect on the Irish landscape but contacts with the Roman provinces were inevitable. In A.D. 97–98 Tacitus wrote that in soil, in climate and in the character and civilization of its inhabitants, Ireland was much like Britain. Its approaches and harbours were tolerably well known from merchants who traded there. Pottery, glass and jewellery were imported from various Roman provinces while hides, cattle and Irish wolfhounds were exported to Britain. Trade, together with the influx of refugees from Britain and Gaul and, notably during the fourth and fifth centuries, the looting of valuables and slaves – including incidentally the boy who later became St Patrick – brought many new ideas to Ireland. The heavy iron plough was introduced from Britain, an event of great material significance to the evolving landscape. Metal-working and enamelling revived under the stimulus of provincial Roman work in Britain but, with the eclipse of Roman culture, art soon acquired a Celtic expression as new life was infused into the dying La Tène styles that lingered in the west.

When converted to Christianity during the fifth century, Ireland was still characterized by a preliterate Iron Age culture to which common social and economic customs, language and laws gave some semblance of unity. Numerous tribal groups were ruled by minor kings who were responsible for land fertility and communal safety, paying tribute to over-kings and to the high king. During the subsequent early Christian period, early Irish literature and laws combine with abundant field evidence to paint a vivid portrait of the essentially rural Celtic landscape, most of whose distinctive qualities were to survive somewhere into modern times. Celtic society weathered the Viking onslaught of the ninth and tenth centuries and the later Anglo-Norman incursions, while traditional settlement patterns and agricultural practices survived in many parts into the nineteenth century. An understanding of the Celtic contribution is thus basic to any appreciation of the developing Irish rural landscape. Such understanding is provided most clearly by the evidence from early Christian times, a period of some seven centuries during which Celtic traditions were impressed firmly on a landscape devoid, at least initially, of towns.

The Impact of early Christianity

The early monasteries

The Christian message reached the Dési in Waterford, the Corcu Loegde in Cork and other south coast peoples before Patrick returned as a missionary in 432 (or was it 456?), but it was he who first organized the church into territorial dioceses, ruled by bishops. His missionary work was largely concentrated north of a line from Wexford to Galway, an area where most churches that later claimed Patrick in person as their founder are now situated. Following his death in 461 (493?) and Ireland's isolation from Rome, Patrick's ecclesiastical organization withered away as monasteries following the rule of a single founder ousted episcopal sees as centres of religion, learning and artistry. The Irish Church henceforth became a church of monks whose monasteries formed a new item in the landscape.

Monastic ideals spread with missionaries from western Britain, during Patrick's lifetime. Although paganism persisted for a time, existing Celtic society with its stress on kinship and personal rule peacefully accepted the concept of the monastic family ruled by an abbot, usually elected from the founder's family. Monasteries soon arose at Armagh, Clonard, Kildare, and on the Aran Islands. From Clonard, disciples of Finnian founded new monasteries at Durrow, Derry, Clonmacnoise, Clonfert, Devenish, Aghaboe, Glasnevin and also Iona (563) off the Scottish coast, each retaining close ties with one another. Other sixth-century missionaries founded centres at Bangor, Moville, Glendalough, Tuam, Cork and elsewhere. Meanwhile a few religious houses for women were founded at Kildare, in association with the men's monastery, at Killeavy near Newry, Killeady in Limerick, Cloonburren in Roscommon, and Cluain Bronaigh in Meath. Some remote monastic sites, like Kildreelig on Bolus Head in Kerry and Skellig Michael offshore, were quite spectacular.

Early monastic settlements were really adaptations of larger raths whose primitive character well suited the ascetic temper of the early Irish Church. They thus differed considerably from the later Irish foundations by continental orders. Commonly a circular earth rampart or timber palisade enclosed a simple rectangular wooden church, a cluster of round wattle cells, a refectory and adjoining kitchen, a library, some workshops and a forge, a graveyard and perhaps a school. The church, like the other main buildings, was often constructed of oak with a thatched or shingled roof, a stone altar and a tall stone slab near the door. Where timber and thatch were scarce, notably on the west coast, stone buildings, such as the finely corbelled Gallarus oratory in the Dingle peninsula and the beehive cells or clocháns on Skellig Michael, were constructed. The

87

larger monasteries of the sixth century contained a hundred or more monks, mostly laymen but including several priests in holy orders, and many communities expanded to several hundred persons during the golden age of the seventh and eighth centuries. Then as Irish and Latin cultures fused, early Christian scholarship and artistry, notably the art of manuscript illumination, reached their zenith, while monastic workshops, stimulated by the need for sacred vessels, became major centres of metal-working and craftsmanship in wood and stone. Each community contained a cook, baker, miller, cellarer, smith, stonemason, gardener and others, as well as priests and scribes. Undoubtedly, the largest monastic settlements, such as Glendalough and Clonmacnoise with their many churches, were virtually towns in both size and functions. They supported monks whose primary roles were not always as foodproducers and they provided hostels, schools, religious and cultural centres, and places of refuge for their nearby peoples. Many were easily reached by developing systems of roads and paths.

16. The Skelligs off the Kerry coast
On precipitous Skellig Michael in the foreground are three dry-stone, corbelled clochans of the austere early Christian anchoritic monastery, nestling within terraced enclosures some 180 m (600 ft) above the Atlantic Ocean. Little Skellig in the distance is the most southerly breeding place for gannets in Ireland.

The need for economic self-sufficiency demanded that all monasteries should be centres of tillage and pastoralism. Thus, beyond the enclosure, each monastery cultivated cereals and vegetables, pastured cattle, reared sheep notably for wool, and owned farm buildings, a mill and a lime kiln. The Celts had earlier expanded their pastoral farming economy throughout Ireland and now missionaries introduced new farm practices from Europe. The few heavy iron plough coulters and shares so far excavated have all come from sites that post-date the arrival of Christianity. Ploughing, sowing, harvesting and threshing, fishing, milking and beekeeping are all noted in early writings as activities among monks. Their diet consisted mainly of bread, milk, eggs, honey and fish, with meat permitted on special occasions. The role of the early monasteries in the landscape is thus clearly defined.

Later developments

For seven centuries the distinctly Celtic monasteries formed an integral part of the Irish rural scene. Even the decline of pure monasticism after 700, as spiritual fervour inevitably gave way to temporal ambition and greed, served to accentuate their importance. While Emain Macha near Armagh, Cruachain near Elphin, and other Celtic tribal centres near which many early monasteries had been founded, slowly decayed, Armagh, Clonmacnoise, Kildare and Glendalough became wealthy and powerful. Rival monasteries, now often ruled by laymen, competed for land. A large Columban monastery was founded at Kells in 803. Between the Viking raids of the ninth and tenth centuries, stone-masons found time to carve elaborate High Crosses, mortared stone churches such as St Kevin's at Glendalough began replacing earlier wooden buildings, and tall graceful free standing round towers were constructed to serve as belfries and places of refuge. Some eighty round towers, dating from the early tenth to the late twelfth century, survive on early monastic sites. Where complete, they range from 70 to 120 feet in height and, in their unexpected classic simplicity, are unique to Ireland.

Reform of the Celtic Church was inevitable and, although the details need not concern us, the ensuing death blow dealt to the native monasteries, by the re-establishment of episcopal sees after the Synod at Ráth Bresail in 1111 and by the arrival of foreign monastic orders in Ireland after 1127, removed a distinctive component from the Celtic landscape. As early as the eighth and ninth centuries, reforming Céli Dé hermits had sought spiritual retreat by moving to isolated cells, later denoted by *desert* and *dysert* place-names. Near the coast, such foundations, for instance at Finglas and Tallaght, fell easy prey to Vikings. Although the Vikings certainly shattered the scholarly peace of the monasteries and relieved them of much wealth, the overall patterns of the monastic land-scape were little disturbed. If the art of illumination was lost and many Irish monks fled with valuable manuscripts to the Continent, metal-working soon revived. However, monastic corruption and the appearance of local reformers, of Christian Norse communities in towns, and of Gregorian reform on the Continent all stimulated the desire for church reform, although it took forty years to overcome the vested interests of some 180 monasteries before the wishes of the 1111 Synod on diocesan and parochial organization were finally implemented. At the Synod of Kells in 1152, thirty-six sees were created and the papal legate distributed *pallia* to four archbishops – Armagh, Cashel, Dublin and Tuam.

Meanwhile, in 1127, reformed Benedictine monks from Savigny in Normandy had settled at Carrick, near Downpatrick, in the earliest recorded abbey of a continental monastic order in Ireland. By 1135, Benedictine monks from Tiron had founded the Abbey of the Holy Cross in Tipperary. In 1142 Cistercians arrived at Mellifont. A new era of landscape change had dawned.

Celtic society and settlement

Social structure and political organization
Social and economic practices introduced by the Celts several centuries before Christianity reached Ireland persisted long after the demise of the native church. Recognition of the powerful sense of kinship and family among the Celts and of the coexistence of both free and tributary peoples in Celtic Ireland is fundamental to an understanding of the settlements that arose.

The two pivotal institutions of Celtic society were the *fine* or joint-family, the social unit in which ultimate ownership of family land was vested, and the *tuath* or petty kingdom, the semi-independent political unit governed by a king, *rí*, elected by the freemen from among the members of a ruling family. The *fine* comprised all relations in the male line of descent for five generations. There was no system of primogeniture and land was divided equally between brothers, with resultant fragmentation. Individuals had few legal rights and then only as members of the *fine*. There was no public law, but a legal system based on rights and precedents was interpreted by professional lawyers or brehons and enforced, not by regular sanctions, but by private action or public opinion.

The *tuatha* were grouped into over-kingdoms and these in turn formed the seven provinces, which by the fifth century had replaced the five Early Iron Age kingdoms, owing nominal allegiance to a high king, *árd rí*, in Cashel or Tara. The cultural unity produced by the Q-Celtic language, by first Druidism and later Christianity, and by the brehon laws did not extend to political unity. As provincial kings vied for the high kingship, the concept of a Celtic nation-state withered. By the eighth century, at least 150 *tuatha* existed although the total population was probably less than half a million. Their boundaries, although ill-defined because the petty king's authority was personal rather than territorial, often served later to outline many Anglo-Norman baronies. The

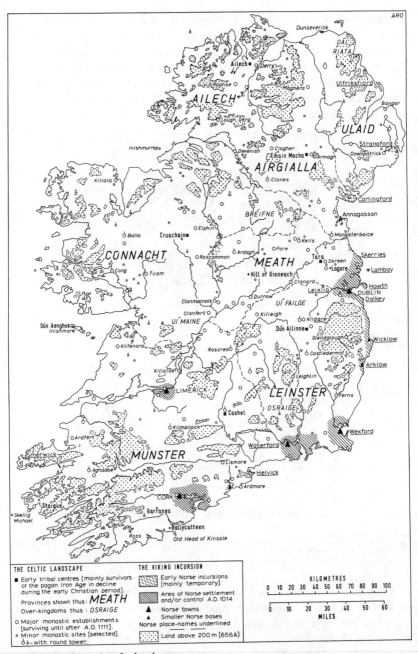

The map shows Early Christian Ireland with the following labels:

Dunseverick · DÁL RIATA · Ulfriksfiord · Bangor · Ailech · Derry · Raphoe · Maghera · AILECH · ULAID · Strangford · Downpatrick · Inishmurray · Devenish · Clogher · Emain Macha ■ Armagh · AIRGIALLA · Carlingford · Killala · Clones · Annagassan · BRÉIFNE · Elphin · Monasterboice · Balla · Cruachain · Kells · Skerries · CONNACHT · Roscommon · Ardagh · Fore · MEATH · Tara · Skreen · Lambay · Cong · Tuam · Hill of Uisneach · Lagore · Howth · Clongrd · Leixlip · DUBLIN · Dalkey · Clonmacnois · Durrow · UÍ FAILGE · Clonfert · Killeigh · Kildare · Dún Aenghus · Inishmore · UÍ MAINE · Dún Ailinne ■ · Glendalough · Wicklow · Kilfenora · Roscrea · Castledermot · Arklow · KillaTaei · Leighlin · LIMERICK · LEINSTER · Ferns · Cashel · OSRAIGE · Wexford · Kilmallock · Ardfert · Waterford · Lismore · MUNSTER · Helvick · Aghadoe · Ardmore · Smerwick · CORK · Staigue · Garranes · Skellig Michael · Ballycatteen · Ross · Old Head of Kinsale

THE CELTIC LANDSCAPE

■ Early tribal centres [mainly survivors of the pagan Iron Age in decline during the early Christian period].

Provinces shown thus: *MEATH*

Over-kingdoms thus: *OSRAIGE*

○ Major monastic establishments [surviving until after A.D. 1111].

• Minor monastic sites [selected].

○ő ő - with round tower.

THE VIKING INCURSION

▨ Early Norse incursions [mainly temporary]

▧ Area of Norse settlement and/or control A.D. 1014

▲ Norse towns

▲ Smaller Norse bases

Norse place-names underlined

⣿ Land above 200 m [656A]

KILOMETRES
0 10 20 30 40 50 60 70 80 90 100

MILES
0 10 20 30 40 50 60

17. *Early Christian Ireland*
(Monasteries simplified from *Map of Monastic Ireland*, 2nd ed. 1964, Ordnance Survey, Dublin.)

Leinster baronies of Forth, Bargy, Slievemargy and Idrone, for instance, each preserve the limits of older *tuatha*. Similarly, many dioceses came to coincide with early over-kingdoms. The diocese of Ossory was once the land of Osraige; Kilmore was previously the twelfth-century kingdom of Bréifne; Kilfenora was the small kingdom of Corcomruad; Down was the over-kingdom of Dál Fiatach which encompassed *tuatha* such as Dubthrian and Leth Cathail that later became baronies; and so on.

18. An early Irish monastery
Redrawn by the author from a reconstruction by L. de Paor in T. W. Moody and F. X. Martin (eds.), *The Course of Irish History*, 1967; Mercier Press Ltd.

19. A crannóg
Redrawn by the author from a reconstruction by W. F. Wakeman in W. G. Wood-Martin, *The Lake Dwellings of Ireland*, 1886.

Early Irish society was rigidly stratified and conservative. The Celtic aristo-cracy formed a dominant minority holding the better land and exerting power over less-privileged and tributary peoples. Rank depended on birth, wealth or learning so that brehons, poets, druids and, later, Christian clergy were of equal status with petty kings. Even unfree persons who professed some skilled trade, such as smiths, physicians and harpists, could acquire freeman status. All freemen were landowners, classified according to their property as valued in *séts* (the basic unit equivalent to a young heifer), and *cumals* (a female slave or bonds-woman equivalent to six *séts*). The higher ranking *bóaire*, a cowlord of similar status to the English yeoman after the fifteenth century, had to have land worth thrice seven *cumals* or sixty-three milch cows. The brehons allowed polygamy and fosterage of children and, while legally married women were important, concubines existed well into early Christian times and women fought in war until the seventh century. Like concubinage, slavery was inherited from the Iron Age and lasted into the twelfth century. Indeed slave girls and labouring chain-gangs undertook most servile tasks around the rath.

The native non-Celtic peoples survived as vassals, labourers and unskilled workmen under Celtic overlordship. They included the Cruithni of Ulster, who survived into historical times as the Picts of Scotland, the Loígis of Leinster, and possibly the Ciarraige of Connacht and north Kerry. By the fifth century A.D. these peoples had completely absorbed Celtic culture and language, and Celtic historians soon reconstructed the past so as to obscure the diverse origins of the population while stressing the heroic activities of the great war-lords of the Early Iron Age. Meanwhile the Dál Riata of Antrim carried the Q-Celtic language to Argyll in Scotland.

Settlement

The Celtic emphasis on kinship and family, their well-ordered society and their strongly pastoral but self-sufficient economy all combined to produce an essentially scattered pattern of settlement. Celtic chieftains and small farmers alike dwelt in isolated raths and crannógs while poorer tributary peoples occupied clusters of simple dwellings. Society had no need for towns and, until the Vikings settled, Ireland was devoid of urban centres.

The rath or ringfort was the isolated homestead of the wealthier *bóaire* and his virtually self-sufficient household. The rath settlement had been fore-shadowed during the Early Bronze Age but reached its finest development after the Celtic intrusion and continued in use into, and locally after, the twelfth century. Over 30,000 such raths survive today as grassy earthworks, mainly in lowland farming country. The simplest and most numerous consisted of one or more wooden buildings and some wattle-and-daub out-houses enclosed by a high earthen bank, sometimes topped with a wooden palisade, and an outside ditch. The raths of more influential persons had several encircling ramparts and ditches. The enclosed space, averaging 60 to 110 feet across, was essentially a farmyard rather than a fort, for the absence of wells within most raths meant that they could afford only temporary protection. Timber was the common building material but where wood was even then scarce, as in Kerry, stone raths – cashels or cahers – arose. Buildings were commonly roofed with timber and thatch, though shingles and slates were also used. Souterrains or underground passages provided storage space and some refuge from sudden attacks. From a contemporary account, one *bóaire's* property included a 27-foot house, a 17-foot outhouse, a barn, mill, kiln, pigsty, and sheep and calf pens. He also owned 20 cows, 2 bulls, 6 oxen, 20 pigs, 4 domestic boars, 2 sows, 20 sheep, a saddle horse, 16 bushels of seed in the ground, and a full selection of household and farming equipment. Separate huts within the enclosure served the functions of different rooms in a modern house. A noble's main hall was richly furnished with articles of gold, silver, bronze and yew, and bed cubicles were arranged along the walls.

Apart from the simple raths, a few elaborate fortresses were built with stone walls, palisaded causeways, wooden gates, sentry boxes and dwellings. The stone fort at Grianan Ailech in Donegal was occupied by the northern Ui Néill into the twelfth century. Other stone forts included spectacular Dún Aenghus on the Aran Islands, the 90-foot-wide Staigue fort in Kerry and Cahercommaun in Clare. The large trivallate ringforts at Garranes and Ballycatteen in Cork were also more than simple farmsteads.

Crannógs were defended homesteads constructed for greater security in lakes on artificial islands built up of layers of brushwood, peat, timber, clay, stones and rubbish, held in place by vertical timber piles. Sometimes natural islands were fortified. Crannógs were surrounded by a timber palisade and sometimes by stone kerbs, walls and breakwaters. They were often approached by causeways submerged beneath the encircling lake. Although lake-dwellings were usually single homesteads containing one or more houses, the large crannóg excavated at Lagore in Meath was an important royal site. Less common than raths, numerous crannógs occupied during early Christian times lay in the west and northwest midlands.

In strong contrast to the above, the unfree members of society probably lived in unenclosed wattle-and-daub dwellings that clustered together in kin groups among open fields. At Lough Gur in Limerick, several round, rectangular and half-circular huts with stone foundations, an animal shelter and nearby fields have been excavated. Much field and literary evidence suggests that the poorer tributary peoples – including those of pre-Celtic stock – lived in simple farm clusters, or *clachans* to use the Scots-Gaelic term, quite distinct from the raths of their Celtic overlords. The farm cluster and the open field system, so persistent in the landscape until recent times, might even be pre-Celtic survivals. There is certainly some tie between these farm clusters and the townlands which are still the basic units of land division in Ireland. V. B. Proudfoot (1959) has argued that the concentration of raths in west Down compared with their less frequent occurrence in east Down is no accurate reflection of the distribution of early Christian peoples. He suggests that in the fertile farmlands of east Down raths coexisted with numerous open farm clusters of which little trace remains – a pattern that accords realistically with the high density of early churches and with later Anglo-Norman settlements in the area. Throughout Ireland, the open farm clusters in which plebeian cultivators dwelt were probably known individually as *baile*, a term that survives today in the place-name prefix 'bally'. 'Bally' place-names are notably dense on fertile lands throughout south and east Ireland, where the successful Anglo-Norman colonists took over the role of the Celtic overlords and strove hard to maintain the rural settlements and agriculture of the native peoples. Significantly, 'bally' townlands are more common in east Down than in the west.

Two features stand out sharply among this settlement pattern. First, the Celtic landscape was essentially rural and was devoid of towns. Secondly, a clear dichotomy existed between the isolated farmsteads of the Celtic overlords and the farm clusters of the tributary peoples. As the Celtic nobility and free-men withered before the onslaught of successive invaders, so their raths tumbled into decay and alien towns arose to usurp their role as foci of society. The farm clusters on the other hand survived to form an integral part of later landscapes.

Celtic economy and the landscape

Rural economy

While Celtic society, customs and laws find their closest modern parallels among Hindu peoples, the Celtic economy closely resembles traditional Zulu practices. Under the Celts, Ireland became a land of cattle. Wealth was counted in heads of cattle, not in land. Lacking currency, the cow was the basic unit of value and exchange. It was also the main source of meat, dairy produce – the principal summer food – leather and hides. The rath was a ranch in a mainly pastoral economy that was not nomadic but which involved short-range transhumance, or booleying, designed to use summer hill pastures for the cattle. The cattleway, or *bóthar*, often became sunken from frequent use. Most cattle were killed and salted in the autumn for winter food, because of the scarcity of winter animal fodder Lagore, Ballinderry, Carraig Aille, Cahercommaun and other sites of early Christian Ireland have yielded bones of the relatively small *Bos longifrons* in abundance. Inevitably, cattle-rustling became a popular and violent blood-sport, a test of manhood and noble status. Pigs, sheep, goats and domestic fowl were common while horses, wolfhounds, sheepdogs, terriers, lap-dogs and cats were kept.

Tillage was common around most dwellings but, with self-sufficiency as the main aim, agricultural surpluses were rare and the area tilled consequently small. In Down most raths farmed about 60 acres each. Wheat, barley, oats, rye and flax were common crops and corn-drying kilns, querns, millstones, plough-shares, coulters, sickles and billhooks have all been found. The plough was generally drawn by four oxen, though the Irish word for a plough team, *seis-*

20. The Rock of Cashel, County Tipperary
A succession of ecclesiastic buildings have occupied this bold limestone knoll since early
Christian times. The present ruins include Cormac's Chapel (1127–34), with its two
unequal square towers, and the large cruciform thirteenth-century cathedral.

reach, implies the use of six oxen at one time. Bee-keeping, for honey and mead,
and watermills were probably introduced from Britain. Because the unfree
tenants had to pay annual food-rents to their cattle-ranching lords and also
provide coshery or free hospitality for their lords and retinue between New
Year and Shrovetide, tillage was particularly important around the farm
clusters. Around most clusters, open fields were worked under the rundale
system, whereby individual tenants tilled unfenced and scattered plots in an
arable infield while the poorer outfield was used for grazing and occasional
shifting cultivation. Enclosed fields, fenced with stones and sods to protect
crops from wandering animals, probably coexisted with open fields. Small
rectilinear fields, none more than 5 acres in extent, were found with excavated
settlements of early Christian age at Beginish in Kerry, Cush in Limerick,
Lissachiggel in Louth, and with two cashels and six huts at Two Mile Stone in
Donegal. Raths situated on drumlins presumably cultivated 12- to 20-acre infields enclosed by contour fences (Proudfoot, 1958). The place-name element
'achadh', as in Achonry, suggests the existence of fields.

Under these stimuli, the existing woodlands underwent further modification.

Following the introduction of the heavy iron plough, around A.D. 300, farmers turned their attention to the heavier clay soils whose woodland cover had previously been little touched. G. F. Mitchell (1956) noting the major change in the pollen record following the introduction of this and other new agrarian techniques, has designated a Zone IX of general deforestation from around A.D. 300 to about 1700. By the seventh century elm had virtually disappeared. Under brehon law elm ranked among the lesser trees whose injury carried only a small fine. Nevertheless, that fines were even considered suggests that, perhaps for the first time, some trees were now regarded as a useful resource rather than a hindrance. The increase of ribwort in the pollen record as Zone IX progresses suggests that the woods were being cleared for pasture rather than for tillage, particularly after the monasteries overcame their early prejudice against dairy produce. Between A.D. 900 and 1100, accelerated clearance of the hazel scrub, followed by attacks on the oak woods, allowed birch and alder to contribute relatively more pollen rain as a new equilibrium was reached. Apples, nuts, wild berries and herbs were plentiful and frequently eaten.

Neither did the native fauna escape. Spear hunting for red deer and wild boar was a popular upper-class sport, causing the latter to die out in the twelfth century. Traps also took a heavy toll of red deer, otters, badgers, hares and foxes. Wild geese, ducks; swans, heron, crane, cormorant, moorhen, coot, owl and gulls were shot with arrows for food. Trout, salmon and wrasse were common fish eaten while coastal settlements commonly ate shellfish and seaweed.

Industry, communications and trade
As in their food needs, the larger raths were also self-sufficient in material equipment and clothing. Iron-working was widespread, and slag and crucibles for smelting iron and copper have been found on many sites. Undoubtedly the demand for charcoal in smelting caused a further drain on forest resources. Iron farm equipment, knives, spears, axes, swords, carpentry tools and pots together with large bronze cauldrons were made. Woodworking and decorative carving in wood and bone reached a high quality. Glass was also made. The paucity of pottery finds from early Christian settlements suggests that wooden and leather vessels were more common. Home-produced flax and wool were spun, woven, dyed and manufactured into clothes by the womenfolk. The aristocracy commonly wore a voluminous woollen cloak (*brat*), fastened with a brooch, over a linen tunic (*léine*), a costume with classical Mediterranean affinities. The less privileged wore a short jacket and trews. Leather belts, shoes and sandals were also worn. Later, the Vikings introduced silks, skin cloaks and a new range of armaments, which the Celts soon adopted.

The self-sufficiency of the raths and farm clusters encouraged neither travel nor trade. For the provincial kings, lawyers, craftsmen and clergy who did travel, a primitive road network existed. The *slige* was an important road for the wheeled vehicles in common use, namely the horse-drawn chariot and the farm cart. The *ramut* was an avenue leading to a king's rath. Rivers were normally crossed by fords but a few flimsy wooden bridges, open causeways and pontoons existed. Tara was apparently reached by five great roads. Coastal and inland water travel was accomplished in *curachs*, skin-covered wicker-framed craft whose canvas-covered equivalents are still used, and wooden vessels. Apart from an important trade in wine and other items with France and some contacts with Britain, overseas trade was limited until the Vikings established their seaports.

Survival of the Celtic landscape

The founding of the Norse seaport towns during the ninth and tenth centuries had little immediate effect on the essentially rural nature of Ireland that had evolved under the twin stimuli of the Celts and the early Christian Church. The seven provinces – Leinster, Munster, Connacht, Meath, Ailech, Airgialla and Ulaid – and their 150 or more component *tuatha* also survived the political turmoil of the eleventh century. At the close of the early Christian period, the Celtic – or more specifically Gaelic – landscape contained innumerable raths practising a mainly pastoral economy, several thousand farm clusters set among open fields worked in rundale, and about 180 self-sufficient monastic settlements. The original forests had diminished with the expansion of pasture and tillage so that most lowland agricultural areas were margined by widespread rough grazings, scrubland and secondary woodland, broken by cattleways and occasional roads. Without central government, without towns and without an extensive trade and communications network, something approaching national consciousness did exist as a result of common social customs, language, laws, religion and economic activity. What then happened to the distinctively Celtic landscape in the centuries following the Anglo-Norman invasion of 1169?

As colonizers, the Anglo-Normans were only partly successful. Thus in Leinster, Meath and parts of Munster and Ulaid, new castles and towns arose as Anglo-Norman barons displaced the Celtic nobility whose raths soon fell into decay. But the invaders encouraged the common people to remain to till the soil and herd cattle as they had done for their previous overlords so that farm clusters survived along with some traditional landholding and agricultural practices. The 'baile' was translated by the newcomers as 'villa' and 'ton', which have come down to us as the 'town' suffix in so many place-names, notably in south and east Ireland. At Caherguillamore in Limerick, Ballymoneymore in Antrim and elsewhere, elaborate field systems around many defunct early Christian raths were evidently inherited by the later medieval occupants of rectangular cottages.

In contrast, neither history nor archaeology has yet revealed much about the medieval landscape in the purely Celtic north and west. Isolation, family loyalties and conservatism probably protected the old social system at first, but, as alien ideas spread, so native culture withered. Raths were abandoned and by the fifteenth century the stone tower-house had been adopted as the normal dwelling by both Anglo-Irish gentry and Celtic chieftains alike. Otherwise, sixteenth-century writers show that many traditional landscape patterns and practices in those hidden parts of Ireland emerged from the medieval period little altered since before the time of the Vikings. Open farm clusters worked by kin groups in rundale even survived the violent disruptions of the seventeenth century and, where their occupants were evicted under enforced resettlement schemes, this form of settlement was often transplanted into previously thinly populated areas, notably into Connacht. We shall return in later chapters to view the gradual disappearance of farm clusters and rundale from the landscape.

The uniformity with which Celtic settlement once enveloped the landscape is shown today by the widespread survival of Gaelic place-names. Some are toponyms describing the physical characteristics of the countryside, some refer to the vegetation, some denote settlement styles. These and other place-name elements which provide such valuable insight into the Irish landscape are summarized in an Appendix.

Chapter 7
Vikings and Normans and the founding of towns

The Viking and Anglo-Norman colonists gave the Irish landscape its first towns. Initially the Viking coastal settlements were mere footholds in a rural environment, but the Anglo-Normans later used them as secure beachheads from which to penetrate inland, establishing new garrison towns. Those towns that weathered the Gaelic resurgence of the later medieval period served in turn as bases from which the English reconquest of the sixteenth century was mounted. Towns were thus colonizing instruments from which successive invaders could subjugate the rural native population. As such, they found little favour in Gaelic society and the commercial interdependence of town and countryside, so vital to the successful functioning of urban centres, often either failed to materialize or otherwise collapsed during the Gaelic resurgence. Some strategically placed inland towns founded by the Anglo-Normans, such as Tullow, Fethard and Athenry, have thus failed to achieve any lasting significance. Others that arose near early religious centres later surrendered their roles to newer towns, better placed in relation to communications and commercial activity: thus Cashel yielded to Thurles, Downpatrick to Belfast. Beyond the towns, the Anglo-Norman colonists organized their newly acquired lands on feudal lines, built new villages, initiated crop rotations, introduced grain production for sale overseas, and exploited forest resources. Under their guidance and that of immigrant monastic orders, the medieval landscape of large areas was gradually transformed.

The towns of Ireland were born as towns. They did not evolve from rural settlements because Gaelic Ireland, with its emphasis on family groups and economic self-sufficiency, had no need for towns and possessed no urban traditions. The number of craftsmen and others not engaged in farming that the raths and monasteries could support depended simply on the amount of food that could be produced surplus to the needs of the local farming community. The lack of extensive commerce before the Viking era also meant that there was little need for markets and seaports. From their inception, the alien market towns had to compete with the Gaelic custom of bartering and selling goods at rural fairs. While larger monastic settlements formed the nearest approach to towns in the early Christian landscape, their scattered distribution often in remote places restricted their development into urban centres. Religious sites like Cashel, Kildare and Kells did attract Anglo-Norman settlement but many others declined. It is futile to speculate about how long Gaelic society might have continued alone without establishing towns but until the seventeenth-century plantation towns were created, again by alien settlers, large parts of Ireland, notably in the north and west, remained devoid of towns and villages.

The Viking contribution

In 795 Norse Vikings attacked Lambay off the Dublin coast and for the next forty years returned again and again to pillage coastal monasteries such as Inishmurray, Bangor, Downpatrick and even remote Skellig at a time when early Christian art, literature and learning were experiencing their golden age. The holiness and fame of the monasteries that suffered under these terrifying onslaughts soon caused the Viking raids to re-echo throughout Christendom but the actual damage caused in the landscape was negligible. To the Viking sea-farers the victualling of their ships for long voyages by means of *strand-hogg* – killing other people's cattle for butcher's meat on the shore – was fully justifiable and the rich, defenceless monasteries offered tempting additional loot. Many early Vikings were adventurers rather than professional pirates. The majority had as their main aim the exploration of the coastlands of Europe preparatory to possible colonization and settlement. The Norse Vikings were but one arm of a series of contemporary Scandinavian migrations across Europe that were motivated by the desire for *Lebensraum* – for more spacious living and better land. Those who reached Ireland came mainly from the harsh environment of west Norway where good farmland and living space were restricted. According to the Vinland saga, they sought land where cattle could graze in the open during the winter. The Norse Vikings thus sailed west to Shetland, then south to Orkney and through the Hebrides, and so to Man in the Irish Sea and to Ireland where they became known as the *Finn-ghaill* or fair foreigners; north County Dublin still bears their name – Fingal. The Danes meanwhile ravaged the Frisian coast and eastern England but reached Ireland only occasionally, often as mercenaries engaged by the Gaels to fight the Norsemen. They became known as the *Dubh-ghaill* or dark foreigners.

With the appearance of Viking fleets off the mouths of the Boyne and Liffey in 837, the Norsemen began determined efforts to found colonies in Ireland, their first attempts lasting until about 880. In 841, the first fortified Norse settlements were built at Annagassan on the Louth coast, where roughly circular earthworks still survive, and at the hurdle ford across the Liffey on a site destined to become Dublin. The Gaelic name *longphort*, given to these defended bases, shows that they began as stockades around the Viking long ships. From these *longphorts* and from temporary camps set up in the estuaries of the Suir, Blackwater, Lee and other rivers, frequent expeditions penetrated inland to plunder such monasteries as Kells, Kildare, Glendalough, Clonmacnoise, Lismore and Armagh. From Viking fleets on Lough Neagh and on the Shannon lakes, Thorgestr pillaged the surrounding country. However, after a northern Uí Néill king defeated a Viking fleet on Lough Foyle in 867 and destroyed Norse strongholds in the north, no Viking colonies were re-established north of the Boyne and their colonizing activities were henceforth restricted to strengthening their beachheads farther south. Following a lull between 880 and 914, large fleets brought fresh settlers to consolidate the earlier camps set up along the south coast. Farming communities settled at Helvick. In 914–15 a permanent settlement was established at Waterford, where the sheltered St John's river enters the Suir. Of the Norse town walls, Reginald's Tower built in 1002 still stands, though in somewhat modified form. In 922 colonists arriving with a Norse fleet on the Shannon founded Limerick around an island stronghold. Permanent port settlements soon followed at Wexford, Cork and Youghal. This phase of colonization lasted until the Viking armies were defeated at Clontarf in 1014, after which the Norse were content to live in their ports as separate communities, manufacturing and trading overseas.

During the later ninth and tenth centuries, Dublin grew into a powerful Norse kingdom. The ridge immediately south of the Liffey was fortified, notably on the site of the present castle from which the town spread west along the modern High Street. Farther west, near Islandbridge, lay a large Viking cemetery while east of the castle lay some burial mounds, or *Haugen*, which later gave their name to Hoggen Green (now College Green). The *Thingmote*, or meeting place outside the town, survived into the seventeenth century. Wharves arose on the Liffey and also on the Dodder estuary. Like other Norse settlements, Dublin has been destroyed and rebuilt so often that little is known about the Norse dwellings and town plan although, after the inhabitants became Christian during the tenth century, they founded Christ Church cathedral in 1040. The Norse kingdom was by no means confined to the Liffey estuary, as such Norse place-names as Skerries, Lambay, Howth, Leixlip, Dalkey, Wicklow and Arklow clearly reveal, but effective colonization was strictly coastal.

Norse settlement in Ireland differed in character from that in the Scottish islands where farmers settled on the land and built long houses and farm villages. If the conquest of Ireland was ever planned it was certainly not successful, and respectable military forces were soon relegated to the defence of the small coastal kingdoms and their ports, whose Norse occupants, with a keen eye to business, sought to exact taxes from the surrounding Gaelic population while also trading extensively overseas in their Irish-based fleets. Towns were a comparatively new feature of Scandinavian society everywhere but, even after the Norsemen became Christian and involved themselves in Irish politics, the dichotomy between rural Gael and urban Norse remained. Towns such as Limerick and Dublin were often sacked by the Gaels but nevertheless survived the 150 years of chaos that engulfed Ireland after Clontarf. The early settlements probably consisted of houses of timber or wattle and daub, protected by earthen ramparts, wooden palisades and towers, similar to Hedeby in Denmark and other early Scandinavian sites. The eleventh-century towns, however, were defended by strong stone walls, beyond which cereals, flax and vegetables were grown for sale by Norse farmers.

The creation by the Norsemen of fortified commercial centres engaged in extensive overseas trade did much to change the simple pastoral economy and the ancient political system of the Gaelic people, and shift the social and political focus for all time from the midlands to the east coast. The Norsemen were skilled metal-workers and shipbuilders, and most Irish words dealing with ships are derived from their language. The iron weapons and tools found in Islandbridge and other Viking cemeteries – axes, spearheads, swords, knives, hammers, forge tongs and sickles – reveal a highly skilled metal industry. Spindle whorls, linen smoothers and bronze scales reflect agriculture and trade, and many Norse words in the Irish language refer to trade, notably *margadh* – market and *mangaire* – merchant. They exploited Irish silver-mines for their silver brooches and sword pommels, and for the coinage they introduced and minted in Dublin. Imports of silk, satin and chased leather, often exchanged for slaves, were traded throughout Ireland. Finally, the number of surviving Norse place-names is small but impressive. Apart from Wexford, Waterford and other settlements noted above, Leinster, Munster and Ulster contain Irish words used in a Norse construction. The name Ireland itself is Norse in origin.

The Anglo-Norman contribution

Pattern of colonization

The reluctant Anglo-Norman invasion of 1169 unwittingly opened a new dramatic phase in the shaping of the Irish landscape. The first invaders were restless Norman–Welsh knights, Flemish colonists from Pembrokeshire, and Welsh archers who came, armed with vague blessings from Henry II of England and the Papacy, ostensibly to reinstate a dispossessed Leinster king. Norman–Welsh names such as Barry, FitzGerald, Carew and FitzHenry, Flemish names such as Cheevers, Fleming, Prendergast, Roche and Synott, and Welshmen who gave Ireland the surname Walsh figured prominently in the subsequent colonization. In language and traditions, their leaders were Norman–French rather than English and only later did the new colonies acquire an English flavour. Landing in southeast Ireland, the Norse cities of Wexford and Waterford soon fell and in 1170 Dublin was taken. By 1175 Henry II was acknowledged overlord of Ireland and had reserved the sizeable Norse states of Wexford, Waterford and Dublin for himself, confirmed the earl of Pembroke's hold over much of Leinster and granted Meath to Hugo de Lacy. Despite recognizing Rory O'Connor as high king over the unconquered areas,

KILOMETRES
0 10 20 30 40 50 60 70 80 90 100

0 10 20 30 40 50 60
MILES

LAND ABOVE 200 m [656 ft]

TIR CONNAIL
TIR EOGHAIN
EARLDOM OF ULSTER
Ards
Lecale
Sligo
FERMANAGH
IRISH ORIEL
BRÉIFNE
Dundalk
Granard
Ardee
Kells
LOUTH
Drogheda
Fóre
CONNACHT
MEATH
ROSCOMMON
Trim
Athlone
KILDARE
DUBLIN
Galway
Athenry
DUBLIN
Loughrea
Athy
Wicklow
Athy
Arklow
Nenagh
TIPPERARY
KILKENNY
CARLOW
Adare
Croom
Callan
Iderone
LIMERICK
Kilmallock
Clonmel
WEXFORD
Clanmaurice
Clonmel
New Ross
Wexford
KERRY
Ida
Forth
Tralee
Buttevant
WATERFORD
Bargy
Dingle
Barrymore
Hook Head
CORK
Decies
Dungarvan
Kilmokilly
Youghal
Cork
Kinsale

TOWNS
▲ Norse foundations
■ Anglo-Norman foundations
• Motes (rural areas only)
ADMINISTRATIVE UNITS circa 1300
--- Boundaries (▼▼Pale c.1515)
Counties thus : DUBLIN
Liberties thus : CARLOW
Baronies thus : *Lecale*
Gaelic Irish areas : *BRÉIFNE*

MEDIEVAL MONASTIC FOUNDATIONS
[Established after A.D. 1111 and
surviving until the 16th century]
▽ Augustinian Canons
△ Benedictine Monks
○ Cistercian Monks
× Mendicant Friars :—
— Dominicans 1224
— Franciscans 1231
— Carmelites 1270
— Augustinians 1282
— 3rd Order Reg. of St Francis

ARO

21. Medieval Ireland: selected facets of colonization and settlement
(Monastic foundations simplified from *Map of Monastic Ireland*, 2nd ed. 1964, Ordnance
Survey, Dublin; mottes based partly on G. H. Orpen, *Ireland under the Normans
1169–1216*, vol. 2, Clarendon Press, Oxford, 1911, with additions.)

Henry was unable to curb the whetted appetites of the land-hungry barons who subsequently seized more and more native territory. Thus in a piecemeal and unsystematic fashion, and often with insufficient settlers for effective colonization, the frontiers of Anglo-Norman settlement were extended and the better lands throughout the south and east were gradually brought within the feudal framework. The newcomers were intent on staying and, while they failed to subdue Ireland, their colonizing processes have left many indelible marks on the landscape.

In 1177 John de Courcy daringly invaded Ulster and captured Downpatrick, capital of Ulaid. From garrison castles established there and at Carlingford, Carrickfergus, Dundrum, Dromore, Newry and Coleraine, the Anglo-Normans soon controlled much of Antrim and Down, though neither de Courcy nor his successors ever extended their colony effectively west of the river Bann. Meanwhile Henry II unilaterally signed away extensive Gaelic lands in Munster and castles arose to defend the favoured lowlands and coastal areas, notably in south and east Cork, north Kerry, Limerick and Tipperary. Reserving the Norse cities of Cork and Limerick for himself, Henry conveyed the MacCarthy kingdom stretching from Youghal to Dingle to Robert Fitz-Stephen and Milo de Cogan, and the O'Brien kingdom embracing Tipperary, Limerick, Clare and north Kerry to Philip de Braose. The village of Buttevant in Cork, though recalling the battle-cry of the founding Barry family, '*Boutez-en avant*', is in fact named after the Norman-French word for a defensive outwork – *botavant*. Farther north, fortresses at Roscrea, Terryglass, Clonmacnoise and Athlone brought the Anglo-Normans to the middle Shannon, while a castle at Clones brought part of the north midlands under their control. The O'Connor kingdom of Connacht was treacherously invaded in 1235 and, excepting Roscommon and Leitrim which were left to the Gaelic Irish, the province was soon apportioned among Normans, Flemings and Welsh.

Within eighty years of the invasion, three-quarters of Ireland had been overrun by the Normans and with varying success the new tenants-in-chief had carved their acquired lands into feudal manors occupied by subtenants, founded villages and abbeys, and granted charters to new towns. The former kingdom of Meath, embracing the modern counties of Meath, Westmeath, Longford and parts of Cavan and Offaly, was skilfully organized by de Lacy who built his chief fortresses at Trim and Drogheda and distributed lesser castles such as Delvin, Dunmore, Granard and Skreen throughout the territory. The castles were occupied by his vassals – the Plunketts, Nugents, Daltons, Barnewalls and others – while other subtenants lived in stone manor houses with courtyards. In contrast, there were never sufficient Anglo-Norman settlers in Connacht for that turbulent province to become feudalized like Meath or Leinster, and even the towns that arose at Galway, Athenry, Dunmore, Ballinrobe, Loughrea and Sligo were gradually infiltrated by the Gaelic Irish. Indeed, as the colonizing impetus of the Anglo-Normans lost momentum after 1250, so native resistance stiffened, the MacCarthys and O'Sullivans regained south Kerry from the FitzThomas family in 1261, the O'Donnells consolidated their independence in Donegal, and the O'Connors temporarily regained much of the northwest between 1270 and 1316. These marginal setbacks in the wild west did not at first vitally impair the prosperity of Anglo-Norman settlement elsewhere, but in effect the expansion of the colonies was halted and, as their frontiers later contracted and chaos spread through the countryside, settlers in the south and east were forced on to the defensive.

The Anglo-Normans soon extended English concepts of common law, feudal obligation, local and central administration, state finance and representative government to Ireland, or at least to those parts that they effectively occupied for such alien ideas found little acceptance among traditional Gaelic customs and practices. Many of the administrative units that the Anglo-Normans either introduced or adapted from pre-existing land divisions have survived, despite boundary modifications and subdivisions, into the present. The invaders adopted many existing Gaelic *tuatha* as administrative units which they renamed cantreds, roughly equivalent to hundreds in England and later to become known as baronies. Other cantreds were newly created as colonization progressed. For instance, *tuatha* in west Kildare came to serve as cantreds – Cairbre became Carbury – but farther east entirely new cantreds based on Norman land grants arose around the new towns of Kilcullen Bridge, Naas and Maynooth. Each cantred was subdivided into vills, many of which focused on pre-existing *bailes* while others centred around the homesteads and farm villages of the colonists and added the place-name suffix 'town' to local Anglo-Norman patronymics or to prefixes denoting a local church, mill or castle. Many such vills have survived as modern townlands, frequently subdivided during the intervening centuries. At the other end of the scale, by 1260 the settled area had been grouped into eight counties – Dublin, Louth, Waterford, Cork, Kerry, Limerick, Tipperary and Connacht – each with its own sheriff and shire court, and into the feudal liberties of Meath, Kildare, Carlow, Kilkenny, Wexford and Ulster. These were administrative units quite new to Ireland.

The medieval rural landscape
As the colonists distributed castles, abbeys, manors, villages, grazing commons and broad open fields tilled in strips through the countryside, so occupied Ireland became part of the wider feudal landscape of western Europe. The effectively feudalized areas are today reflected in a legacy of earthworks, ruined castles, numerous place-names ending in 'town', family names of distinctive Anglo-Norman origin and, less tangibly, in certain field patterns and agricultural practices. Following invasion, wooden motte-and-bailey castles soon arose

at strategic intervals along lowland corridors, such as the Barrow valley, throughout the south and east. The motte or mote was a 20 to 40-feet-high, steepsided, artificial mound of earth, topped by a 30 to 100-feet-wide summit flat defended by a timber palisade and blockhouse or *bretesche*. The motte was separated by a

22. The Manor of Cloncurry, County Kildare, in A.D. 1304
(Reconstruction based on a text by J. O'Loan and a sketch by P. J. Tuite in Department of Agriculture *Journal*, Vol. 58; Mr O'Loan's interpretation was in turn based on the official transcript of *The Red Book of Ormond*, a fourteenth-century cartulary of rentals and deeds relating to the Irish property of the Butler family, published by the Irish Manuscripts Commission, 1932.)

surrounding ditch from a circular or semicircular courtyard or bailey which housed barracks, stables and workshops and was protected by one or more earthen palisaded ramparts. After 1200, these early timber structures were often replaced with massive stone keeps and some formidable fortresses arose, notably at Trim and Carrickfergus. Mortared stone buildings were not new to the landscape but in their castles, churches and abbeys, the Anglo-Normans brought fresh sophistication to Romanesque styles and soon introduced revolutionary Gothic techniques.

Behind fortified frontiers, landholdings and agricultural production developed along manorial lines with stone-built manor houses, and their numerous outbuildings, forming the focal points of lands that also normally coincided with the evolving pattern of territorial parishes. In the more closely settled areas, the lord cultivated part of his manor as a home farm, the remainder being subdivided among dependable tenants from western Britain who held land either freely, or by burgage tenure, or on lease for a number of years. The small extent of many such holdings indicates a virtual peasant colonization. Exceptionally, the colonists outnumbered the Gaelic Irish but, commonly, the lack of settlers for the lands available, particularly along the margins of the colonies, was reflected in the encouragement given to the native peoples to return as betaghs (serfs) and cottiers (cottagers), and sometimes even as gavillers and free tenants, to till the land and herd livestock. Norsemen, such as those occupants of Wexford who were resettled in the nearby parishes of Rosslare and Ballymore, were also brought into the feudal system. Gradually the landscape became studded with farm villages, clustered around their church and mill, and with individual cottages.

Anglo-Norman mixed farming, with its emphasis on cereal production for export, on crop rotations and on estate management, contrasted strongly with

23. Doornane, County Kilkenny

A rare survival of a medieval courtyard-farm village as viewed in 1954 when it contained 17 farmsteads. Doornane was noted on Petty's Down Survey maps of 1654–6 and possessed 30 houses and 243 inhabitants in 1841. Such villages were once common in the areas settled by the Anglo-Normans and as late as 1841 similar villages survived in the Ards and Lecale in Ulster, in the Cooley peninsula and in secluded parts of the former Pale in Leinster.

24. The ruins of Mellifont Abbey, County Louth
Cistercian monks first came to Mellifont in 1142 and by 1148 had established daughter
houses at Bective, Boyle, Monasternenagh and Baltinglass. By 1272 these in turn had
established 20 further houses, mostly in Leinster and Munster. Mellifont, one of the first
Irish examples of the integrated monastic architecture of medieval Europe, was sup-
pressed in 1539.

the pastoralism of the Gaelic Irish. Under the colonists more land was ploughed,
and fruit and vegetable farming became important. Apple, pear and plum
orchards up to 5 acres in extent grew up around medieval farms in Tipperary
and elsewhere. Further land reclamation became economically desirable and
accelerated forest clearance clearly shows in the pollen record as grass, plantain
and cereal pollen increase. Extensive clearances in the wetter low-lying woodlands, initiated by the Cistercians and hastened by the Anglo-Norman influx,
allowed birch which still thrived on poorer dry soils to contribute relatively
more pollen rain as oak, alder and hazel fell away. Oak forests were widely
exploited for building materials and timber was exported from many south and
east coast ports to Wales, Bristol, London, Holland and elsewhere. As if existing
environmental restrictions on forest regeneration were not enough, rabbits and
fallow deer were introduced, ostensibly as game. Nevertheless extensive woodlands, such as the Duffry oak forest west of the lower Slaney in Wexford, did
survive – often as enclaves of Gaelic resistance within Anglo-Norman territory.

The continental monastic orders that entered Ireland during the twelfth
century were lavishly endowed with lands by Gael and Anglo-Norman alike.
Thus early Cistercian foundations such as Mellifont (1142), Baltinglass (1148),
Bective (1146) and Boyle (1148–61) were supplemented after the invasion by
abbeys founded both in the Anglo-Norman areas, such as Jerpoint (1180) in
Kilkenny, Dunbrody (1182) and Tintern (1200) in Wexford, and on Gaelic
lands farther west as at Kilcooly (1182), Corcomroe (1182) and Knockmoy

(1189). Cistercian estate management and farming practice made a significant impact on the landscape, as the widespread survival of the place-name 'grange' clearly indicates. The grange was a consolidated landholding with its own farm buildings, often some distance from the abbey, on which the Cistercians with their ample labour supply practised mixed farming on a scale previously unknown in Ireland. Other orders such as the Benedictines at Fore in Westmeath, the Augustinian Canons at Athassel in Tipperary and Killagh in Kerry, and the military and canonical orders that followed in the wake of the invasion also made major contributions to the medieval Irish scene. During the thirteenth century, progressive Dominican, Franciscan, Carmelite and Augustinian friars spread throughout Ireland evangelizing and building churches and schools. By the early 1500s, 400 religious houses existed in Ireland, comparing well with the 850 houses throughout England and Wales, but most were destined to fall into decay following the Reformation.

The growth of towns and commerce

Around many Anglo-Norman castles, new towns and ports arose as chief tenants and merchants sought to exploit the commercial possibilities of the conquered lands. As workshops, mills, houses for artisans, merchants and officials, a church and perhaps a monastery arose under the protection of a local garrison, so the fabric of a town took shape. As trade expanded so regular markets and annual fairs were held and craft guilds of carpenters, tailors, bakers and others flourished. Streets were paved and water supplies organized. The Normans instituted town charters, the first municipal charter in Ireland being granted to Dublin in 1172, mayors, freemen and the entire administrative framework so familiar to modern towns.

In the decades following 1169, boroughs were freely created by chief tenants and subtenants alike in the hope that burgess status would attract settlers from Britain. Although given primitive urban constitutions with burgage holdings and hundred courts, many such boroughs were never more than large agricultural villages. A. J. Otway–Ruthven (1965) has indicated that, of such places, Drumconrath and Sidan in Meath, Ardscull and Dunfert in Kildare, Leys in Laois, Moyaliff in Tipperary and Glenogra in Limerick never acquired any real urban character. Nevertheless, many existing inland towns owe their origins to the Anglo-Normans, the most successful being strategic centres, such as Carlow, Kilkenny and Clonmel in the Barrow, Nore and Suir valleys respectively, that acquired commercial significance amid rich agricultural hinterlands. Eventually Anglo-Norman towns developed throughout the feudalized south and east, their fortunes fluctuating with the strength or weakness of the colonized areas. Some were enclosed within strong walls but, while many early walled centres such as Nenagh function in important roles today, others, such as

Athenry which has shrunk within its walls and Fore which has virtually disappeared, have lost their significance.

Meanwhile, along the coast the former Norse ports flourished as agricultural and forest produce from their hinterlands arrived for export. The existing Norse inhabitants were either allocated quarters within the walls or resettled nearby. The Dublin Norsemen founded the suburb of Villa Ostmanorum ('the town of the easterners') at Oxmantown north of the Liffey, while their old city received a strong infusion of colonists from around the Bristol Channel. In addition, the Anglo-Normans founded new ports at Dundalk, Drogheda, New Ross, Dungarvan, Kinsale, Dingle, Tralee, Galway and Sligo to cater for their territories. New Ross was established by William Marshal for the export of wool, hides, wheat and dairy produce from his extensive Leinster estates and,

25. *Dromore, County Down*

The 12 m (40 ft) high English Mound in the foreground was built on a good defensive site above an entrenched bend of the river Lagan during the late twelfth century and is perhaps the best preserved Anglo-Norman motte and bailey in Ulster. The small settlement that grew up below the castle suffered repeated disasters during medieval and plantation times and the present town traces its growth mainly to the expanding linen industry of the eighteenth century. Just right of centre in the middle distance is Ballymaganlis rath.

soon after it was walled in 1265, numerous craft guilds and over 500 separate properties existed in the town. The exports of wheat, hides, skins, fish and linen that Dublin and Drogheda traded with Chester throughout the medieval period, and of wool, woolfells, cattle, hides, skins, leather, timber, grain, fish, linen, flax, horses and lead that Waterford, Youghal, Cork, Kinsale, Limerick, Galway and Sligo sent to Bristol and other British ports in return for salt, iron, wine, cloth and household goods, clearly reveal the nature of economic activity in the Anglo-Norman landscape. Under the Anglo-Normans, the Norse settlement at Youghal was incorporated (1209) and walled and, as the port, market and service centre for the colonists in the Blackwater valley and east Cork, often rivalled Cork and Waterford in the value of customs duties received and the size of its merchant fleet which traded from Portugal to Scandinavia. Youghal, Kinsale, Dingle, Galway and other west coast ports carried on a significant trade with southwest France and Spain, exporting wool and hides in exchange for wines, salt and cloth. While their hinterlands developed peacefully, the market towns and ports flourished but, as the conquerors' control over the country collapsed, so urban prosperity dwindled, property decayed and the Gaelic Irish began inheriting what were to them meaningless agglomerations of buildings.

The English colony in decline
As native resistance to the colonists stiffened into a tangible Gaelic resurgence, the feudalized 'land of peace' shrank and by 1400 covered less than one-third of Ireland. By the mid-fifteenth century only the English Pale, a bridgehead thirty miles deep behind Dublin and Drogheda comprising modern County Dublin and parts of Kildare, Meath and Louth, together with a few outlying towns, remained under effective English administration. The rest of the country was in the hands of either Gaelic-Irish chieftains or Anglo-Irish nobility owing varying loyalties to the English Crown. The colonization process failed for several reasons but, from the geographical viewpoint, the settlement of English people on the land was neither planned methodically nor executed with sufficient numbers to ensure lasting success. Ecologically, there were generally too few settlers to withstand eventual overcrowding and displacement by more vigorous native elements. Excepting English and French merchants in the towns, there was no substantial middle-class population and, beyond the southeast, settlers were few and far between. Enclaves of Gaelic Irish survived in north Wexford, the Wicklow mountains, Offaly and elsewhere. In rural areas 'degenerate' colonists began speaking Irish and adopting Gaelic customs, laws and dress until they were almost indistinguishable in the eyes of the Dublin government from their Gaelic neighbours. The statutes of Kilkenny in 1366 and other restrictive legislation aimed at preserving the identity of the 'land of peace' largely failed to arrest this cultural assimilation of colonist and Gael. Thus as the tide turned against the less flexible colonists, feudalism

crumbled both along its frontiers and from within. The ensuing chaos was soon transmitted to the landscape as recurrent fighting caused much material damage and encouraged rural depopulation.

During the fourteenth and fifteenth centuries, rural depopulation of the feudalized areas became rife. Absenteeism by barons and tenants alike and the drainage of men and supplies to costly English wars in France increased the vulnerability of the colonists remaining. In 1349 the Black Death (a plague caused by the bacillus *Pasteurella pestis* which is spread by fleas living on certain rodents, chiefly black rats), having swept through Europe killing more than one-quarter of the population, struck Ireland, causing panic among the settlers. Many fled from outlying areas to the towns and from there to England, leaving fields untilled and manors and villages deserted. The plague swept through the narrow streets and insanitary dwellings of such walled centres as Dublin, Drogheda and Kilkenny which within a few weeks were virtually depopulated. Bad harvests, cattle-rustling and sporadic warfare added to the poverty and insecurity of the country districts. As tillage collapsed for want of labour, sheep-rearing replaced grain production and many farms were abandoned. Bracken, gorse and hazel scrub crept back into lands that had been cleared and oak and alder woods expanded. Some of the deserted villages, whose overgrown ground plans can still be discerned in the present landscape throughout the southeast, were probably abandoned at this time. While the wealthier inhabitants, Gaelic Irish and Anglo-Irish alike, protected themselves from the general anarchy of the fifteenth century by building strong tower-houses, large numbers of which still exist, others were less fortunate. For example, in the vicinity of Clonmacnoise and Ardagh, whose cathedrals were in ruins by 1517, many Irish dwelt in fields and caves with their cattle. In southeast Wexford, attempts to stem the Gaelic resurgence saw frontier castles erected along the marshy Corock valley in 1441 to defend the surviving English settlers in the baronies of Forth and Bargy. In Ulster, effective English settlement became restricted to the Ards and Carrickfergus.

The towns commonly remained English in language and sympathy long after their hinterlands had reverted to the Gaelic Irish. Their continued existence as market centres, however, came to depend on the produce of the Irish who infiltrated in growing numbers until their language was commonly spoken, even in such large ports as Galway. As depicted on sixteenth-century maps, some forty-three walled towns apparently survived the medieval period in various states of disrepair. Behind massive stone walls and strongly fortified gates, streets were narrow, dark and winding in response to site factors and were separated by elongated housing blocks. These were composed mainly of wooden buildings or timber-framed houses faced with mud and rubble held together by laths and ties, interspersed with the more substantial stone houses of the wealthier merchants and officials. The employment opportunities of medieval

26. Fore, County Westmeath

Little now remains of the medieval walled town but the west gate in the foreground and the massive fifteenth-century towers of the ruined Benedictine priory, founded around 1200, recall Fore's one-time role as a fortress outpost in central Ireland.

towns had long induced the Gaelic Irish to settle – sometimes by choice and lack of money for taxes but more often by the purposeful design of the burgesses – in ghettoes just beyond the main walls. Such settlements, consisting of wattle-and-daub huts covered with turf or thatch, developed at Athlone, Kilkenny and Limerick, particularly after English artisans and labourers had left Ireland for more secure employment, and have come down to us as the 'Irishtown' sectors of our modern towns. By the close of medieval times, most smaller inland towns, such as Castledermot and Fore, had fallen to the Gaelic Irish and only a few larger centres retained any semblance of their former prosperity. On the other hand, many ports remained in English hands to serve as bases for the Tudor conquests.

Chapter 8
The plantations of the sixteenth and seventeenth centuries

Despite the growth of towns and commerce during medieval times, the sixteenth-century Irish landscape and its peoples were still overwhelmingly rural. Where Anglo-Norman influences had been strongest, numerous agricultural villages or their charred skeletons, focusing on a church or a central open space, survived among large arable open fields, worked in regular strips, and nearby grazing commons. Although often frustrated by recurrent turmoil, attempts to enclose fields and consolidate holdings had increased during later medieval times and consequently many compact farms had also evolved. Apart from these villages, open farm clusters occupied by Gaelic-Irish kin groups existed on most former manorial lands, notably in such marginal areas as Wicklow, Waterford and Westmeath. Their open fields were organized along less formal rundale lines, smaller in scale but more flexible than the alien field systems. In contrast, towns and villages were virtually non-existent in the north and west where traditional Gaelic-Irish pastoralism persisted and where, in Donegal and other remote localities, some raths continued to serve as farmsteads well into the sixteenth century. Despite widespread reclamation for farmland and the disappearance of much high forest, possibly 15 per cent of the countryside remained well wooded. Extensive woods survived around the Wicklow mountains and in western Ulster, Sligo, Mayo, Offaly, Laois, Tipperary, Cork and Kerry. Hazel scrub flourished on abandoned farmlands everywhere. Communication between settlements was difficult and hazardous, and accomplished if at all along ill-kept tracks and 'passes' through the woods and bogs, routeways inherited from the early Christian and Anglo-Norman periods.

The commercial activities of those towns that had survived the troubled later medieval period revived during the sixteenth century, and many cities experienced urban renewal within their walls and some suburban growth beyond before the century closed. Substantial two-storey freestone houses were built in Cork, Galway and Limerick, while suburban dwellings arose outside the gates of Dublin, Cork and Youghal. As the century progressed, however, many smaller, less privileged seaports such as New Ross, Dungarvan, Kinsale and Dingle fell victims to repeated attacks by pirates and rebels, to the frequent devastation of their hinterlands, and to various restrictions imposed on their foreign trade. The miserably poor inhabitants of Kinsale were unable to repair their walls while, in 1579, Youghal was sacked by the sixteenth earl of Desmond and temporarily abandoned by its townspeople.

During the later sixteenth century, the Irish landscape entered on a new dramatic phase of development which stemmed from the successful English reconquest and may be summarized in one word – plantation. Reconquest was undertaken for two main reasons: first, to restore royal authority and English

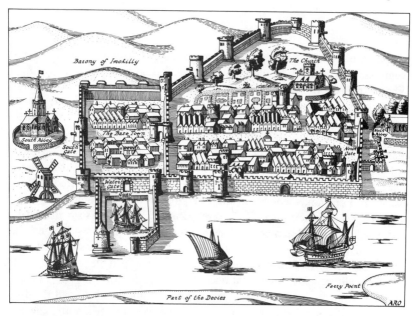

27. Youghal, County Cork, in the later sixteenth century
(Redrawn by the author from the original published in *Pacata Hibernia* in 1633, showing Youghal probably about 1587.)

interests in a country racked by local wars, poverty and famine, and largely controlled by so-called 'Irish enemies' and 'English rebels'; and secondly, to prevent Ireland from falling into the hands of England's continental rivals at a time when the Tudor nation-state was becoming involved in European power politics. When negotiation failed, the Tudors embarked on a series of costly military campaigns which led ultimately to the subjugation of Ireland in 1603. Meanwhile, attempts to impose the Protestant Reformation on the country added religious bitterness to the political conflict. Grants of former monastic lands at first reconciled many Gaelic and Anglo-Irish magnates, but later doctrinal innovations met with scant success and the bond of Roman Catholicism served to unite all classes of Irish society in a common cause.

English government circles realized that military conquest would not by itself secure the territories confiscated from rebellious chieftains. They instigated a policy of plantation whereby loyal English and Scots colonists were substituted for disloyal Gaelic and Anglo-Irish (or Old English) landholders. The plantation policy served as insurance against further rebellion, as an outlet for England's expanding population, commercial interests and investment capital, and as a painless way of rewarding loyal soldiers and civil servants through grants of Irish land. The plantations had many farreaching effects on the landscape and on the subsequent social, economic, political and religious development of Ireland. During the seventeenth century, numerous new towns and villages were created, old towns were revitalized, agriculture, industry and trade were stimulated, woodlands were extensively felled, and most land was transferred to the ownership of New English Protestants.

Arising from the need to implement the plantation policy, the government commissioned surveyors to make maps of the confiscated lands and their work has provided an invaluable record of the contemporary landscape, additional to the other documentary and field evidence of the period. The maps drawn from the plantation surveys of Jobson in Munster, of Barthelet, Bodley and Pynnar in Ulster, and of Raven in Derry and Connacht foreshadowed the famous parish and barony maps of the Down Survey (1654–56) organized by William Petty (1623–87) to aid the Cromwellian land settlement. Other cartographic advances of the period included the publication by John Speed (1611) of the earliest printed town plans of Cork, Dublin, Galway and Limerick.

The plantations

Laois and Offaly

The first experiment in systematic plantation was made in 1556 in the O'Moore and O'Connor territories of Laois and Offaly, country which had largely escaped permanent Anglo-Norman influence and still retained extensive woodlands, heaths and bogs. Although earlier attempts after 1548 to found garrison settlements on the more fertile lands had met with little success, the collapse of a native rebellion in 1556 opened the way for a general English plantation. The territories were shired and vested in the crown, Laois being named Queen's County after Mary of England and Offaly named King's County after her husband, Philip of Spain. Likewise, the garrison forts established earlier in Laois and Offaly were renamed Maryborough (now Portlaoise) and Philipstown (now Daingean) respectively, destined to become the first towns in an otherwise rural landscape. Although given markets and incorporated in 1567, neither these proposed centres nor their hinterlands could develop peacefully until the seventeenth century dawned. Indeed in the intervening period, much land either fell to waste or was let to the populous Gaelic tenantry, and the plantation was acknowledged a failure.

Munster

The collapse of the Geraldine rebellion in Munster in 1583 provided the government with the opportunity to develop a more elaborate scheme of plantation, combining state direction with private enterprise along lines later repeated in the North American colonies. In 1586 some 400,000 acres of confiscated land was divided into seignories varying from 4,000 to 12,000 acres in extent. In 1587 these were granted to English 'undertakers', men like Walter Raleigh, Edmund Spenser, Robert Payne and William Herbert, who agreed to plant them with English families. On paper, according to the contemporary Carew manuscripts, Walter Raleigh received 42,000 acres in Cork and Waterford, Edward Fitton 32,000 acres in several parts of Munster, Arthur Robins 18,000 acres in Cork, William Herbert over 13,000 acres in Kerry, while many others received over 10,000 acres each. In effect, the scheme soon foundered on incompetence, inaccurate surveying, poor defences and the general reluctance of grantees and potential colonists to occupy a countryside devastated by war, famine and disease. In 1592, out of fifty-eight 'undertakers' only thirteen were resident and only 245 English families had settled in. Only parts of Munster were planted, and the thin veneer of colonists could not survive without local labour and rackrents. Many 'undertakers', anxious for quick returns, accepted Irish tenants at high rents and exploited their forest, soil and human resources without regard to long-term planning. The plantation had scarcely made any imprint on the landscape when it was virtually swept away by the 1598 rebellion. In 1602 Raleigh's 42,000 acres, mainly in the lower Blackwater and Bride valleys and costing him £200 a year in upkeep, were purchased for £1,500 by Richard Boyle, who after 1620 became earl of Cork.

Boyle partly retrieved the situation and, under his direction, much of Cork and west Waterford experienced unprecedented urban and industrial growth. He diligently rebuilt Lismore, Tallow and Youghal and expanded the commercial activities of their hinterlands. In order to recolonize the desolate lands acquired from Raleigh, Nuce and others, and to infuse New English Protestants into the population, he shipped in a variety of settlers from southwest England. To shelter the planted areas from the Gaels in west Cork and south Kerry, Boyle planned four new frontier towns at Bandonbridge (now Bandon), Clonakilty, Enniskean and Castletown, to be occupied by loyal Protestant traders, leather-tanners and linen-weavers. Bandon soon became a flourishing, strongly fortified settlement covering some 27 acres and divided by the river Bandon, which was bridged in two places, into two parts, each with a symmetrical grid-iron plan, a market-place, sessions house and church (Butlin, 1967). Its houses were solidly built of freestone or with timber frames and plaster, each with a tree-studded garden. As in Youghal, Boyle later provided almshouses and a free school. Bandon, like less successful Clonakilty, was incorporated in 1613 and by 1641 allegedly contained 7,000 inhabitants. Enniskean and Castletown were less

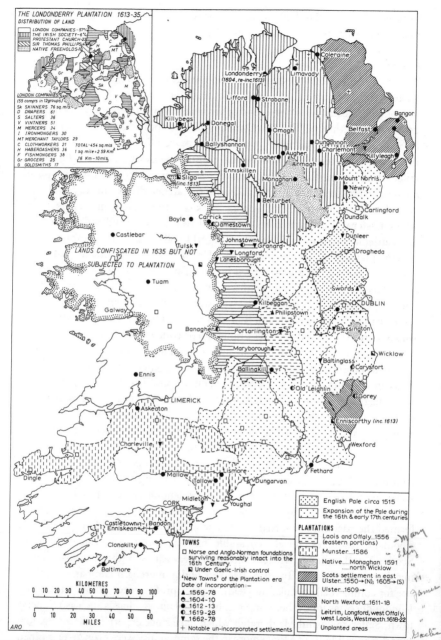

28. *The plantation of Ireland 1550–1640*
(For further details on the Londonderry plantation see T. W. Moody, *The Londonderry Plantation 1609–41*, Mullan, Belfast, 1939.)

119

fortunate. Lacking Bandon's strong defences, they were sacked in 1641 and are today mere villages, 8 or 9 miles west of Bandon.

Ulster

The chief source of unrest in later sixteenth-century Ireland lay in remote Ulster, the last stronghold of Gaelic traditions, where the O'Neills and O'Donnells – earls of Tyrone and Tyrconnell respectively – openly flouted government authority. The MacDonnells, Gaelic-speaking and Roman Catholic Scots from the western isles, were settling peacefully in north Antrim during the 1550s, but attempts at more formal plantation elsewhere after 1569 largely failed. The land settlement imposed on Monaghan in 1591 and the establishment of several strategically sited garrisons threatened the Gaelic way of life and contributed to the outbreak of fighting in 1594. After a costly nine years war in which Ulster was devastated, its crops and livestock destroyed and its churches and settlements plundered, the Gaelic world collapsed in 1603. Anticipating general plantation, Montgomerys and Hamiltons from Scotland and other colonists from England soon settled in Down and Antrim respectively, which were thus excluded from later confiscation. With the help of immigrant masons and carpenters, old towns like Newry were rebuilt and new towns such as Donaghadee, Newtownards and Belfast were constructed. In the Lagan valley, woods were cleared and marshes drained to provide farmland.

The flight of the earls of Tyrone and Tyrconnell to the Continent in 1607 left their peoples defenceless and invited comprehensive plantation. Their lands in counties Armagh, Cavan, Coleraine (now Londonderry), Donegal, Fermanagh and Tyrone were declared forfeit, and most remaining native landlords were deprived of their estates. These lands were then granted in parcels of between 1,000 and 2,000 acres, either to Scots and English undertakers, pledged to recruit only loyal Protestant tenants, or to 'servitors', men who had served the Crown in Ireland and who could take Gaelic tenants. Despite the change in land ownership, the proposed removal of the native population from certain areas failed to materialize and many former landlords were accepted as new tenants. In the years following 1609, English and lowland Scots colonists transformed the pastoral non-urban landscape of Ulster. They zealously exploited woodland resources, developed arable farming, produced grain for sale in Scotland, and built neat villages and towns near garrison forts established during the nine years war. In 1610, twelve London merchant companies with an eye for commercial speculation yielding quick profits began colonizing county Londonderry, as it now became, establishing planned villages such as Draperstown, Salterstown and Magherafelt which have since experienced varying fortunes. The residents of Moneymore in the same county were even given a piped water supply. In retrospect, the Ulster plantation settlement of 1609 was the first reasonably successful attempt at regional planning in Ireland. Ecologically,

29. The Ulster plantation town of Donegal
The town with its imposing Diamond or market place was designed by Sir Basil Brooke. The castle ruins include the great square tower erected by an O'Donnell in 1505 and altered by Brooke who also added the Jacobean fortified house in 1610. See also Fig. 66.

it ensured that immigrant communities of rural Protestants were sufficiently numerous to maintain their identity in the face of competition from a resurgent Roman Catholic Irish population later in the century. Even so, by 1628 only 2,000 British families dwelt in the six escheated counties and the difficult 1640s still lay ahead.

Among the corporate towns proposed in the plantation scheme, Dungannon, Clogher, Omagh, Loughinsholin and Mountjoy were planned for Tyrone; Limavady and Dungiven for Londonderry; Lisgoole and Castlekeagh for

Fermanagh; Derry, Killybegs, Donegal, Rathmullan, Lifford and Bally-shannon for Donegal; Cavan and Belturbet for Cavan; and Armagh, Mount Norris, Charlemont and Tanderagee for Armagh (Camblin, 1951). Many proposed towns were to be sited near garrisons and this emphasis on strategy and security rather than commercial viability was reflected in the short lives of some settlements and in the complete absence of towns from remote areas like north-west Donegal. Nevertheless, most towns envisaged in the plantation scheme

30. Londonderry, looking northeast
The seventeenth-century walled town which forms the core of the modern city occupies a low hill above the left bank of the River Foyle. The central market square or Diamond lies at the intersection of four main streets leading from the four original gates. Beyond the walled core the townscape is dominated by drab nineteenth-century industrial housing, by factories, warehouses and port facilities stretching down the Foyle and, east of the river, by the Waterside suburb. The modern Maydown industrial complex with the large Coolkeeragh oil-fired power station appears in the distance.

developed over the next thirty years and, despite the upheavals of 1641 and 1689, eventually acquired a permanent place in the Ulster landscape. Meanwhile, other urban settlements arose at Bangor, Castleblayney, Dowcoran, Manorhamilton, Monaghan, Strabane and elsewhere. With Ireland apparently secured, official policy now sought to ensure an adequate Protestant majority in the Irish parliament by incorporating some forty-four additional towns as boroughs between 1604 and 1613. Of these, the twenty-one new boroughs of Ulster served to redress, at first on paper but later in the landscape, the previous imbalance in the distribution of towns in Ireland.

Ulster plantation towns developed many features in common. Frequently a well-fortified town wall enclosed a formal or gridiron street plan dominated by two main streets that crossed in the central market place or 'diamond', a design beautifully preserved in Derry. A market house, a church and the grantee's fortified residence, with its 'bawn' or defensive enclosure, were also conspicuous, particularly in the smaller settlements. Apart from stone houses roofed with slate and simpler wattle-and-daub dwellings thatched with rushes, normal and prefabricated timber-framed houses were widely constructed. With timber readily available, prefabrication to a standard design was a means of countering the critical shortage of skilled labour. Brickmaking was also introduced as part of the planters' material culture and brickfields and brick buildings soon dotted the settlement landscape. As markets and local industries thrived, so craftsmen, merchants, shopkeepers, vegetable growers and others who peopled the new towns flourished and schools were built.

The impact of the Ulster plantation was dramatic and far reaching. As the pendulum of change swung far across, Ulster changed from being the last stronghold of pastoral, non-urban Gaelic traditions to become the powerful bastion of peoples whose speech, habits, traditions, unwavering loyalties and resolute Protestantism differed totally from native ways, and whose new towns and villages, commercial and industrial enterprise, and land-use methods were to transform the landscape. The seeds of Ireland's present political division were sown and fertilized in the seventeenth century.

Other early seventeenth-century plantations

The desire to extend effective royal authority west of the Shannon led, in 1585, to the 'composition of Connacht' in which landholders were confirmed in their estates by English law in return for quit rents payable to the Crown. Succession by primogeniture was imposed and tenants were required to pay money rents instead of rendering feudal services or making contributions in kind. Gaelic customs were thus undermined but, for a while, the people of Connacht were undisturbed by plantation. During the early seventeenth century, however, the Crown's desire to obtain revenue for its depleted exchequer while also curbing the powerful Roman Catholic landowners led government lawyers to attack the titles to estates in Wexford, Laois, Offaly, Longford, Westmeath and parts of Connacht. Where such titles were invalidated, one-quarter of the land was commonly reserved for plantation and the rest regranted to the former occupant on payment of a fine. In practice these plantations came to little because few undertakers ever visited their estates and most were content to profit from existing landholders. Some new towns, such as Carrick-on-Shannon and nearby Jamestown in Leitrim, were established, but little is yet known of their early form. In 1635 Thomas Wentworth, Charles I's deputy in Ireland, confiscated one-quarter of all Roman Catholic land in Connacht, making no distinction between Gaelic and Old English landlords, and thus exposed the province to sporadic plantation.

The Cromwellian land settlement and its aftermath

The prolonged disturbances of the 1640s eventually exposed Ireland to the unrelenting dictates of the regicidal English Parliament, expressed notably in the vicious land settlement of 1652. By that year, Ireland lay unconditionally at the mercy of a Parliament resolved to pay its creditors from the fruits of conquest which, in effect, meant depriving existing landholders, Roman Catholic and Protestant, Gaelic and Old English, of their estates. Those landholders who had been involved in rebellion simply lost all their lands. Those who had not been involved but who nevertheless failed to prove their 'constant good affection to the interests of the commonwealth of England' were transplanted to Connacht and Clare where, in the poorer country west of the Shannon, they were allowed to own a proportion of the amount of land which they had previously held elsewhere. The remaining twenty-six counties became the property of Parliament for redistribution among its creditors and army men. Those soldiers and adventurers who received substantial land grants generally settled down, and many a Smyth or Williams of modern Ireland may trace his family back to this plantation, but others, finding their smaller plots insufficient, sold out and returned to England. The restoration of Charles II in 1660 ushered in a spate of claims from dispossessed landlords which could not be met in full simply because there was not enough land available. A compromise was reached in 1665 which, by requiring Cromwellian settlers to surrender one-third of their holdings so that a land fund could be created to meet various claims, largely satisfied Protestant interests but left Roman Catholics discontented.

The Cromwellian confiscations, as modified at the restoration, had far less immediate effect on the landscape than the Ulster plantation. By confining its attentions to the removal of landlords and wealthier tenants, Parliament did indeed transfer the sources of wealth and power from the Roman Catholics to a fresh wave of enterprising Protestant colonists but the bulk of the population – craftsmen, small farmers and labourers – were left undisturbed. In the countryside, uncertainties about land ownership, combined with the acute labour

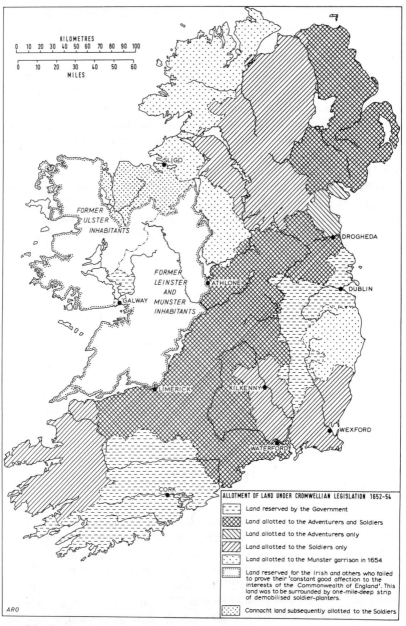

KILOMETRES
0 10 20 30 40 50 60 70 80 90 100

0 10 20 30 40 50 60
MILES

SLIGO

*FORMER
ULSTER
INHABITANTS*

*FORMER
LEINSTER
AND
MUNSTER
INHABITANTS*

GALWAY

ATHLONE

DROGHEDA

DUBLIN

LIMERICK

KILKENNY

WEXFORD

WATERFORD

CORK

ALLOTMENT OF LAND UNDER CROMWELLIAN LEGISLATION 1652-54

Land reserved by the Government

Land allotted to the Adventurers and Soldiers

Land allotted to the Adventurers only

Land allotted to the Soldiers only

Land allotted to the Munster garrison in 1654

Land reserved for the Irish and others who failed to prove their 'constant good affection to the interests of the Commonwealth of England'. This land was to be surrounded by one-mile-deep strip of demobilised soldier-planters.

Connacht land subsequently allotted to the Soldiers

ARO

31. The Cromwellian land settlement 1652–4
(Based on the 'Act for the settling of Ireland' 1652, and subsequent legislation.)

shortage caused by war, famine, disease and the emigration of some 30,000 soldiers from disbanded Irish armies, at first discouraged the careful development of estates. Neither was there much attempt to organize rural Protestant communities. However, economic recovery began before 1660 and prosperity was soon transmitted to the towns and seaports where between 30 and 75 per cent of the population were commonly New English. After the restoration, further new towns were incorporated, notably at Midleton, Charleville (now Rath Luirc), Portarlington, Longford and Lanesborough, thus more or less completing the main urban framework of Ireland's present landscape, though a few very small towns were to be created in Connacht and elsewhere along the Atlantic seaboard during the ensuing landlord era. These events, which reduced the amount of land held by Roman Catholics from 59 per cent in 1641 to 22 per cent in 1688, placed most of Ireland in the hands of a vigorous Protestant minority who, as a consequence, acquired the power and wealth to reshape the landscape at will. The eighteenth century was to witness such developments.

Economic activity and the landscape

Sixteenth-century attempts at plantation made little difference to the forces already shaping the landscape but the collapse of Gaelic power in 1603 and the subsequent large influx of new colonists initiated a century of sweeping change. Remaining woodlands were cleared, commercial sheep and cattle-rearing expanded, tillage revived, more fields were enclosed, industries were introduced, old towns broke free of their outdated medieval walls, and new towns and villages arose almost everywhere. Ireland, however, became controlled by social and economic forces designed in England, about which Irish people generally could do little. As these forces, ranging from plantation policy to restrictions on the import into England of Irish cattle and woollen goods, were manipulated to suit England's needs, so their effect was transmitted to the Irish landscape.

Fortunately, these landscape changes were recorded as they happened by surveyors, government officials and natural historians whose documents, when added to the surviving field evidence, provide invaluable tools for the historical geographer's craft. The Ulster plantation maps and new town plans, the few surviving maps of the Connacht plantation survey (1636), and Petty's Down Survey of the cultivable and other lands involved in the Cromwellian confiscations are noteworthy cartographic records. The Civil Survey (1654–56) was a valuable estimation of land use and ownership, settlement, roads, woods and bogs covering twenty-seven counties. Meanwhile, comparison of John Dymmok's writings on Ireland around 1600 with Gerard Boate's *Ireland's Naturall History*, published in 1652, and the regional descriptions collected by

William Molyneux between 1682 and 1685, shows that the art of landscape description improved as the century progressed. During the later seventeenth century, crude population estimates were computed from unreliable taxation returns and statistics of births and deaths. Despite their limitations, these and other information sources suggest that Dublin's population increased from about 60,000 to some 80,000 during the last quarter of the century and that by 1700 Ireland's population exceeded 2,500,000, of whom at least 75 per cent were Roman Catholic.

The most striking landscape change arising from the economic revival of the seventeenth century was the clearance of the remaining woodlands. Despite widespread clearances for farmland and timber, Elizabethan state papers could still comment on the problems of conducting military campaigns in extensive woods that sheltered both rebels and wolves. Some Munster and Ulster woods were certainly felled for reasons of military expediency, but seventeenth-century colonists soon came to regard the woodlands less as a threat to their security and more as a source of quick profit. With the titles to their estates rendered uncertain by the vagaries of Irish and English politics, the new land-owners naturally wished to convert their forest resources into a more liquid form of capital as quickly as possible. Thus, by catering to the demands of the leather industry for tanner's bark, of the Welsh coal-mines for pit-props, of the French and Spanish wine trades for barrel staves, of the expanding iron-smelting industry for charcoal, and of the housing and shipbuilding industries at home and overseas for prepared timber, the woods were ruthlessly felled with complete disregard for future resources. By 1700, Ireland was virtually devoid of woodlands. Oak, alder and hazel almost disappear from the pollen record at this time and are replaced by grass and weeds. The Munster woodlands suffered particularly severely from profit-conscious grantees and later from the flourishing charcoal–iron industry established by Boyle in the Blackwater and Bride valleys above Youghal. Furthermore, the wild woodland animals, deprived of their cover and forage, were exposed to relentless hunting and decimation, eventually reflected in the declining export of deerfells and wolf, fox, wild dog, otter and marten skins from Munster ports.

Much of the land cleared of trees was either left as rough grazing or converted to improved pasture to accommodate the expanding sheep and cattle-rearing industries intent on exploiting the British market for livestock, wool, hides, beef and dairy produce. During the peaceful 1620s and 1630s, Munster in particular was transformed into a vast unenclosed sheep run with almost two-thirds of Ireland's annual wool exports passing through Youghal, Cork, Kinsale and New Ross en route to Bristol Channel ports. The cloth manufacturers of Devon drew upon southern Ireland for wool to supplement their home supplies. Cattle-rearing was the other mainstay of Ireland's economy and, in view of the shortage of labour and capital and of the insecurity of tenure, played a leading role in the commercial revival of the 1650s. By the early 1660s, cattle formed the country's most valuable export, tens of thousands being sent annually from Dublin and Drogheda to the rising port of Liverpool for fattening on rich English pastures. Thus began in earnest a pattern of commercial activity which is still the dominating feature of Ireland's landscape and economy. In these fields, England's interference with Ireland's trade had little direct effect on the landscape. The restrictions imposed by restoration England on Irish wool exports to the Continent were countered by smuggling while, following the exclusion of live cattle from England by acts of 1663 and 1666, Irish traders soon found lucrative continental markets for their cattle products. On the other hand, the English commercial interests, which tightened restrictions on the overseas sale of Irish woollen manufactures until the industry was virtually destroyed in 1669, prevented Ireland from broadening her industrial base in an obvious direction. Conversely, linen manufacturing was encouraged because it did not clash with any English interests. In Munster where flax-growing and linen-weaving had flourished before the devastating Elizabethan wars, Boyle promoted the industry in Bandon, Clonakilty and elsewhere.

The settlers encouraged tillage, grain cultivation flourished in Ulster and Leinster, expanding vegetable gardens catered for the growing towns, and the newly introduced potato was gradually adopted as the main support of poorer folk. Villages, single farms, cornmills, markets and fairs flourished, except during the 1640s and other troubled times when much land fell out of cultivation and was invaded by scrub and bracken. Enclosure became more frequent, notably around expanding centres like Limerick and Dublin, but neither the new hedges nor the numerous orchards of Kilkenny and Tipperary could compensate for the loss of the woodlands. In the 1680s, extensive areas of farmland in Westmeath and elsewhere were still open or 'champain' country, the arable being protected in summer by light temporary fencing. For various reasons, several old villages fell into disuse during the plantation period. Clonmines and Bannow in Wexford were both finally abandoned during the seventeenth century and subsequently achieved some notoriety as 'rotten boroughs'. The failure of any public authority to provide new planned highways between growing commercial centres meant that communications remained poor throughout the period.

While the new settlers introduced many changes, the rural population remained overwhelmingly Gaelic and, where possible, traditionally pastoral. In 1684 O'Flaherty, describing booleying among the inhabitants of west Galway, wrote of how 'in summer time they drive their cattle to the mountains, where such as look to the cattle live in small cabins for that season'. Along the nearby coast, applications of seaweed to poor land yielded the local farmers a marketable surplus of grain. Undoubtedly, Gaelic traditions found new expression among the peoples transplanted west of the Shannon during the Cromwellian period. Farther south, in areas repeatedly exposed to plantation, the so-calle census about 1659 revealed that New English Protestants formed only 5 per cent of the west Limerick population, only 8 per cent of the west Waterford community, and in all the Munster towns achieved majorities only in Bandon and Mallow.

Apart from woollen and linen manufacturing, iron smelting was among the most significant industrial features of the seventeenth-century landscape. Initially, the widespread occurrence of low-grade iron ores, charcoal resources and water power presented few locational problems for the industry. During the early seventeenth century Boyle's furnaces at Ardglin, Cappoquin and Mocollop, his forges at Lisfinny and Kilmakoe, together with their associated steelworks and slitting mills in west Waterford, produced iron for shipment downstream to Youghal and thence coastwise to ports as far afield as Drogheda and Sligo (Andrews, 1956). For a while, this area was the principal centre of the Irish iron industry, but, having depleted its local ore and charcoal resources, only one forge near Tallow survived beyond mid-century and this had been abandoned by 1685. Other early centres of the industry in the once dense woodlands of the Lagan valley near Belfast, north and west of Lough Neagh, and around Castlecomer suffered similar fates. The industry later came to focus either on less accessible native ores, such as those of the Shannon basin, Connacht, Kerry and Wicklow, or on coastal and river sites, such as Enniscorthy in Wexford, favourably placed to import high-grade English ores for smelting with cheap local charcoal. From our viewpoint, the indiscriminate rape of the woodlands for charcoal had a more significant long-term effect on the landscape than the transitory existence of furnaces and forges. Even judicious coppicing, as a means of ensuring a steady fuel supply, was ignored until it was too late. The charcoal–iron industry had virtually died from lack of fuel by the mid-eighteenth century although the last Irish charcoal furnace at Enniscorthy was still smelting Lancashire ore in 1785. Youghal, which had exported timber and iron during the early seventeenth century, was importing both commodities from Scandinavia by 1719.

ord and landscape in Ireland, 1690–1850

The Williamite victory on the Boyne in 1690 launched the Irish landscape on a century and a half of unparalleled development and remodelling at the hands of a favoured minority, the Protestant ascendancy. By confiscation, the Roman Catholic share of profitable land fell from 22 per cent in 1688 to 14 per cent in 1703, a much smaller loss than had resulted from the combined effect of the Cromwellian and restoration settlements. Colonization of Ireland from outside was, however, almost at an end. No settlers came from Scotland or England to occupy the confiscated lands and neither the Huguenot infusion into Irish towns, after the revocation of the Edict of Nantes in 1685, nor the 3,000 Palatine immigrants of 1709 exerted much influence on rural landholding. The land of Ireland was thus confirmed in the hands of the existing Protestant, chiefly Episcopalian, minority and of those formerly Roman Catholic landlords who went over to the established Church. Indeed the penal laws of the eighteenth century brought so many pressures, inducements and prohibitions to bear on Roman Catholic landowners that, before the relaxation of these laws began in 1778, scarcely 5 per cent of Ireland remained in their hands.

Under the driving force of the 'improving' landlords, the eighteenth-century landscape acquired a more orderly and well-furnished appearance, notably among the better lands of the south and east. New farming practices were adopted, lands drained, fields enclosed, crops and livestock improved; trade and industry were fostered, new roads and canals built, and harbours extended; country houses were built, demesnes laid out and woodlands planted; existing towns were rebuilt in accordance with Georgian planning concepts, and new towns and villages were created in the gaps inherited from the seventeenth-century framework of settlement.

Despite these deliberate, often revolutionary, changes in the landscape, Ireland's physical and human resources remained grossly underdeveloped, owing to poor management, absenteeism and lack of capital among many land-lords, combined with the rigid duality of a society whose two scarcely compar-able components were commonly out of touch and out of sympathy with each other. To the discredit of landlordism generally, pernicious social and economic forces condemned the mass of the Roman Catholic peasantry to exist as serfs in a state of abject poverty, wretchedness and squalor, dependent on agriculture for a livelihood and on potatoes for food. The century advanced in company with a grim progression of rising population, increasing rents and diminishing holdings, tempered by high mortality rates, famine as in 1740–41, and emigration, notably of 'Scotch–Irish' Presbyterians who, driven initially from the land by unreasonable rent increases after 1718, fled from Ulster to America. While

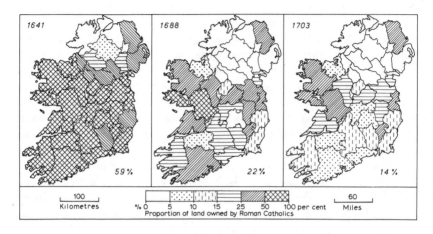

32. *The proportion of land owned by Roman Catholics according to counties in 1641, 1688 and 1703*
The effect of the Cromwellian confiscation as modified at the Restoration is indicated by comparing the first and second maps; the effect of the Williamite confiscation is shown by comparing the second and third maps (after J. G. Simms, 'The Williamite confiscation in Ireland, 1690–1703', London, 1958, Faber & Faber Ltd.).

material legacies of landlordism abound in the modern landscape, events of the landlord era cannot be viewed in isolation for they were to culminate in the great famine of 1846–48, in vastly increased emigration and eventually in the collapse of the dual society. These negative legacies have furnished a striking epilogue to landlordism – a relict landscape abandoned by the landlords who shaped it and by the faceless masses who occupied it.

Information on pre-famine Ireland is fortunately abundant. The cartographic record includes Grand Jury county maps, town plans and estate maps by John Rocque and others, Charles Vallancey's military surveys, and the 6 inches to 1 mile Ordnance Survey maps published between 1833 and 1846. The writings of travellers such as Loveday (1732), Young (1776–78), Hall (1807) and Inglis (1834), the exhaustive compilations of Wakefield (1812), Lewis (1837) and others, the statistical county surveys published under the auspices of the Dublin Society in the early 1800s, contemporary papers such as Walker's *Hibernian Magazine*, Faulkner's *Dublin Journal* and the *Freeman's Journal*, and the remarkable census of 1841 provide a wealth of material on the period.

The rural landscape

Agriculture

Owing to their complete control over landholding, landlords influenced the nature of agricultural activity and rural settlement throughout eighteenth-century Ireland. Even so, within this framework a broad gulf existed between the commercial farming practices of the landlords and the largely subsistence economy of the majority of the people. Landlords with capital and initiative could respond to changing economic stimuli either by rearing livestock or by expanding cereal production as occasion arose. Most of their tenants, meanwhile, were condemned by poverty, uncertain tenure and rising population to eke out a meagre existence on potatoes and buttermilk, supplemented by the occasional sale of a pig. This dichotomy of the 'two Irelands', which was social and economic rather than regional, was vividly expressed in the prefamine landscape.

Despite restrictions on wool and cattle exports, the eighteenth century saw a remarkable expansion of pasture as landlords and privileged tenants alike exploited the lucrative continental and North American markets for provisions of salted beef, mutton, pork, dairy produce, tallow and hides while also smuggling much wool to France. After Irish cattle imports to England were de-restricted in 1759 and provision imports decontrolled some years later, this process accelerated. Tenants were evicted from their farms, whole villages and communal open fields swept away, and common lands enclosed. Extensive sheep walks and cattle ranches spread through Roscommon, Sligo, east Mayo, east Galway, Clare, Limerick and Tipperary as graziers took advantage of rising prices. Tens of thousands of sheep and cattle were sold annually at Ballinasloe and other Connacht fairs to Cork and Limerick provision merchants and to Leinster graziers for fattening either for the home market or for shipment live to Bristol and Liverpool. Commercial dairying expanded in Carlow, Kilkenny, Waterford, Cork and elsewhere. Drogheda, Waterford and Cork exported live pigs and Limerick became the centre of ham curing in the 1820s.

Around mid-century, the adoption of new agrarian practices and the growing awareness that efficient arable farming could alleviate poverty, hunger and unemployment in rural areas led to an expansion of land under the plough. In 1759 a subsidy was paid to farmers who brought grain to Dublin. When Roman Catholics were again allowed to own land freely in 1781 and Foster's corn law of 1784 provided large bounties on wheat exports, tillage expanded farther, much pasture was broken up, and large flour mills and grain stores were built. The traditional tillage counties of the south and east grew vast quantities of oats, wheat and barley for the developing industrial population of Britain, particularly after the outbreak of war with France curtailed alternative supplies. The grain ports reached the zenith of their prosperity on this thriving trade. The wealthy merchants of Youghal, for example, reclaimed land from the Black-water slob, erected new quays, warehouses and corn stores, opened new streets and built elegant Georgian town houses. This prosperity rested insecurely on inflated wartime grain prices but, with the inevitable collapse of the boom in 1815, many landlords evicted their tenants in order to consolidate their farms and maintain cash crop production. In fact, large amounts of grain continued to be exported until the great famine and the repeal of the corn laws in 1846 led to belated agrarian adjustments. Flax, the most profitable tillage crop in early nineteenth-century Ulster, various fodder crops, potatoes, clover and grasses helped to vary field rotations.

Before the adoption of new agrarian practices, farming had been hampered by exhaustive rotations, few crops, limited use of fertilizers, excessive fallow and waste, indifferent livestock, primitive implements and few farm buildings. Poor management, irresponsibility and wet weather commonly prolonged harvesting and haymaking, and reduced crop values. As the eighteenth century progressed, however, new agricultural societies and landlords with capital and initiative imported new techniques. The Dublin Society, founded in 1731, imported new ploughs and other implements, experimented with new methods, encouraged afforestation, fruit-growing, flax cultivation, cider-making, fish-curing, spin-ning and weaving, and gave bounties for agricultural and industrial proficiency. By 1800 the light iron swing plough and the Scots cart had entered Ireland through Ulster and were helping to transform the landscape. Improving land-lords such as Richard Edgeworth in Longford, Anthony Foster of Collon in Louth, Lord Altamont of Westport, Joshua Cooper of Markree in Sligo, the Trenches of Ballinasloe and Thomas Mahon of Strokestown in Roscommon reclaimed mountain and boggy lands, introduced new crops and improved live-stock breeds, planted trees and hedgerows, erected limekilns and solid farm-houses for their tenants, built roads and bridges, and stimulated local woollen and linen industries. Some absentee landlords, such as the 1st marquis of Lansdowne who owned much of south Kerry, were similarly enterprising but the majority did little or nothing for their tenants.

Enclosure was undoubtedly the most lasting change to befall the rural land-scape during the eighteenth century. As no act of Parliament was needed before an estate was enclosed, many landlords soon set about reorganizing their lands to suit the needs of their expanding cash economy. The growth of commercial grazing provided the initial stimulus. Open fields and associated settlements were swept away, notably throughout the midlands and the south, holdings were consolidated, sown with grass, and enclosed by earthen banks or quickset hedges of furze and hawthorn. After 1755 numerous common lands were also enclosed. Predictably, these events generated much rural unrest throughout Ireland, culminating in the 'Whiteboy' terrorist campaign in Munster and similar movements in Leinster and Ulster. Later in the century, various agrarian improvements necessitated further enclosures to protect valuable cash crops and improved livestock breeds. This process varied considerably from one area to another but, when the field surveyors were preparing the 6 inches to 1 mile Ordnance Survey maps between 1825 and 1841, the essentials of the present pattern of enclosed fields throughout eastern Ireland already existed. Some landlords had of course inherited hedgerows from earlier eras, while others allowed open field systems to survive intact well into the nineteenth century.

Improving landlords and privileged tenants, motivated by the profit incentives of the cash economy, were thus the main agents of durable change in the pre-famine agrarian landscape, notably in the southeastern tillage counties and the pastoral midlands. In contrast, most tenants were too poor and insecure to benefit from new agrarian practices. Their impact on the landscape was thus less revolutionary and less durable. The encroachment of pasture upon arable and of cash crops upon subsistence plots, together with the mounting pressure on the land exerted by a population which rose from about 2,500,000 in 1700 to over 4,750,000 in 1800 (Connell, 1950), meant that farms were repeatedly subdivided in order to maintain bare subsistence. Middlemen and agents took high rents for short leases until most tenants had sunk to the level of mere cottiers, dwelling in wretched hovels and scraping a miserable living from a few acres paid for in labour, cash or kind. Seaweed and animal manure helped to sustain arable production and when weather and crops were good the people, fortified by their rich folk culture and religious piety, probably lived a carefree enough existence. The poorest families, however, shared miserably furnished, windowless, single rooms in squalid turf-covered mud cabins with their poultry, cow and pig – 'the gentleman who paid the rent'. Many such cabins were quite ephemeral, as wandering families squatted in one area after another seeking food and employment. Their plight was worst in the economically marginal areas, notably in the overcrowded west where landless families reclaimed and colonized mountain sides and bogs. These conditions were to be terminated in a most terrible way by the great famine. In the north, the tenant farmer's lot was rather better, although this did not stem the flow of discontented emigrants to North America. The 'Ulster custom' protected tenants against eviction and unjust rents, and entitled them to sell their interest in the farm on leaving. Agriculture was more widely based. Punishing rotations of potatoes, oats, barley, flax and short leys provided a subsistence diet of potatoes, buttermilk and oatmeal, and a cash income from domestic linen production and the sale of barley, butter, poultry and eggs.

Throughout pre-famine Ireland, regional variations in agriculture were functions more of the complex pattern of landlord control and of varying economic and demographic pressures than of any qualities of the physical environment. In the mainly subsistence areas, these forces led to the disintegration of traditional rundale practices, the dispersion of clustered settlements, and the creation of individual strip holdings based upon scattered farmsteads. These processes began long before the great famine, accelerated afterwards, and culminated in the decline of kinship and Gaelic speech.

Planted woodlands and orchards

The savage deforestation of the seventeenth-century landscape led in 1698 to an Act that made tree-planting compulsory on all sizeable estates in Ireland. The response was generally disappointing. Many landlords did nothing and most tenants naturally avoided planting trees which, on the expiration of their leases, would revert to their landlords for only nominal compensation. Thus, in 1776–78, Arthur Young noted that 'the greatest part of the kingdom exhibits a naked, bleak, dreary view for want of wood, which has been destroyed for a century past with the most thoughtless prodigality and still continues to be cut and wasted'. In contrast, new hedgerows ran wild for want of trimming. When, in 1781, tenants were granted property in the trees they planted, many made more serious attempts to establish plantations.

Meanwhile, having forsaken fortified residences for stately country mansions, many eighteenth-century landlords began improving the scenic and sporting amenities of their demesnes with groves, belts and avenues of indigenous and exotic trees and shrubs. Some were motivated by a sense of duty, others by their aesthetic sensibilities. Among the trees widely introduced to the country's demesnes and deer parks by 1700 were various elms, beech, Scots pine, lime, Spanish chestnut, walnut, hornbeam, sycamore, evergreen oak, plane, robinia, mulberry, Lombardy poplar, Lebanon cedar and Norway spruce (McEvoy, 1958). European larch and silver fir arrived around 1738. Elm, beech and pine, the most commonly planted trees, soon revealed themselves in the pollen record and G. F. Mitchell (1956) has justifiably recognized a pollen Zone X commencing around 1700. In Munster, Arthur Young also noted the frequent occurrence of cider-apple orchards, many averaging 14–21 acres, on larger farms where tenure was more secure and more land was available. Even mounting population pressure on the land did not totally eliminate all these orchards before the famine.

In 1791, despite a century of planting, only an estimated 105,000 acres of woods and plantations yet covered Ireland, 20 per cent of which comprised oak woods. This total represented about 0·5 per cent of the land area, although the figure probably took little account of relict woodlands outside demesnes. Forestry practices were confined simply to coppicing the natural oak woods on a 30–40-year rotation for small timber and charcoal. Changes were, however, imminent. About this period, commercial forestry commenced as landlords became attracted by the profits to be gained from the high wartime prices for hardwood and particularly for oak timber and bark. Between 1791 and 1800, some 2,500 acres of timber were planted yearly. After this market collapsed in 1815, many oak coppices were allowed to develop into high forest. After 1820 forestry came to rely increasingly on those European and American conifers which grew satisfactorily under Irish conditions. Between 1831 and 1840 some 6,500 acres were planted annually and by 1840 Ireland's wooded area had more than trebled in fifty years to 350,000 acres.

Country houses and demesnes

As the seventeenth-century colonists found greater security, so their domestic architecture began to shed its military characteristics and before the century closed several handsome brick-built country houses had appeared, such as Beaulieu on the Boyne estuary, while Huguenot refugees were popularizing the use of Dutch gable ends, projecting eaves and imported bricks. Until well into the eighteenth century, however, most landlords possessed neither the capital nor the incentive to initiate vast building projects. Then, after 1720, the comparative peace of the countryside and the plentiful supply of cheap labour led many larger landowners to lavish the wealth they derived from rising rents either on converting existing castles or on building stately Georgian mansions set amid carefully planned demesnes. Constructed to imported designs, these houses were, like their owners, quite alien to the surrounding landscape. The taste for classical exteriors and rococo interiors was soon expressed in Castletown House, begun near Celbridge in Kildare for the influential William Conolly in 1722. This and many later mansions commonly consisted of a stone-built, three-storey central block, prolonged on each side by colonnades or concave curtain walls leading to smaller blocks at both wings. The most noteworthy country houses of this period include those designed by Richard Cassels between 1728 and 1751 at Carton near Maynooth, Hazelwood near Sligo, Summerhill and Ballinter in Meath, and Westport in Mayo. Powerscourt, built for the Wingfield family near Enniskerry around 1730, was later provided with beautiful gardens, terraces and parklands. Cassels collaborated with Francis Bindon to design Russborough near Blessington, while the latter also created Bessborough and Woodstock in Kilkenny. Impressive later eighteenth-century houses include James Wyatt's designs at Mount Kennedy in Wicklow and Castle Coole, faced with imported Portland stone, near Enniskillen, and the houses built for Frederick Hervey, 'the edifying bishop' of Derry, at Ballyscullion, north of Lough Neagh, and Downhill near Coleraine. During the last quarter of the century, Abbeyleix and Heywood in Laois, Headfort in Meath and many other houses were given Adam-style interiors. Around 1800 Francis Johnston enlarged Killeen in Meath, and designed Pakenham in Westmeath and Rokeby with its thirty estate farmhouses in Louth; John Nash designed Lough Cutra in Galway and remodelled Rockingham in Roscommon and Caledon in Tyrone; Richard Morrison and his son created Shelton Abbey and Kilruddery in

Wicklow, Castle Freke in Cork, Ballyheigue in Kerry and many others in the Gothic revival styles with which the Romantic age had by now replaced classical Georgian designs.

The creative extravagances of the landlords were not confined simply to their main houses. During the early eighteenth century, formal Dutch and French style gardens were widely adapted to individual means. Huguenots introduced continental horticultural practices, together with many exotic plants, flowers and vegetables, wherever they went. Bullen and other landscape gardeners constructed terraces, fishponds and summerhouses, trimmed yew and laurel bushes into remarkable shapes, marshalled trees into rows alongside gravel avenues and walks, and laid out lawns, flowerbeds and vegetable gardens sprinkled liberally with vases, statues and grottoes, all to preconceived symmetrical plans. Later in the century symmetry was abandoned in favour of flowing natural lines and formal gardens gave way to rolling tree-studded lawns. Botanic gardens were sponsored in Dublin by Trinity College and the Dublin Society. Beyond the country houses and gardens, demesnes were frequently walled, partly to protect deer and plants, partly to provide work for starving tenants during lean famine years. Thus Low Grange, in Kilkenny, and Carton both had walls en-

33. Powerscourt demesne near Enniskerry, County Wicklow
Looking southeast towards the Great Sugar Loaf. The beautiful terraced gardens, laid out between 1843 and 1875, lead away from the mansion which was designed originally by Richard Cassels for the Wingfield family around 1730.

g over 1,000 acres, and the 200-acre deer park at Burton Hall near Carlow was bounded by a 9-foot wall.

The above country houses and demesnes were among the most extravagant of their age and, where they survive intact, still add considerable if unrealistic grace to the landscape. They were by no means typical of lesser landlords and middlemen, most of whom built less pretentious, more comfortable homes. With the subsequent collapse of landlordism, many estates fell into decay, buildings were abandoned or burnt, and demesne lands were subdivided among local farmers.

The urban landscape

The 200 years that separated the Cromwellian confiscations from the great famine saw vast changes befall Ireland's urban landscapes, changes of quality and design rather than distribution. With the growth of population and commerce, existing towns and villages increased in size and importance. Settlements which had grown continuously throughout medieval times rarely escaped reconstruction while the newer plantation towns were also remodelled. Landlords were, once again, the main agents of change. Their attentions were not confined to the renewal of existing settlements for they also exerted much energy in creating numerous estate villages and some new towns. The landlords thus completed Ireland's framework of nucleated settlements as it now exists.

Owing to sporadic warfare and ensuing economic slumps, many towns were sadly in need of reconstruction as the turbulent seventeenth century drew to a close. The redundant walls and fortifications of many had fallen into decay or largely disappeared, but there had been little renewal of the cramped core areas and virtually no rationalization of the unplanned rows of squalid mud cabins which comprised the suburbs. Inland towns such as Athlone and Kilmallock had often suffered considerable damage and many villages had degenerated into unkempt collections of miserable dwellings. On to this scene came the 'improving' landlords and, if so many Irish towns are today remarkably uniform in plan and composition, it is because their wide main streets, squares, long terrace blocks and treelined avenues were laid out more or less simultaneously by eighteenth-century landlords, architects and town planners, imbued with the creative uniformity of their age.

With the growth of the cash economy, directed primarily towards British and continental markets, the favourably located south and east coast ports, together with outliers like Limerick and Sligo and prosperous inland centres like Clonmel and Kilkenny, were soon affected by eighteenth-century ventures in town planning, public works and private building. Town centres had their old buildings swept away and their streets widened and lined with new brick-built Georgian houses. Nevertheless, these changes rarely erased the cramped,

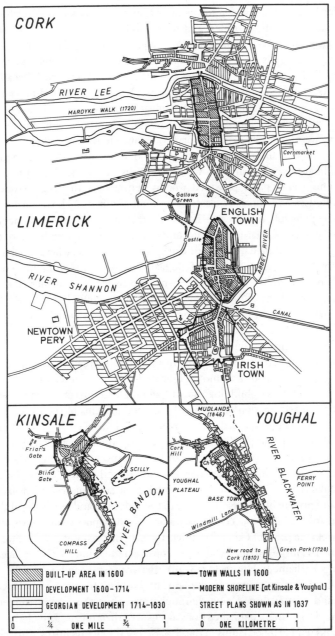

CORK

RIVER LEE
MARDYKE WALK (1720)

Cornmarket

Gallows
Green

LIMERICK

ENGLISH
TOWN

Castle

ABBEY RIVER

RIVER SHANNON

CANAL

NEWTOWN
PERY

IRISH
TOWN

KINSALE

MUDLANDS
(1846)

YOUGHAL

Friar's
Gate

Cork
Hill

Ch

RIVER BLACKWATER

SCILLY

Blind
Gate

YOUGHAL
PLATEAU

FERRY
POINT

BASE TOWN

RIVER BANDON

Windmill Lane

COMPASS
HILL

New road to
Cork (1810)

Green Park (1728)

	BUILT-UP AREA IN 1600		TOWN WALLS IN 1600
	DEVELOPMENT 1600–1714		MODERN SHORELINE [at Kinsale & Youghal]
	GEORGIAN DEVELOPMENT 1714–1830		STREET PLANS SHOWN AS IN 1837

0   ¼   ONE MILE   ¾   1

0   ONE KILOMETRE   1

34. *The ground plans of Cork, Limerick, Kinsale and Youghal as they appeared
in 1837, following the major urban developments of the Georgian era*

irregular ground plans which towns like Dublin, Limerick and Waterford had inherited from medieval times, and which still characterize their old sectors. Beyond the old town walls, which were now generally dismantled, changes were far more striking, as once open country was progressively submerged by the building boom. Here, in vivid contrast to the congested core areas, broad regular streets, treelined walks, paved footpaths, elegant squares and pleasant gardens were laid out along formal rectilinear lines. Streets and squares were flanked with three- to four-storey residential blocks whose plain, rather severe exteriors were offset by ornate doorways, stone steps, iron railings and lamp arches, and often hid richly decorated interiors. Such blocks were commonly built of light red brick but a few were faced with local stone, at least to the first floor. The overall plans provided worthy settings for the larger stone-built private houses and superbly classical public buildings, such as court houses, exchanges, custom houses and hospitals, that most larger towns acquired. Many towns had similar features in common. Thus broad, tree-lined, riverside malls arose at Drogheda, Youghal, Cork, Kinsale and elsewhere. Fashionable assembly rooms were a feature of Belfast, Newtownards, Dublin, Youghal, Cork, Limerick, Galway and other towns, and society was further catered for by a liberal sprinkling of theatres, clubs, bandstands, coffee houses and bowling greens. Military garrisons often contributed to urban social and economic activities.

Georgian planning concepts reached their fullest expression in Dublin, about which one correspondent wrote in 1785 that 'there never was so splendid a metropolis for so poor a country'. During the later seventeenth century, the old walls disappeared, buildings spread along Dame Street, Cornmarket and Capel Street, reclamation of the poorly drained margins of the Liffey estuary began, quays were extended downstream, and Phoenix Park (1662) and St Stephen's Green (1664–5), once an unenclosed common, were laid out. The eighteenth-century city, functioning in every respect as its country's capital, expanded rapidly within the framework subsequently provided by the canals and circular roads. The planned thoroughfares, elegant squares and magnificent public and private buildings that arose to the southeast and northeast of the old city effectively shifted the centre of gravity to a new north–south axis aligned along Sackville (now O'Connell) Street, Carlisle Bridge (1793), Westmoreland Street and College Green, where a reconstructed Trinity College faced the imposing Parliament House (1728–39). Between 1757 and 1841, the Wide Street Commissioners improved many of Dublin's narrow and dangerous streets and created broad new thoroughfares, while the Commissioners for Paving and Lighting, established in 1806, ensured their repair, provided covered sewers and tended 6,000 lamps in the city. Before the eighteenth century closed, Dublin's population exceeded 200,000 but, with the coming of the legislative Union with Great Britain in 1801 and of declining economic prosperity after

35. Classical and modern Dublin
The Custom House built to the design of James Gandon between 1781 and 1791 and
Liberty Hall built in 1962–4.

1815, the city's brief glory faded. Many elegant town houses were sold and soon
degenerated into wretched tenements and, although expansion continued,
artistic town planning died.

Profiting from the rich provision trade, Cork also acquired several handsome
public buildings and paved streets such as Grand Parade and South Mall, lined
with good shops and elegant houses belonging to the merchants. The Lee's
various distributaries were canalized and bridged, the marshes drained, and
large warehouses erected along the quays. The Mardyke walk was laid out west
of the town in 1720. Waterford's share in the provision trade and the Newfoundland fisheries was vividly expressed in the merchants' handsome houses
ranged along its broad mile-long quay which, like the Mall which it crossed at
Reginald's Tower, was constructed beyond the dismantled town walls.
Medieval Limerick had consisted of two walled sectors, the insular English
Town and the Irish Town to the southeast. Now, in the eighteenth century, the
flourishing city was given a new fashionable sector southwest of these old twin
sectors by the local landlord, Edmond Pery. Newtown Pery, as it was called,
was provided with clean, broad streets, paved footpaths, good shops and
Georgian residential blocks, all conforming to a rectilinear town plan. As in
Dublin, the principal new axis soon became the social and commercial focus of
the city. Similar patterns of reconstruction and expansion could be observed
on a smaller scale in most contemporary Irish towns. In the north, textile towns
like Dundalk, Banbridge, Lurgan, Lisburn, Belfast, Coleraine and Londonderry expanded, notably after factory production was introduced towards the

141

36. Limerick

Looking northeast along O'Connell Street, the main axis of Newtown Pery, towards the decayed English town on King's Island. Norsemen founded a settlement on King's Island in 922 which, following the Anglo-Norman invasion, developed into a powerful frontier trading colony dominated by English merchants while across the narrow Abbey river an equally distinctive Irish Town emerged. Both English and Irish Towns were walled. When Limerick ceased to be designated a fortress in 1760 the way was open for the planned gridiron development of Newtown Pery and this fashionable sector soon displaced the cramped older parts as the city's social and commercial focus.

close of the eighteenth century. Belfast in particular acquired a grid of wide, well-paved streets as a prelude to the rapid urban and industrial expansion it was to experience during the nineteenth century.

These outward expressions of the wealth, security and creative ability of the Protestant ascendancy should not hide the deplorable living conditions of the urban poor who, without even a potato patch, were probably worse off than their country cousins. In Dublin and elsewhere, the outward movement of wealthier people into freshly built suburbs was countered by an inward migration of poor folk to the increasingly congested town centres where thirty or forty persons might share a single house. As social and economic conditions worsened during the early nineteenth century, poverty and overcrowding were further aggravated by the accelerated drift of country folk into the towns, on whose outskirts numerous thatched cottages arose. As in the country, these primitive dwellings were mainly transient features of the landscape but some decayed examples still survive around smaller towns. Sometimes, the overt squalor of these suburbs was more a reflection of the low living standards passively accepted by their inhabitants than of unrelenting poverty. Thus, although Galway did not share in the general prosperity of the eighteenth century, the closely knit community of the nearby Claddagh, a picturesque but squalid collection of thatched cabins housing some 3,000 fisherfolk ruled by their 'admiral', reaped a good harvest from the sea and was for the most part happy and contented.

Many landlords demolished existing settlements to make way for newly designed towns and villages alongside their demesnes. Thus, the King family swept away old Mitchelstown and created a new town with two elegant squares, two main north–south streets and five cross streets between 1770 and 1830. Jefferyes transformed a dismal collection of mud cabins at Blarney into a thriving textile manufacturing town. John Anderson's new town of Fermoy began replacing some old estate cottages in the 1790s. Lord Altamont's Westport was redesigned by James Wyatt in the 1780s and the local river diverted along the centre of a broad, treelined Mall. Adare in Limerick owes its attractive English appearance to the third earl of Dunraven (1812–71). Tyrrellspass in Westmeath, a settlement with Anglo-Norman connections, owes its well-proportioned crescent to the countess of Belvidere. Many villages initiated by seventeenth-century planters such as Castlebellingham, Cootehill, Blessington, Castlecomer and Eyrecourt were radically replanned during the eighteenth or early nineteenth century. Kenmare, founded by William Petty in 1670, was mainly developed by a descendant, William Lord Sherburne, 1st marquis of Lansdowne (1737–1805), in the last quarter of the eighteenth century. A typical estate village was created alongside the Seaforde demesne in Down. Mallow, Castleconnell, Lucan, Swanlinbar and Ballynahinch (Down) developed as fashionable spa towns.

Finally, new towns arose during the landlord era in areas where there had previously been little or no nucleated settlement, notably in the trackless lands of west Connacht. In the remote Mullet of Mayo, Binghamstown, a half-mile-long alignment of some seventy dwellings, was founded in the 1790s, but

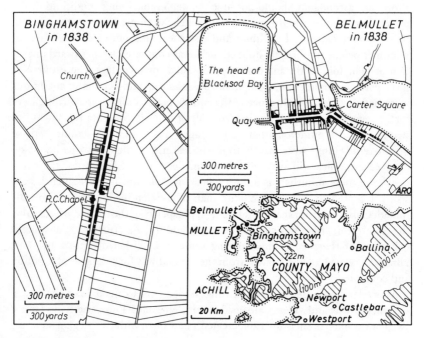

37. Binghamstown and Belmullet

Two small nucleated settlements created by landlords in remote northwest Mayo, as they appeared in 1838. Binghamstown, a half-mile-long alignment of 70 indifferent dwellings, was founded on the Mullet peninsula by Major Bingham in the 1790s. It ultimately failed owing to the growth of rival Belmullet, strategically located by William Carter on the neck of the peninsula in 1825 and still, today, a small service centre. Its population of 694 in 1966 was a 4·1 per cent decrease from 1961.

ultimately failed owing to the growth of rival Belmullet, established by William Carter in 1825 (Jones Hughes, 1959). Louisburgh was founded by Lord Alta-mont for refugee Ulster Catholics around 1800. In isolated Connemara, John D'Arcy established Clifden around 1812. After a Scots engineer, Alexander Nimmo, had built the first road to Clifden, he laid out a small village at Round-stone in the 1820s and brought in Scots fisherfolk. These and other new settle-ments were planned by their landlords, not as garrison or planter towns to secure the neighbourhood as had happened during the seventeenth century, but as growth points and service centres for the scattered rural population. Athea, Abbeyfeale, Dromcolliher and Knockaderry in west Limerick arose in this way.

In many landlord settlements, the grand entrance to the demesne lay at one end of a broad, treelined main street and the established church at the other, a feature beautifully represented in Mitchelstown, Cootehill and Strokestown.

Industry and communications

For much of the eighteenth century, industrial production remained organized along domestic or workshop lines and thus made little direct or lasting impression on the landscape. Larger towns possessed workshops making quality leather goods, silver, glass, furniture and earthenware within a framework of trade guilds but, apart from iron foundries in the Lagan valley, Newry, Dublin, Enniscorthy and elsewhere using English ore or pig iron, there was little heavier industry. The main legacies of the widespread domestic linen industry, which was stimulated by the Huguenot refugee influx and by both English and Irish parliaments, are the few surviving weavers' cottages that improving landlords built in their towns and villages. Large communities of linen-weavers once lived in or around Ballymote, Castlebar, Westport and Galway in Connacht, and in Dunmanway, Cork, Bandon, Clonakilty, Waterford and Kilkenny farther south. As the century progressed, however, production was increasingly concentrated in the north where the industrious and loyal Protestant element

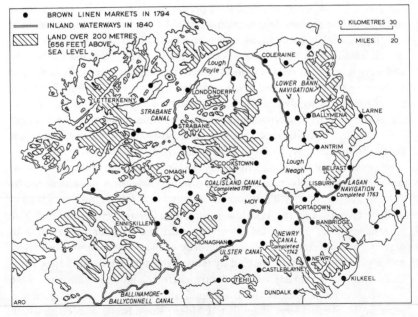

38. Brown-linen markets in the north of Ireland in 1794

and the 'Ulster custom' generated confidence and capital. Ulster farming families grew and dressed flax for spinning and weaving at home and then sold their cloth at linen halls in the towns. By 1794 there were some sixty brown-linen markets functioning throughout the north. As home and overseas demands outran domestic flax supplies, so increasing amounts of flax seed and undressed flax were imported. The domestic woollen industry revived temporarily during the 1780s, particularly in southern towns like Carrick-on-Suir, Clonmel, Carlow, Kilkenny, and several north Cork villages, but declined in the face of English factory production after the 30 per cent protective duty was removed in 1820.

Ironically, it was the comparatively new cotton industry, established in several east coast towns during the eighteenth century, that introduced factories to Ireland and led the linen-weavers of the north and the woollen manufacturers of the south into similar mills. Factories, steam power, advanced machinery and other aspects of the industrial revolution were already established among the textile industries of east Ulster before the century closed but, because industrialization was a continuing feature of the nineteenth century, their impact on the landscape will be considered in the next chapter.

While the domestic industries of the landlord era have left little trace, the various road, canal and harbour projects of the period are still very much part of the contemporary landscape. Large-scale road planning began in Ireland around 1700 and continued until the mid-nineteenth century, by which time the lowlands had largely acquired their present road network. By 1700 existing roads were in a deplorable condition, scarred by deep ruts, liable to frequent flooding, and plagued by highwaymen and footpads. They had evolved over several centuries from twisting woodland tracks, field paths and cattleways, and were more often related to local rather than national needs. As peace and economic growth stimulated trade and travel, however, the need for better gravel roads was keenly felt. With cheap labour and raw materials abundant, the next 150 years saw a multitude of road schemes implemented by county Grand Juries, turnpike trusts, military and post-office engineers, individual landlords and, latterly, by the government Board of Works (Andrews, 1964). The 'presentment' roads, sanctioned by the Grand Juries to link market towns, and the turnpike roads connecting more distant centres were prominent results of such road planning. Military roads were constructed through County Waterford in 1788–96 and the Wicklow mountains after the 1798 rebellion. The government later participated directly in road and harbour construction in order to provide employment and stimulate economic growth in those areas, notably in the west, most troubled by famine and agrarian distress after 1815. Few roads had previously crossed the treacherous bogs and mountains of the remote western peninsulas and it is significant that the growth of nucleated settlements like Belderg, Belmullet, Clifden, Roundstone and Cahersiveen awaited the arrival of government-inspired roads. The fine Antrim coast road, which follows the coastline from Larne to Cushendall, was begun after 1830 as a famine relief measure.

The unwavering straightness of many modern Irish roads is a vivid reflection of the ideals of earlier eighteenth-century road-builders. The roads from Monasterevin to Portlaoise (1731), Kinnegad to Mullingar (1733), Lanesborough to Roscommon (1737) and Urlingford to Cashel (1739), together with many sections since abandoned as impracticable, are good examples. Only exceptional physical obstacles or sacrosanct demesnes caused any deviation from their Roman precision which was otherwise pursued regardless of hills, valleys and bogs. After 1760 straight roads were gradually abandoned in favour of more reasonable curving roads with gentler gradients. Not only did heavier road traffic accompany the expansion of tillage but, after the first Irish mail coaches were introduced in 1790, post-office engineers sought to provide routes with gradients less than one in thirty-five. Many existing roads were thus partly realigned and, although straight roads continued to be built in areas of favourable relief, as between Dublin and Slane (1827), by the 1820s most new constructions were sensible compromises between the flattest and the straightest routes. The new roads of the eighteenth and early nineteenth centuries exerted an interesting influence on the adjacent landscape. Where they passed through open country, later enclosures caused hedges to be thrown up alongside and at right angles to the new roads. Existing settlements gravitated to the roads and intersections, new farm boundaries were demarcated, and new street villages such as Ballylynan in Laois and Ashbourne in Meath came into existence. Finally, the new arteries injected fresh life into several distressed western areas. Road works provided paid employment, opened a wider market to local fish and grain, and accelerated the redistribution of population and the break up of rundale.

Ireland's derelict canals are vivid reminders of the misplaced enthusiasm with which their eighteenth-century builders once sought to develop the country's agricultural and industrial potential with the aid of water transport. Commissioners of Inland Navigation were appointed in 1729 and over the next hundred years much money was lavished on a system of navigable waterways. Some were entirely artificial; others were rationalizations of existing rivers such as the Boyne below Navan, the Slaney below Enniscorthy, the Barrow between Athy and St Mullins, the Maigue below Adare, the Shannon between Lough Allen and Killaloe, and the Bann above Coleraine. The most successful waterways lay in the northeast where economic activity was more widely based. The first undertaking, the Newry Canal, was built from Lough Neagh to Newry in 1731–42 and extended as a ship canal to the sea in 1761. Newry's substantial eighteenth-century homes and warehouses testify to its former entrepôt role, exporting Ulster's agricultural produce and linen cloth to Britain in return for raw materials and manufactures. The Lagan Navigation, built between 1756 and 1793 to connect Belfast with Lough Neagh, was particularly successful between 1810 and 1930, but was finally closed in 1958. Feeder canals, such as the Ulster Canal between Lough Neagh and Upper Lough Erne, the Ballinamore–Ballyconnell Canal linking Upper Lough Erne with the Shannon but closed in 1869, and the Coalisland Canal, opened in 1787, played important parts in maintaining the flow of traffic but, as in the south, their demise was hastened by the advent of railways and road transport. The two extravagant waterways linking Dublin with the Shannon were great disappointments to their optimistic instigators. The Grand Canal system, begun in 1756, reached Athy and the Barrow in 1791, with a branch to Mountmellick. The main midland section was built from Robertstown in Kildare to Tullamore (1798), Shannon Harbour (1804) and on to Ballinasloe, the whole system having cost about £6,000 a mile to construct. The freight traffic, for which the canal and its warehouses and wharves were primarily designed, was less than anticipated, but between 1780 and 1852 passenger services flourished and the hotels built for this trade can still be seen at Portobello in Dublin, Sallins, Robertstown, Tullamore and Shannon Harbour. The ill-conceived Royal Canal, built between 1789 and 1817 at an estimated cost of £15,000 a mile, was a miserable failure and fell into railway ownership as early as 1845.

Chapter 10
The nineteenth century and after

Three major events occurred during the nineteenth century which were to have far reaching consequences for the shaping of the Irish landscape. First, the great famine of 1846–48 dramatically reversed the rising population trend of preceding decades, stimulated migration from rural areas to the towns, and accelerated emigration. Secondly, a series of land acts commencing in 1870 tackled the iniquitous land problem, dismantled landlordism and created a country of peasant proprietors. Thirdly, the industrial revolution transformed northeast Ireland which now emerged as the most industrialized part of the country. Although landlordism remained a dominant process until after the famine, each of the above events can trace its origins back to the eighteenth century. However, the long-term social and economic ramifications of famine, land redistribution and industrialization are also very much part of the contemporary scene.

The nineteenth century was also a period of continuing rural change and reorganization in which both landlords and government played leading roles. In particular, the rundale system and its allied farm clusters were gradually dismantled and small compact family farms, entrenched in mid-Ulster and the north midlands since the seventeenth century, emerged as Ireland's nearest approach to the mainly subsistence holdings of European peasants. Long before the famine, the rundale system could barely cater for the rapidly growing population, particularly as its main strongholds survived on the already marginal lands in the congested west. Land hunger was met by savagely subdividing the communal open fields and by allowing potato plots to encroach on the booley lands, so that livestock were removed from the unfenced cultivation strips during the growing season to diminishing summer pastures. Efficiency thus declined and attempts to integrate new crops and rotations were frustrated. Reform was inevitable and from the early 1800s onward many landlords rearranged rundale lands and farm clusters into consolidated holdings based on single farmsteads, often strung out along new roads. Fields were enclosed and the new single-farm units organized so as to take in land of different qualities. In this way, the long thin 'strip farms' ranged up and down the hillsides throughout the west were created. One land agent in Donegal, Alexander Hamilton, rearranged 2,639 farms and built 2,601 new houses. Even so, in 1845 2 million acres of Irish land were still held in common or in joint tenancy, although not all was necessarily farmed under the rundale system. The famine partially re-lieved pressure on the land and many farm clusters developed naturally into single farmsteads whose lands were consolidated by absorbing abandoned holdings. Nevertheless, it has remained for the various governments of the past eighty-eight years to complete, through the agency of the Congested Districts Board (1891–1923) and the Land Commission (founded 1881), the processes of farm consolidation and rural settlement initiated by the landlords.

The rural revolution of the nineteenth century inevitably signed the death warrant of the primitive methods and traditional ways of the Gaelic-speaking peoples. The spade and crude native plough gave way to the light iron swing plough; the wheel-less slide-car and the cumbersome Irish cart gave way to the

39. Ashleam
A landlord-reorganized settlement on Achill Island. Individual farmsteads are strung out along a road located between the turf cuttings and rough grazings on the higher slopes and the enclosed strip fields running down to the valley floor. The ribbing effect in some pastures reflects the lazy-beds or spade ridges of former tillage plots.

light flat Scots cart. Although many farm clusters survived the abolition of rundale the majority soon dispersed. As their kin groups scattered, so social life decayed, the community spirit was lost, and the Gaelic language disappeared, no doubt aided by the rapid spread of National Schools teaching through the medium of English through the country during the 1830s. The proportion of Irish speakers fell from around one-half of the population in 1800 to one-quarter (1,500,000) in 1851 when the vast majority were already confined to the poorer, less accessible west of Ireland, and to one-eighth in 1911. New approaches to farming were sought and communal work among kin groups was replaced by co-operative farming between neighbours, as seen in the spread of the co-operative creamery movement during the 1890s.

The Great Famine, 1846–48

Prelude

Ireland's dual social and economic personality was accentuated by the agrarian depression after 1815. The living standards of most people plunged downwards until only a very narrow margin separated them from starvation. The unbalanced economy stagnated while the population rose from 6,802,000 in 1821 to 8,175,000 in 1841. The increase exceeded 30 per cent in Kerry, Clare, Galway, Mayo and Antrim and, except for marked migration into Dublin and Antrim's growing industrial towns, was essentially rural. Population growth was partly offset by emigration, notably from Ulster and the north midlands where the collapse of the domestic textile industry in face of British factory competition aggravated rural unrest and where the 'Ulster custom' provided cash for the passage. Elsewhere during the 1820s and 1830s, emigration was rarely feasible for the poor without some assistance. Between 1780 and 1845 Ireland probably lost 1,140,000 persons to North America and a further 600,000 to Britain. Between 1831 and 1841 the loss exceeded 400,000 and in 1841 there were 420,000 Irish-born persons in Britain. Seasonal migration by Irish workers seeking harvest employment in Britain, commonly to pay rents back home in the west, was also a notable feature of prefamine times. Within Ireland, rural poverty drove increasing numbers into the towns, but even in 1841 only one-fifth of the population lived in nucleated settlements of twenty houses or more. In eastern Ireland before the famine, inability to obtain cultivable land other than by sub-division had already delayed marriages and retarded the population's rate of natural increase (Cousens, 1966). Where some submarginal lands were still available, namely in the west, birth rates were much higher and population growth was retarded mainly by excessive mortality. Nevertheless, despite emigration, delayed marriages and high mortality, the population had risen to about 8,500,000 by 1845.

In a country in which two-thirds of the people sought a livelihood from agri-

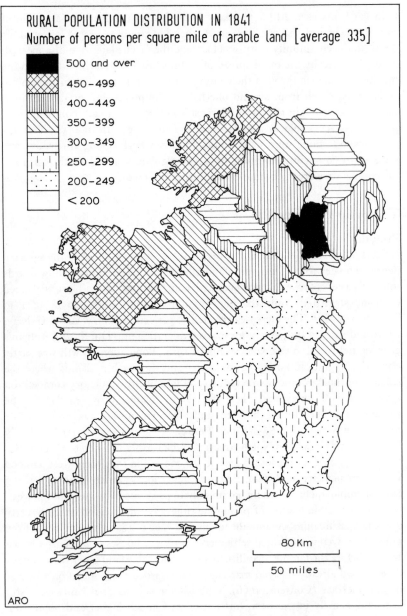

RURAL POPULATION DISTRIBUTION IN 1841
Number of persons per square mile of arable land [average 335]

500 and over
450 – 499
400 – 449
350 – 399
300 – 349
250 – 299
200 – 249
< 200

80 Km
50 miles

ARO

40. *The rural population of Ireland per square mile of arable land in 1841*
The rural population, defined for this purpose as those persons living outside towns with
2,000 or more inhabitants, numbered 7,040,000 out of a total population of 8,175,000
(based on *Census of Ireland, 1841*).

culture, the rising population inevitably increased pressure on the land and dependence on the high-yielding potato crop. Land hunger led in turn to microscopic subdivision of holdings, higher rents, insecurity, unemployment, poverty and sickness. By 1841 Ireland's rural population (defined for this purpose as those living outside towns of 2,000 or more persons) averaged 335 persons per square mile of arable land, but in Connacht, where 78 per cent of the people depended directly on agriculture, the figure was 386 and in Ulster 406. Owing to the growing industrial and urban population in the latter province, however, only 61 per cent relied on agriculture. Population density thus bore little relationship to land quality for Armagh with 511 persons and Mayo with 475 persons had the highest numbers per square mile of arable land, while Meath with 201 persons and Kildare with 187 persons had the lowest densities. As dependence on potatoes intensified, cultivation was extended beyond its economic limits on to the bogs and higher mountain sides where, today, abandoned spade ridges or 'lazy beds' may still be seen, as above Killary Harbour and in the Beara peninsula. Clearly, if the potato failed the consequences would be disastrous but, prior to the famine, most landlords were too obsessed with self-interest and successive governments lacked the initiative to tackle such a vast problem effectively, namely by ensuring a more equable distribution and intensive usage of the better lands and by widening the country's economic base. Realizing that the burning and liming of marginal wastes made limited cultivation possible, the government did once envisage widespread reclamation of the bogs in order to combat land hunger. The bogs were surveyed in 1809–14 but, apart from the construction of a village with a model 300-acre farm and limekilns at Kingwilliamstown on the new Kanturk–Tralee road in 1833, the scheme soon collapsed.

Aftermath

Famine first struck in the autumn of 1845, reached its peak during 1846 and 1847, and declined during 1848. It was not the first nor the last disaster of its kind to befall Ireland but its exceptional duration, severity and consequences have left an indelible impression on the country and its people. The immediate cause was the failure of the potato crop when blight, in the form of the fungus *Phytophthora infestans*, spread rapidly through Ireland with the encouragement of the mild wet climate. The ultimate cause was the iniquitous neglect that allowed a situation to develop wherein the vast mass of the people were condemned to bare subsistence on one crop. Had economic development progressed along more rational lines, there was little reason why the population could not have been supported. The terrible consequences need only be summarized in the present context: over 1 million people died from starvation and related epidemics of typhus, relapsing fever and bacillary dysentery during the famine years; a further million emigrated, mostly in 'coffin ships' to North

America. By 1851 the population had fallen to 6,552,000, although an un-interupted continuation of the 1841–45 rate of increase could have produced 9 millions. Between 1841 and 1851 Connacht lost 28·6 per cent of its population, Munster 23·5 per cent, Ulster 16 per cent and Leinster 15·5 per cent, although even here losses ranged from 29 per cent in Longford to only 11 per cent in Wexford.

What immediate effects did this catastrophe have on the landscape? First, many roads, harbours and river embankments were built as relief projects during the famine years and are still with us. Counties were encouraged to provide immediate road work for the destitute regardless of the long-term utility of such roads, many of which have since been abandoned. Reclamation of the North Slob in the Blackwater estuary began in 1846 as relief work but the Youghal Mudlands thus enclosed have been put to little use. The Fergus drain-age scheme was implemented in Clare, wastelands were reclaimed at least temporarily, and landlords built new cottages and farm premises for their tenants. All these may be considered positive additions to the landscape. Secondly, death, eviction and emigration produced a spate of negative changes: deserted farmsteads and villages, walls and hedges in decay, abandoned fields invaded by rushes, bracken and scrub. Between 1841 and 1851 at least 360,000 cabins disappeared. Continuing heavy emigration from the physically less favoured areas, such as the north midlands, has given these derelict landscapes a melancholy expression.

The impact of the catastrophe continued to be felt long after the worst years were past. The famine formed a watershed in the social and economic life of the country. Ireland's population reached an unprecedented peak in 1845 but the subsequent prolonged decline reduced the pre-famine total to half by 1926. Emigration reached a peak during the famine period, later slowed down, but has never ceased. The famine transformed harvest migrants into permanent emigrants, checked the growth of the rural population and increased the pro-portion of towndwellers, who today constitute more than half the total popula-tion. For a while at least, slums and ramshackle suburbs proliferated. Although the pre-famine agrarian situation persisted for some time along the western seaboard, elsewhere the decline of population prevented former conditions from reasserting their worst aspects. Ireland could never be allowed to return to its pre-famine state and, in the years following, new avenues of social and economic development were sought, the results of which again transformed the landscape and were generally beneficial – at least for those who had not died from starvation or emigrated. The drastic reduction of wheat acreages after the corn laws were repealed in 1846 was confirmed by the poor harvests of 1861–62 and by the agrarian depression of the 1870s. Tillage declined generally, flour mills and grain stores fell derelict, and much of rural Ireland reverted to pasture. The small compact family farm engaged in mixed tillage, intensive haymaking and livestock production began to emerge as Ireland's typical farm unit. Its cash income was derived from livestock rather than grain and, even where there had previously been little cash income, oats, hay, potatoes and green crops were now grown in rotation for marketing in the form of animals and animal products.

The land problem and its solution

The great famine was symptomatic of a deep-rooted evil – the land problem – which originated with the wholesale confiscations of the plantation era and was aggravated by the rapid population increase and the unbalanced social and economic dichotomy of the landlord era. Holdings multiplied as landlords sought to increase their power and wealth and as tenants, evading the subletting acts of 1826 and 1831, subdivided for profit or to provide for their many children. Compact farms diminished in size, rundale lands became increasingly congested. By 1841, Ireland contained 685,000 holdings and in Connacht 64 per cent were between 1 and 5 acres. In 1845 there were 65,000 holdings not exceeding 1 acre. Meanwhile, the number of 'encumbered estates' increased as landlords squandered their resources. The famine was followed by consolidation and by gradually rising standards of rural living. Holdings of 1 to 5 acres fell from 45 per cent of the total in 1841 to 15·5 per cent in 1851; holdings exceeding 30 acres rose from 7 to 26 per cent over the same period. But consolidation accentuated competition for land among those remaining and hostility between landlord and tenant, already embittered by the famine, increased. For many, the price of holding together the family farm was to remain unmarried. Gone were the days of early marriages and a countryside thronged with children and young people. Not surprisingly, tenants began pressing with growing insistence for the three Fs – fair rents, fixity of tenure and freedom to sell their interest in the farm – the last demand being the tenant-right which had long formed part of the 'Ulster custom' but was rarely practised elsewhere. Even so, by 1870 one-fifth of Ireland's 19,000 proprietors still owned 80 per cent of the cultivated area. These fortunate few were augmented by 135,000 leaseholders, mainly non-Gaelic families of either longstanding Roman Catholic or planted Protestant stock, who held land in perpetuity or on favourable long-term leases. The remaining tenantry were totally at the mercy of the landlords and their middlemen and agents, and had been hardest hit by the famine. They included 525,000 annual tenants of the 'small farmer' group paying money rents and liable to eviction on six months' notice; and the cottiers, some of whom rented wretched cottages and gardens and normally hired a patch of conacre land for part of the year to grow potatoes and pasture stock, while others were quite landless and depended on labouring work to provide the means for hiring conacre.

The famine had revealed the need for land reform but, apart from the disastrous encumbered estates acts of 1848 and 1849 when properties were sold at absurdly low prices and no protection was given to tenants, some twenty years passed before the government took its first faltering steps in this direction. In 1869 Gladstone disestablished the anglican Church of Ireland and its glebe lands were gradually transferred to tenant purchasers. Gladstone's first Land Act of 1870 was the government's first, but unsuccessful, attempt to intervene on behalf of the tenants. For a while, agrarian distress worsened. During 1878–79 falling farm prices, crop failures and exceptionally wet weather brought most small tenant farmers to the verge of bankruptcy, starvation and eviction, and agrarian agitation culminated in the formation of the Land League in 1879 and the 'land war' of 1879–82. Gladstone's second Land Act of 1881, based on the three Fs, transformed landlord-tenant relationships, introduced dual ownership, extended tenant-right throughout Ireland and, by reducing land-lord interest in the land, prepared the way for eventual peasant proprietorship. These processes were implemented and fair rents were fixed by the newly

41. Slievemore deserted village on Achill Island
The tillage practices of the earlier nineteenth-century population are clearly revealed by the informal ribbing effect of former 'lazy beds'. Subsequent reorganization into 'strip farms' is indicated by the way in which later stone walls and field banks cut obliquely across the 'lazy beds' as they run directly downslope.

created Land Commission. Further Acts in 1885 and 1891 combated the lack of capital among farmers by providing money loans up to 100 per cent and by fixing the annual repayments at levels below existing rents. By 1896, 80,000 tenants had purchased their holdings and Acts of 1903 and 1909 added a further 320,000 owners.

Meanwhile, the Congested Districts Board was established in 1891 to tackle the problems facing more than half a million persons still barely subsisting in the most densely populated areas of the west. Scattered holdings were consolidated, roads and light railways built, improved stock and fresh crops introduced, fishing encouraged and rural industries stimulated. Chronic overcrowding was countered by transplanting tenants to less densely populated areas and, when more estates were needed to accommodate this resettlement programme, government agencies were given wide powers. The 1903 Act allowed the state to subsidise the prices given to landlords from whom estates were purchased and the Estates Commissioners were created for this purpose. In 1909 legislation was extended beyond the original congested districts to cover nearly all the west and the Congested Districts Board and the Land Commission were given compulsory purchase powers. The government thus resolved the land problem by breaking the monopoly of the landed few and creating a country of small farmers who owned the land that they worked. The state bodies that implemented these measures thereby took over from the 'improving' landlords the work of reshaping the rural landscape, work which still continues.

The industrial revolution

Human rather than physical factors explain Ireland's strongly localized pattern of industrialization during the nineteenth century. Despite the paucity of coal and iron-ore resources, the widespread abundance of cheap manpower during pre-famine times might have been organized into large-scale industrial employment had not lack of capital and Ireland's commercial subjugation to Britain inhibited initiative. As it was, when new machines and factory production were introduced during the late eighteenth century, they came mainly to northeast Ireland where the 'Ulster custom' made for happier landlord–tenant relationships, where an unfettered domestic linen industry provided a pool of skilled textile workers (there were 40,000 Ulster weavers in 1784), and where greater confidence in the people's loyalty and industriousness generated capital investment. The personal initiative of several leading industrialists, the astute policies of the joint stock banks after 1825, and improved transport facilities subsequently ensured that Ulster's industrial momentum was maintained.

Although linen manufacturing and shipbuilding were to be the principal agents in shaping Ulster's industrial landscapes, the industrial revolution was introduced to Ireland initially through the cotton industry. When damaging restrictions were replaced with government bounties after 1780, this industry expanded rapidly. Water-powered cotton mills were built and new spinning jennies were adopted. In 1789 Ireland's first steam engine was installed in a Lisburn spinning mill, and by 1811 fifteen of the thirty-three mills around Belfast were steam-powered. Some mills were five storeys high and employed 200 workers. The need to import raw cotton and coal from Britain tended to confine the mills to the Belfast area and the number of spindles in Belfast rose from 8,000 in 1790 to 13,500 in 1800 and to 50,000 in 1811. Weaving remained a domestic process and the goods produced were readily absorbed by the home market. After the abolition of protection in 1821 and the slump of 1825 the industry declined in the face of Lancashire competition. In 1839 only twenty-four mills employing 4,622 workers survived in Ireland. By 1850 these figures had fallen to eleven mills with 2,937 workers, and in 1890 only eight mills with 1,375 workers remained.

Despite its decline, the cotton industry had brought large numbers of industrial workers into Belfast, created allied engineering workshops, and provided a model for the reorganization of the domestic linen industry. After Kay's wet-spinning process, patented in 1825, made it possible to spin fine linen yarn by powered machinery, many cotton mills were converted to linen production and new flax mills were built. By 1838 there were fifteen flax-spinning mills in Belfast compared with only three or four cotton mills. Meanwhile, bleaching firms built spinning mills in Lisburn, Bessbrook, Castlewellan, Banbridge and Dromore, gave out millspun yarn to the several thousand domestic weavers in their employ and collected the cloth for finishing. To avoid the cost of installing steam engines when the river Bann could no longer satisfy the demands of the water-powered mills in the vicinity, reservoirs were constructed at Lough Island Reavy and Corbet Lough which increased the volume of water power fivefold. This revolution in linen manufacturing was concentrated in south Antrim and Down. By 1850, three-quarters of Ireland's flax spindles were located in these two counties, there were thirty flax-spinning mills in Belfast, some employing 600 to 800 workers, and most bleach greens lay in the Lagan and Bann valleys. During the 1850s power looms were adopted for weaving because famine and emigration had reduced the number of handloom weavers. The industry was now fully equipped to play its dominating role in transforming Ulster's personality.

Shipbuilding began in Belfast in 1792, but the great expansion came in the 1850s when Edward Harland bought Hickson's shipyard on Queen's Island and invited, in 1858, a young Liverpool man named Wolff to become his assistant and later his partner. By developing new designs and exploiting the new market for iron and, later, steel ships, the Harland and Wolff shipyard expanded rapidly. Its payroll increased from 500 workers in 1861 to 2,400 in

1870 and to 9,000 by the beginning of the twentieth century. The industry reached its peak during World War II. Meanwhile the Workman and Clark shipyard was founded in 1880 and by 1902, when its output was larger than any single yard in Britain, its site covered 50 acres. This yard closed in 1934. The two staple manufactures, linen and ships, also gave rise to iron foundries, rope-works and engineering industries. For instance, Harland and Wolff success-fully added iron and engineering concerns that had arisen initially to serve the linen mills.

The impact of these industrial developments on the landscape was twofold. On the one hand lay the mills, shipyards and workshops directly responsible for the process of industrialization; on the other lay the railways, docks, re-claimed lands and monotonous rows of industrial housing brought into existence to serve the needs of industry and the industrial population. But this impact was strongly localized, even in Ulster. The industrial revolution remained an intrusive element in an agricultural country and did not advance far beyond its urban bases in east Ulster where raw materials and fuel were easily imported and from which markets were more readily accessible. The textile industries of Dungannon, Coleraine, Sion Mills, a factory village founded in 1835, and Londonderry where shirt making was introduced around 1850, were essentially outliers of the main industrial core. Indeed, the concentration of textile factories in south Antrim and Down and of shipbuilding at Belfast led to social and economic decay in the rural areas of south and west Ulster. Deprived of their cash income as the domestic linen industry withered away, farming folk sought to escape from poverty and famine either by migration to the rising industrial towns or by emigration. Furthermore, while the outlying textile towns absorbed female labour, there were, unlike in Belfast, no heavy industries for the men-folk. This imbalance between male and female employment opportunities is a continuing feature of the Irish industrial scene.

The impact of industrialization is thus vividly expressed in the townscapes of east Ulster. As Emrys Jones (1960) has convincingly shown, Belfast is *par excellence* a product of the industrial revolution, having once shared the worst evils of the factory system and of squalid overcrowded tenements with similar cities in Britain. In the early nineteenth century it was still a small market and textile town contained within the level sloblands where the river Farset, flowing along the High Street commercial axis from the old market place to the quays, entered Belfast Lough. With the growth of industry and trade, Georgian plan-ners had transformed the open town parks to the north into a regular grid of streets filled with small houses, mills, timber yards and warehouses. To the south, another street grid centred on the White Linen Hall (1783) had acquired fashionable Georgian terrace blocks and, in 1827, building started along the drives radiating south from this zone. Industrial sectors lay along the Farset valley to the west, where textile mills were surrounded by tiny streets and con-

42. A nineteenth-century industrial quarter of Belfast
Looking northwest across York Street and Gallahers' tobacco factory (the older part of which occupies a large nineteenth-century flax-spinning mill) to the rows of industrial terrace housing.

gested courts housing the industrial population, and across the Lagan estuary in Ballymacarrett where chemicals, glass and iron were manufactured and nearly every cottage housed a weaver.

Rapid expansion during the Victorian era confirmed Belfast as Ireland's leading industrial town and shaped much of the present urban landscape. The population rose from around 20,000 in 1800 to 50,000 in 1830, 100,000 in 1850 and 350,000 in 1900. Little control was exercised over the urban and industrial sprawl that spread beyond the sloblands on to higher ground, overrrunning the brickpits from which the town's houses came. The industrial nature of west Belfast was accentuated as flax mills replaced cotton mills and as steam power was applied first to spinning and then to weaving. By mid-century, Belfast contained thirty flax mills and was also manufacturing textile machinery, iron, ships, rope, chemicals, soap, flour, ale, whiskey, tobacco and mineral waters. Three railway termini had reached the expanding town boundaries and were gathering more factories and industrial housing around them. Most of the narrow 'entries' of the town centre and the back-to-back houses to the north and west had degenerated into congested slums and bye-laws were introduced to standardize house construction. In the 1840s roofing thatch and cellar dwelling were forbidden, every house was to have a 10-foot-square yard and piped water, and every room had to have a window. In 1878 back entries, water closets and ash-pits became obligatory. The new bye-laws, whose minimum legal requirements were rarely exceeded, gave Belfast much of its present character as street after street of identical brick-built terrace houses was constructed. But behind their drab exteriors there lurked a deep religious gulf, expressed most vividly by the way in which the Protestant communities along Sandy Row and Shankhill Road were segregated from the intervening concentration of Roman Catholics along the Falls Road axis. Meanwhile, the former residential sector around the White Linen Hall was overtaken by commerce, and those who could afford better homes moved into pleasant suburbs overlooking Belfast Lough from the north, along the Malone ridge in the south, and along the Holywood and Newtownards roads east of the Lagan. Between 1870 and 1900 Belfast Corporation widened many streets, built new bridges across the Lagan, provided better water and gas, installed electricity, and linked the sprawling suburbs with the city centre by means of a horse-tramway system that was electrified in 1904.

During and since the Victorian era, some four square miles of slobland at the head of Belfast Lough have been reclaimed and the landscape transformed by the addition of new docks, storage sheds, grain elevators, shipbuilding yards, engineering works, power stations and an oil refinery, oil storage depot, sewage outfall works, park and airport to the areas reclaimed. Earlier schemes had done little more than straighten the Belfast waterfront but, after 1837, the bends in the Lagan estuary were eliminated with the deep Victoria Channel (1849), islands of slob and spoil were created and then, as with Queen's Island, absorbed, and the Musgrave (1903) and Herdman (1933) channels formed. Dublin is the only other Irish port to experience reclamation of this magnitude.

Beyond northeast Ireland, the industrial revolution had little effect on the landscape. Neither the few cotton and linen mills that arose in Dundalk, Drogheda, Balbriggan and Dublin, nor the isolated woollen mills that dominated many country towns, gathered large industrial populations around them. The woollen industry did, however, expand during the later nineteenth century and the number of mills scattered throughout Ireland increased from only nine, employing 553 workers, in 1850 to 114, employing 3,325 workers, in 1899. Most mills were located on or near water power and many occupied the site or even the buildings of old flax or flour mills. The principal forms of industrial activity in most towns outside east Ulster depended, like woollen manufactures, on local agricultural output rather than on imports for their raw materials and

43. Portlaw, County Waterford
A model industrial village built by the Quaker Malcomson family in the 1820s for the 1,000 or more workers of their large cotton-spinning mills (1825–1904, converted to flax-spinning in later nineteenth century). The web of streets lined with single-storey terrace dwellings converges on the small market square from which a short factory road leads to the former mills, occupied since 1935 by a leather tannery.

existed to supply home rather than overseas markets. Tanneries, shoe-making, brewing, distilling and flour-milling were thus commonplace. Without the stimulus of new industries, the larger towns stagnated while most smaller towns and villages lost population. Many countryfolk continued to view emigration as their only hope.

Likewise, with little industrial freight available, the railways that Ireland acquired during the nineteenth century soon came to rely on passenger traffic. The first railway was opened in 1834 between Dublin and Kingstown (now Dun Laoghaire) and Ulster's first line, between Belfast and Lisburn, opened in 1839. With the completion of an impressive viaduct across the Boyne at Drogheda in 1855 Belfast was finally linked directly to Dublin, and by the 1860s Ireland's broad-gauge (5 feet 3 inches) network was largely complete. During the later nineteenth century several picturesque narrow-gauge light railways penetrated the west. The railways certainly ended the isolation of many inland and west coast towns, stimulated suburban growth around Belfast Lough and

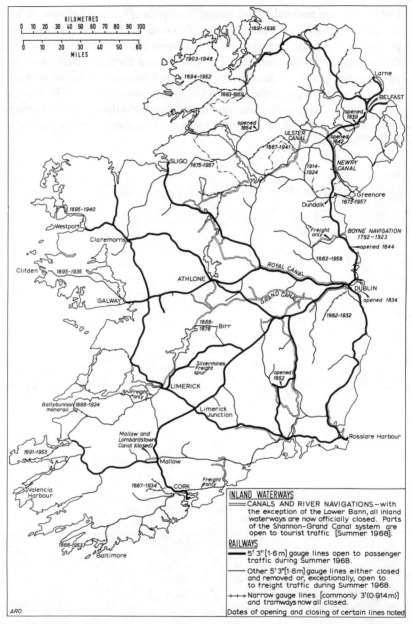

KILOMETRES
0 10 20 30 40 50 60 70 80 90 100

0 10 20 30 40 50 60
MILES

1891-1935

1903-1948

1894-1952

1883-1959

opened
1854

ULSTER
CANAL
1887-1941

opened
1842

opened
1839

Larne

BELFAST

NEWRY
CANAL

SLIGO   1875-1957

1914-
1924

Dundalk

Greenore   1873-1957

1895-1940

Westport

Claremorris

Clifden   1895-1935

GALWAY

ATHLONE

Freight
only

BOYNE NAVIGATION
1792-1923

opened 1844

ROYAL CANAL

1862-1958

GRAND CANAL

DUBLIN
opened 1834

1882-1932

1868-
1878   Birr

Silvermines
Freight
spur

opened
1852

Freight
only

LIMERICK

Ballybunnion 1888-1924
monorail

Limerick
Junction

Mallow and
Lombardstown
Canal (closed)

1891-1953

Mallow

Rosslare Harbour

Valencia
Harbour

1887-1934   CORK

Freight
only

1886-1953   Baltimore

INLAND WATERWAYS

CANALS AND RIVER NAVIGATIONS—with the exception of the Lower Bann, all inland waterways are now officially closed. Parts of the Shannon–Grand Canal system are open to tourist traffic [Summer 1968].

RAILWAYS

5′ 3″ [1·6 m] gauge lines open to passenger traffic during Summer 1968.

Other 5′ 3″ [1·6 m] gauge lines either closed and removed or, exceptionally, open to to freight traffic during Summer 1968.

Narrow gauge lines [commonly 3′ (0·914 m)] and tramways now all closed.

Dates of opening and closing of certain lines noted

ARO

44. *Ireland's inland waterways and railway network, past and present*

Dublin Bay, and fostered seaside resorts like Bangor, Bray and Greystones, but anticipated industrial expansion rarely followed in their wake. During the present century, road transport has progressively usurped their role in all but the heaviest carrying traffic. All light railways and tramways have vanished, many branch lines have closed and several main lines converted to single track. Beyond the few surviving trunk routes and the commuter spheres of Belfast and Dublin, the railway interlude has almost closed and only the overgrown cuttings and embankments of the once 'permanent way' and some derelict or converted railway buildings survive.

Part Three
The contemporary landscape

Chapter 11
The rural landscape

Despite the sporadic growth of towns during recent centuries, the Irish landscape has remained overwhelmingly rural. Today the countryside is dominated by a dispersed pattern of rural settlement focusing upon small compact family farms, and by extensive grasslands carved by untidy hedgerows into enclosed pastures that support large numbers of livestock. Recent statistics clearly illustrate this picture. In 1961 57 per cent of the Republic's population lived outside the fifty-three towns with 3,000 or more inhabitants and agriculture occupied 35 per cent of the working population. In 1965 pasture accounted for 48 per cent of the Republic's total land area, hay for 12 per cent, crops and fruit for only 8 per cent, while the remainder was largely rough grazing or bog. There were over 5·3 million cattle, 5 million sheep and 1·2 million pigs. Of those agricultural holdings exceeding 1 acre, 70 per cent were smaller than 50 acres and almost 90 per cent were below 100 acres. Only one-eighth of the permanent farm labour force came from outside the family circle and these hired labourers were concentrated almost entirely on the larger farms of the south and east. In value, agriculture provided two-thirds of the Republic's total exports. Even in Northern Ireland, 47 per cent of the people lived beyond the thirty towns with 3,000 or more inhabitants in 1961. In 1965 33 per cent of the land lay under pasture, 15 per cent under hay, 11 per cent under crops and fruit, and 19 per cent under rough grazing. The cattle, sheep and pig populations each exceeded 1 million, only 8 per cent of the permanent farm labour force was drawn from outside the family, farm-size ratios were similar to the Republic and, in 1967, agriculture employed 11 per cent of the working population as against 4 per cent in the United Kingdom as a whole. Owing to the high value of manufactured goods, agriculture provided little more than one-fifth of Northern Ireland's exports.

The rural landscape has acquired this personality largely over the past hundred years. The expansion of pasture and commercial livestock farming at the expense of cereal cultivation, the solution to the land problem, emigration, co-operative farming, improved agrarian technology, rural electrification and other forms of state activity have all played a part. Nevertheless, the countryside contains many relics of bygone eras. Some, such as prehistoric tombs, medieval castles, derelict mansions, walled demesnes, abandoned farmsteads and booley huts, empty corn mills and old spade ridges, are now quite dead or, like open-field systems, rapidly vanishing. On the other hand, country villages, enclosed fields, strip farms and certain traditional land-use and farm practices are living reminders of the many distinctive colonizing forces that have given the landscape its many facets. Strong regional variations in the character of the rural economy and settlement pattern continue to express potent historical, as well as physical, factors. Few parts of the Irish countryside fail to evoke memories of the past.

The role of the state

Over the past hundred years, landlordism has been dismantled and discredited and it has fallen to the state, the prime mover in this social revolution, to foster the peasant proprietors that its land acts called into being. Since the creation of two states in 1921, government actions have played a major role in shaping the rural landscape on both sides of the Border. Direct state intervention is most vividly expressed in the work of resettlement, afforestation and drainage, but indirect activity through the media of financial aid, marketing policies and advisory services has also strongly influenced rural land use.

The Republic's responsibility for land settlement and afforestation falls upon the Irish Land Commission and the Forestry Division respectively, both of which come under the Department of Lands. Founded in 1881, the Land Commission soon developed into a land-purchase agency and, by 1921, had assisted almost 320,000 tenants in purchasing 11·3 million acres of the 17 million acres within the twenty-six counties. Nevertheless, over 25 per cent of all holdings still remained under landlords, consisting mainly of uneconomic plots in the overcrowded west. Since the 1923 Land Act, which was designed to expedite these outstanding cases, a further 100,000 holdings comprising 2·8 million acres have been improved, enlarged or rearranged by the Land Commission and then revested in the occupiers. The latter have received freehold title to their lands in fee simple, subject to repayment of the advance made by the Commission to purchase the former landlord's rights. While the advance is being repaid, the farm is deemed to be personal property for inheritance purposes, passing on the death intestate of the owner to his next of kin. The Land Commission has now virtually completed this work outside counties Donegal, Mayo, Galway, Roscommon, Kerry and Cork. In these western counties and locally elsewhere, a residual hard core of 7,300 tenanted holdings needs major improvements before revesting. In Northern Ireland, where 84,000 holdings had been transferred by 1921, over four-fifths of the farms are now owner-occupied.

By enlarging uneconomic holdings, consolidating scattered plots, relieving congestion and resettling farming folk, the Land Commission has made a forceful contribution to the rural scene. In 1923 the Commission inherited the Congested Districts Board's problems and relief of the acute congestion that pre-

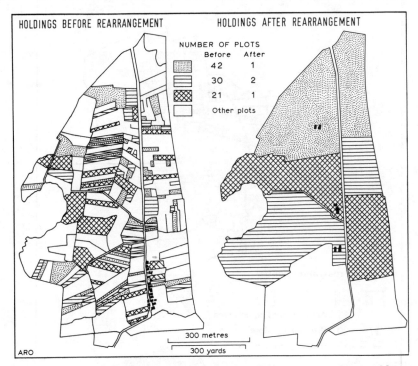

45. *Land holdings at Cloondeash on the former Peyton estate, County Mayo, before and after rearrangement by the Irish Land Commission*

vails in the west has been its main task in recent years. The most daring solution to this problem has involved transplanting numerous families from the over-crowded parts of Mayo, Galway and Kerry to untenanted former estate lands in Meath and nearby counties. For example, between 1935 and 1940, 122 such families were resettled in a compact colony around Gibstown, Allenstown, Clongill, Kilbride and Rathcarran in Meath where new cottages, outbuildings, seed, stock and equipment were provided for them. Many Gaelic-speaking families were chosen deliberately for these transfer schemes in a defiant attempt to establish Gaeltacht colonies in the east. Otherwise, no element of coercion or compulsion was involved. Economically, the change replaced large beef-producing farms with several smaller units of about 40 acres each, devoted mainly to intensive liquid milk production for the nearby Dublin and Drogheda markets. Although comparatively few of the total number of families needing assistance have been resettled in this way, there have been some significant local increases of population in the east midlands while, back in the west, an element of stability has been introduced where lands thus vacated have been used to enlarge other holdings. In the west, also, the regrouping of

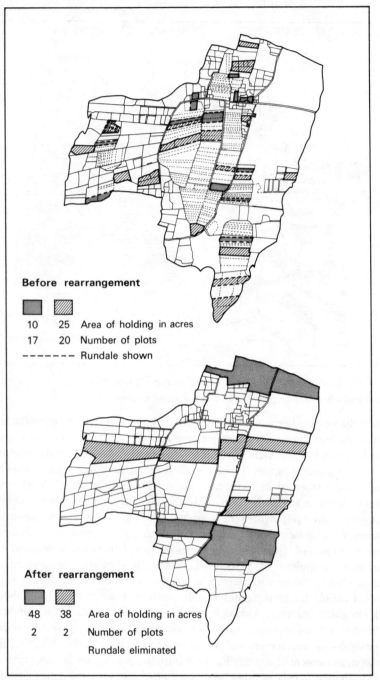

Before rearrangement

10	25	Area of holding in acres
17	20	Number of plots
- - - - - -		Rundale shown

After rearrangement

48	38	Area of holding in acres
2	2	Number of plots
		Rundale eliminated

46. Tooreen townland near Ballinrobe, County Mayo, before and after rearrangement of holdings by the Irish Land Commission in 1962 scattered rundale plots into compact workable units continues while, throughout the country, the enlargement of uneconomic holdings to a minimal 45–50 acres of good land is being implemented by means of voluntary and compulsory purchases. Such improvements have often allowed farm machinery to be used for the first time and have encouraged some farmers to reclaim more land from nearby wastes.

The material legacies of Land Commission work, such as the simple rectangular cottage, the enlarged field and the rationalized field boundary, are common features of the countryside. Between 1923 and 1965 the Commission spent £18 million on the erection of dwellings and outbuildings, and on the provision and repair of access roads, fencing and drainage works. About 60 per cent of this figure was spent in the western congested counties. The Land Commission has thus played a vital role in extending the country's scattered pattern of rural settlement, notably where rundale clusters have given way to dispersed farmsteads set amid small compact holdings.

By dismantling landlordism, the land acts also brought two centuries of private tree-planting to a close. In terms of composition and productivity, private forestry reached its peak in 1891 when Ireland contained over 300,000 acres of scattered woodlands dominated by such conifers as Scots pine, European larch (*Larix decidua*) and Norway spruce (*Picea abies*). As the Land Commission had no funds with which to purchase standing timber, these woods soon became an embarrassment to landlords and state alike and thus fell easy prey to timber merchants. During the years that followed, woodland clearances so exceeded plantings that Ireland was soon left with the lowest percentage area under forest of any European country. In 1908 the state finally acknowledged that the surviving private woods could not possibly meet home timber requirements and thus advocated planting some 200,000 acres of bare land over a forty-year period and further acquiring any private woods that came on to the market through Land Commission activity. The Irish Forestry Commission was established to implement these plans just as western American conifers were coming into general use for afforestation purposes. For the next thirty years, afforestation was largely confined to the relatively favourable hill country in the south, the east, and the south midlands, for example on Slieve Bloom. Remembering the dismal failure of an 820-acre trial plantation in Connemara in the 1880s and of later Congested Districts Board projects, the exposed west was for the time being avoided. During the 1930s, however, planting on upturned turves in wet and peaty soils was generally adopted and the hardy lodgepole pine (*Pinus contorta*) was found suitable for poor exposed sites. Foresters thus began tackling the poorer, wetter areas of the west and, after tractor-ploughing and phosphatic manuring were adopted during the 1950s, plantations even spread on to shallower blanket bogs in Donegal, Mayo and Galway. By 1967 some 460,000 acres or 2·7 per cent of the Republic lay beneath 213 state-owned woods and plantations and the Forestry Division, employing over 4,000 persons, had during the previous ten years planted between 20,000 and 26,000 acres of new land per annum, with particular emphasis on western and southern counties. Private woods raised the wooded area to a little over 3 per cent and the state continues to encourage private planting by giving grants and technical advice to farmers. In Northern Ireland, where 55,000 acres of a projected 150,000 acres had been planted by 1961, woods and plantations now cover 4 per cent of the total area.

As in Britain, regimented rows of conifers, forest roads, employees' houses and sawmills form minor but locally conspicuous elements of the Irish rural scene. State forests are particularly visible in Cork (63,000 acres), Wicklow (52,000 acres), Galway (45,000 acres), Tipperary (38,000 acres), Donegal (33,000 acres) and Waterford (31,000 acres), but no Irish county is now without at least one sizeable plantation. Sitka spruce (*Picea sitchensis*), accounting for 56 per cent of all trees planted in 1966–67, is the commonest species and, like lodgepole pine (22 per cent), has played a leading role in afforestation in exposed western areas. Norway spruce (8 per cent) is conspicuous in the moist fertile soils of the more sheltered lowlands farther east but other once-important conifers such as Scots pine, Japanese larch, Corsican pine, European larch, Douglas fir and silver fir are now little used. Broadleaf species account for only 4 per cent of the trees currently planted but this deficiency is compensated in part by longstanding parkland and hedgerow trees, notably in Meath and Louth, which contain only one state plantation each. As in many farming countries, the difficulty in obtaining good land condemns most state forests to submarginal areas that cannot economically carry stock or crops. But Irish forests possess two unique characteristics. First, owing to the rapid acceleration of afforestation in recent years, over half the trees are less than ten years old while only one-eighth are over thirty years old. Secondly, because farmers are reluctant to part with land and because the Forestry Division has of necessity acquired small, often fragmented holdings, the typical state forest now consists of several detached plantations separated by rough grazings and is quite unlike the traditional concept of a forest as a large unbroken tract of woodland. Apart from economic incentives, afforestation throughout Ireland also has avowed social objectives – to provide work in areas of serious rural depopulation.

In recent years, both states have completed important drainage projects along their rivers and estuaries. Flooding has been minimized by building embankments, straightening streams and removing obstacles from their courses, while new farmlands have been reclaimed from fens and marshes. Previously, the lack of funds, co-operation and technical resources among the local landowners in whom responsibility for such projects formerly lay had retarded many desirable schemes. During the 1930s, however, the Northern Ireland government trebled the discharge capacity of the Lower Bann in order to minimize flooding around

Lough Neagh and, since the 1947 drainage Act and later legislation, has been particularly active in drainage works along most of its rivers, streams and lakes. Between 1955 and 1964, twelve miles of sea embankments protecting 3,500 acres of land along the south shore of Lough Foyle were reconstructed. The Moy drainage scheme in Mayo is a notable recent project within the Republic. Cross-Border co-operation has brought a large area of formerly waterlogged land along the Flurry river between Armagh and Louth into cultivation, and work in the Erne basin has reduced the likelihood of serious flooding, particularly around Upper Lough Erne which had benefited little from a late nineteenth-century scheme.

State financial aid to farming is conspicuous on both sides of the Border and reveals itself in three ways. First, grants for the improvement of field drainage, buildings, water supply and livestock, for the provision of lime, phosphates and potash, and for the removal of scrub, boulders and unnecessary fences have countered lack of capital among farmers, increased productivity and smartened the appearance of the countryside.

Secondly, agricultural activity has been channelled by price guarantees, marketing policies, protectionist measures and advisory services along those lines most suited to national needs in the prevailing economic climate. The state thereby hopes that under commercial conditions Irish farmers will make optimum use of the country's environmental resources. One visible expression of this policy is that pastures and animal feedingstuffs now grow where, under the different economic aims of the landlord era, wheat was once widely cultivated. Northern Ireland farmers have long benefited from unrestricted access to British markets while at home guaranteed milk, beef and pig-meat prices provide a welcome measure of stability. In the Republic, price policies are less systematic. Store cattle and sheep sold to Britain and Northern Ireland benefit from the United Kingdom guaranteed price system. Inside the country, there are guaranteed prices for pigs sold to bacon factories, for creamery butter, millable wheat and feeding barley, but malting barley and sugar-beet prices are fixed by contract. Minimum prices are prescribed for liquid milk sales to the Cork and Dublin regions. The few restrictions on exports from the Republic to the United Kingdom will shortly disappear. The Agricultural Institute operates several centres around the country, engaged in all forms of agricultural research including the subsequent use of cutaway peat bogs. Private firms like Guinness and Goulding also undertake research while county committees for agriculture operate a variety of advisory services, for example in horticulture, poultry-keeping and butter-making.

The third and most daring form of state assistance places social objectives before economic considerations and is vividly expressed in the Gaeltacht – those residual Gaelic-speaking areas, mainly in the west, which have long concerned the Dublin government. In 1926 a Gaeltacht Board began promoting the social, economic and cultural welfare of these areas in the belated hope that the Gaelic-speaking population might be preserved and expanded. The problems were enormous, the solutions controversial. Even today, after forty years during which local domestic crafts have been stimulated and new factory industries introduced, agriculture still occupies three-quarters of the working population although 8o per cent of the Gaeltacht's 1,860 square miles comprises rough grazing and bog. Realizing this, state grants to agriculture, horticulture, housing, education, fishing, tourism and roads are in excess of those offered elsewhere. Glasshouses form one unexpected expression of this aid, notably along the north shore of Galway Bay. The production and marketing of handwoven tweeds, knitwear, embroidery and toys are controlled in thirty-four centres by the state-sponsored *Gaeltarra Eireann* which has recently extended its tweed factory at Kilcar and built a new toy factory at Spiddal and new knitwear premises at Tourmakeady. Seaweed-processing factories provide part-time employment for about 1,000 seaweed collectors along the west coast, and small turf-fired generating stations at Screeb in west Galway and at Gwee-dore in Donegal provide further work. Like similar plants using hand-won sod peat at Cahersiveen in Kerry and Miltown Malbay in Clare, both outside the Gaeltacht, they operate at a loss. Thus, through the provision of employment opportunities and financial aid, the state is helping to maintain a Gaelic-speaking population in several disjoint areas that offer few natural opportunities.

The agricultural scene

Farm size and economy

Ireland's farms are commonly divided into three size categories – small farms of 1–30 acres, medium-size farms of 30–100 acres, and large farms of over 100 acres. The proportions in each category have changed radically since 1841 when 93 per cent of the country's 685,000 holdings were between 1 and 30 acres. Today there are 345,000 holdings, 52 per cent of which lie between 1 and 30 acres, and 40 per cent between 30 and 100 acres. Small farms, which currently occupy one-fifth of the fertile area, have thus decreased numerically owing to the growth of medium-size farms, a trend which both states have done much to encourage. Together, these two categories constitute the family-farming community which is such a noteworthy element of Irish society. In 1961, for example, the small farms of the Republic occupied 118,000 farmers and their relatives but only 3,000 labourers; medium-size farms occupied 157,000 farmers and relatives but only 19,000 labourers. The farmers alone provided two-thirds of the labour force on these farms, which reveals a critical lack of employment opportunities on most farms of this size under prevailing methods of land use and helps to explain why young folk continue to leave the land. In

47. *Connemara landscape near Ballyconneely*

contrast, large farms gave work to 25,000 labourers and several hundred managers in addition to 42,000 farmers and their relatives.

Small farms exist all over Ireland but predominate, by virtue of historical design rather than land quality, in Ulster and Connacht. Many small farmers in Ulster may trace their roots back to planter families who, protected by the 'Ulster custom', once specialized in growing flax for their main cash income. Today, livestock farming is their most profitable activity. Many small farmers in Connacht may trace their origins to the Cromwellian transplantations and to ancestors for whom congestion, land hunger, small fragmented holdings and famine were commonplace. Despite emigration and state intervention, problems of overcrowding and under-employment survive in several areas, notably along the western seaboard. Owing to congestion and poor land quality, many small farmers possess little more than subsistence holdings and derive their cash income from craft industries, emigrants' remittances or labouring elsewhere. For example, many Achill farmers work for most of the year on building and motorway sites in Britain, returning for a few weeks each summer to save the hay. While proper organization and modern techniques may have turned many of Ireland's small farms into economic units, those holdings on the poorer lands remote from markets are a continuing problem. Attempts to stimulate dairying and co-operation have been poorly received by the ageing rural population. In the Republic, the Land Commission hopes eventually to replace most small farms with units of 45–50 acres of good land. To this end elderly persons are encouraged to sell their lands to the Commission in return for cash or life annuities, while retaining their dwelling houses for life. Western landholders who also sell their lands to the Commission can obtain loans to enable them to buy farms elsewhere in the state. In Northern Ireland, 'golden handshakes' are given to those small farmers who give up their land for amalgamation into larger farms. Operating against these incentives is the conservatism of the small farmer to whom farming is often more a way of life than a commercial enterprise geared to strict market demands. Market gardening, as around Rush in north Dublin, and intensive pig- and poultry-farming are obvious exceptions to normal small farm practice, making maximum use of small acreages with heavy capital investment where markets are reasonably assured.

Medium-size farms characterize most of Leinster and Munster. Within a mixed farming framework, their emphasis may vary from commercial dairying or cattle-fattening to sugar-beet or cereal production. Their size allows greater mechanization than on small farms and co-operation is often notable. Large farms are most common in Meath and Kildare but are also scattered throughout the south and east. They are most frequently engaged in cattle-fattening for home and overseas markets although many large farms practise mixed farming, dairying or sheep-rearing.

This summary reveals two critical features. First, farm size exerts a strong influence on agricultural activity. Small farms must necessarily devote much of their output to family subsistence, their marketable surplus is small, capital is scarce and, in view of the general reluctance to accept credit, opportunities for adopting new techniques and for specialization are limited. As farm size increases, so commercial production expands and specialization becomes more feasible. Secondly, there is a remarkable paradox between farm size and land quality, largely owing to historical factors already examined. Thus, small farms occur most commonly along the harsh western seaboard and on the difficult drumlin soils of Ulster, while larger farms lie in more favoured environments to the south and east. These features are expressed in the landscape through land use and field size. On the large cattle-fattening farms of Meath, lush hedgerows with numerous trees enclose rich permanent pastures and meadows in fields averaging 10 acres. On the medium-size farms of Wexford, tillage is important and fields averaging 6 acres are separated by hedges with relatively few trees. On the limestone drift that mantles the east shore of Galway Bay, 30-acre farms mixing pasture, hay and tillage have fields averaging 2·5 acres separated by straight, solidly built stone walls. In the Curraun peninsula in Mayo, a typical congested district where small farms crowd on to the improved land near the coast, fields of ·5 acre or less are separated by crude stone walls.

Each farmer may have some walled paddocks of hay and pasture, a patch or two of oats and potatoes, a few cattle and, farther inland, a peat cutting and some rough grazing shared with his neighbours. Seaweed farms offshore yield manure for the poor soil.

Irish farms are mainly family holdings passing directly to the owner's issue or to a near relative and attachment to land ownership is such that farms change hands much less frequently than in Britain. Furthermore, the land tenure system created by the Land Acts produces few farms for rent. Legal complexities and traditional antagonisms towards leases both militate against letting. There is thus little mobility among the farming population and virtually no 'agricultural ladder' whereby an individual may progress from labourer to tenant, to owner subject to mortgage, and ultimately to owner free of mortgage debt. Letting is confined mainly to the conacre system, the leasing of land for less than one year. Conacre takers range from small farmers who need more land to make their farms economic, to cattle dealers and graziers who want land near their urban markets. The system, which is particularly common in Northern Ireland, is simple and flexible but rents are often disproportionately high and constant letting endangers soil fertility.

Land use

The present pattern of land use evolved during the later nineteenth century and, apart from wartime adjustments, has since undergone little change. Between 1861 and 1901 the area under pasture and hay expanded by 1·25 million acres and dry cattle numbers increased by over 1 million; tillage contracted by 1·5 million acres, corn crops alone falling by 1 million acres. Then as now, the nearby British market exerted a dominating influence on Irish agriculture. After the repeal of the corn laws and the consequent influx of cheap American grain to European markets, Irish farmers concentrated on meeting part of the growing demand for meat and other livestock products in Britain. The advent of re-frigerated shipping in 1882 also introduced strong competition in this field but its favoured location combined with restrictions on British imports from conti-nental Europe have allowed Ireland to maintain a virtual monopoly of the live cattle export trade to Britain. This position has been further strengthened over the past fifty years as British livestock farming has concentrated on milk pro-duction, expanding its dairy herds but not increasing its beef-cattle population outside Scotland. During the earlier half of the present century, Ireland's cattle population fluctuated around the 5 million mark but a steady increase since 1948 has now raised this total to 6·5 million. After an erratic decline, sheep numbers have also increased since 1948 and now exceed 6 million. In 1965 pasture and hay occupied 88 per cent of the Republic's farmland and livestock and their products provided 80 per cent of the total value of farm output. The comparative figures for Northern Ireland were 82 and 87 per cent respectively.

These colourless statistics reveal a countryside whose farmland is over-whelmingly under grass, the cheapest fodder crop in the prevailing climate, and whose cattle and sheep are together three times as numerous as the human population. Nevertheless, while the land is undoubtedly suited to grass, most of it deteriorates when permanently grazed. This, coupled with inadequate use of fertilizers, has reduced about two-thirds of the country's pasture to a thin, weedy and worn-out condition which only extensive ploughing and reseeding can now rectify. Lush grasslands are thus far less common than poor-quality, weed-infested, often ill-drained pastures which restrict livestock-carrying capacity and limit the supply of good hay and silage for winter feeding. Live-stock are thus returned to pasture early in the spring and the overgrazing which results at this time of year perpetuates the cycle of grassland deterioration and animal malnutrition. Government subsidies for fertilizers and agricultural re-search programmes are currently combating these problems. By 1965 the adjoining counties of Longford, Cavan, Leitrim, Sligo and Roscommon in the northwest midlands each had over 95 per cent of their farmland under hay and pasture, much of it of very poor quality. While physical conditions may not favour extensive tillage, continuing heavy emigration from these areas, where social amenities are poor and where 20- to 40-acre farms provide few employ-ment opportunities and stifle initiative, has imposed a certain hopelessness on the landscape. Derelict farm buildings, untidy hedgerows and rush-infested pastures are common, notably in dismal Leitrim, and under such melancholy circumstances grass offers the least troublesome means of using land. Stricter commercial motives explain the high proportion of grassland around Limerick and in the east midlands.

The two periods of compulsory tillage during the present century, in 1917–18 and 1939–45, have had no permanent effect on agricultural land use because the additional areas then ploughed, mainly to increase cereal production, have long since reverted to pasture. The general pattern of declining crop acreages, which has so characterized the past hundred years, soon reasserted itself after each emergency. In the area now covered by the Republic, the dramatic fall in the wheat acreage – from 328,000 acres in 1861 to 21,000 acres in 1931 – was reversed in 1933 when bounties were introduced for home-grown millable wheat and cereal imports were restricted. Since 1945, when wheat occupied 662,000 acres, acreages have again declined, although farmers grew 42 per cent more wheat in 1967 than in 1966. After a less remarkable contraction, barley has expanded steadily since 1939 and by 1965 covered 464,000 acres, the highest acreage ever recorded. The most persistent decline in the tillage sector has taken place in the area under oats and potatoes, each of which now occupies only one-fifth of the 1861 acreage, largely because the demand for subsistence crops has slackened. The need for oats has further diminished over the past twenty years as tractors have replaced working horses on farms, thus releasing land for the production of something other than fodder for motive power. Turnip and mangel acreages have also declined but the expansion of sugar-beet as a main crop after 1926 partly offset the trend of diminishing root crop production. Today nearly all root crops, most oats and potatoes, and three-quarters of the barley crop are fed to animals as befits a livestock-orientated economy. In Northern Ireland, barley acreages have soared over recent years and now occupy half the tilled area. Other crops have diminished in importance and flax has virtually disappeared in face of labour problems, a declining linen industry, and competition from manmade fibres and imported flax.

With most of Ireland under grass, much of it undisturbed for centuries, regional variations in land use are slight and mainly express the significance of various tillage crops. Tillage is more important in the south and east with crops occupying 27 per cent of the farmland in Wexford, 23–24 per cent in Carlow, Dublin and Louth, and 17–19 per cent in Cork, Waterford, Kilkenny, Laois, Kildare and Wicklow. Even so, land-use emphasis may vary appreciably within individual counties. South Kildare and south Cork, with more than 30 per cent of their farmland under the plough, thus contrast markedly with the pastoral north of their respective counties. Tillage occupies 15 per cent of all Donegal farmland, mainly because of the widespread production of oats and potatoes in the Foyle–Swilly lowland. Concentration on particular crops may give further individuality to an area. Thus, Wexford and the Barrow corridor are outstand-

48. Lazy beds – potatoes growing on Inisheer in the Aran Islands

ing producers of wheat, malting barley, sugar-beet and turnips, intensive vegetable production characterizes north Dublin, oats and potatoes dominate the west, and sugar-beet is prominent around the sugar factories at Carlow, Thurles, Mallow and Tuam. Fruit-growing is also strongly localized: strawberries and other soft fruit are grown mainly in Wexford, Dublin and Armagh, and commercial apple orchards feature prominently in north Armagh and less notably in south Tipperary, near the Clonmel cider factory and the co-operative fruit-packing station in Dungarvan. Grass seed, mainly Perennial and Italian ryegrass, is an important cash crop in the lowlands north and south of Lough Neagh and the production of seed potatoes for export is a continuing feature of many Northern Ireland farms.

As land hunger has diminished over the past hundred years, most subsistence holdings on submarginal lands have been abandoned, the upper limits of improved land on hillsides have been lowered and most arable plots have been either invaded by scrub or converted to pasture. For instance, improved pastures around the Wicklow mountains rarely reach 800 feet today but above this level a legacy of decayed field boundaries and old spade ridges all but obscured by bracken reveals that cultivation once reached 1,000 feet, a view endorsed by evidence from pre-famine maps. Similar expressions of the past occur on most hillsides where mountain sheep now graze on lands that once barely supported a desperate peasantry.

Regional contrasts

Regional contrasts in farming are mainly a function of the varying aims of livestock production in a mixed farming economy in which tillage is largely designed to supplement animal fodder requirements. Specialized forms of livestock farming, such as cattle-fattening, dairying and sheep-rearing, may give a distinctive expression to certain landscapes but the mixed character of most Irish farming, in which changes from one area to another commonly reflect variations on a theme, makes regional boundaries difficult to distinguish. Where physical influences are marked, for instance where uplands rise abruptly from extensive lowlands, one type of farming may rapidly replace another. Frequently, however, historical and economic factors are more important, boundaries between farming regions are blurred and it is more realistic to outline the characteristics of individual core areas.

Cottage farming with much of the farm output devoted to subsistence still characterizes most of the Atlantic seaboard from Donegal to west Cork, reappearing at intervals farther inland. Rugged topography, a wet and windy climate, widespread blanket bog, low-fertility soils and remoteness from markets all restrict agricultural opportunities. Population densities are absurdly high relative to the amount of improved land available. Extremely small, often fragmented holdings, minute fields, poor equipment, rough grazings held in

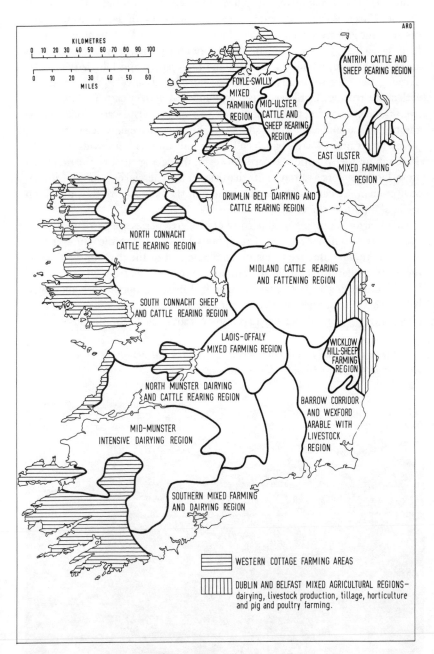

49. *The agricultural regions of Ireland*

common, limited marketable surpluses and negligible capital are all characteristic. Tillage is confined mainly to oats and potatoes for use on the farm and cash income is derived from the sale of young store cattle for fattening on better lands elsewhere. Oats and potatoes are more important as cash crops in north and east Donegal, while in west Cork and the Iveragh and Dingle peninsulas dairying for the co-operative creameries introduced since 1938 is combined with cattle-rearing. Until very recently, numerous donkey carts heading to and from these creameries with their one or two milk churns were a picturesque addition to the landscape in the southwest, but these have now been largely replaced by creamery lorries which collect the milk churns from roadside stands. Throughout the Atlantic seaboard, however, the ageing rural population often views farming more as a way of life than a strict commercial enterprise. Life and environment are closely analogous to those of the Scottish crofters, but sheep are less important than cattle.

Dairy farms supplying milk to co-operative creameries are particularly conspicuous in two major regions of reasonably heavy soils: in the Munster lowlands where medium-size farms predominate and in the drumlin belt across the north midlands where farms commonly range in size from 23 to 35 acres. Intensive dairying is most characteristic in Limerick, north Cork and north Kerry where creameries have been operating since the 1890s and are now supplied by 95 per cent of all farmers (Gillmor, 1967). Lush summer pastures are

50. The walled paddocks and homesteads of the farmer-fisher community on Inisheer in the Aran Islands off the Galway coast.

heavily stocked with dairy cattle but calves are sold rather than reared and pig-rearing is often the most notable ancillary enterprise. In north-central Limerick and around Ardfert in north Kerry, where soils are lighter, dairying is com-bined with tillage, cattle-production and some sheep-rearing. In adjoining Clare and Tipperary, dairying combines with traditional cattle-rearing, creameries are more widely spaced, cattle densities are lower and, in Tipperary, the production of some feeding barley, wheat and sugar-beet for sale gives farming a truly mixed character. On the lighter, better-drained and more easily worked soils of south Cork, Waterford and Kilkenny, wheat, barley and sugar-beet are grown as cash crops, abundant fodder supplies allow cattle to be reared through the winter, but dairying remains important, notably in southwest Waterford and south Kilkenny. In the north midlands, repetitive drumlin topography, heavy clay soils and poor drainage hinder tillage but co-operative creameries provide a ready market for milk. Dairying based upon small farm units is commonly combined with the rearing of store cattle, while pigs and poultry are particularly important in Monaghan and Cavan.

Cattle-rearing and fattening dominate farming across the midlands south of this northern dairying belt. West of the Shannon, in north Roscommon and lowland Mayo, farms specialize in the rearing of young store cattle for sale at the age of $2-2\frac{1}{2}$ years, an enterprise which yields a low return per acre and is not well suited economically to the relatively small farms of the region which average only 32 acres of farmland per holding. Nevertheless, as Gillmor has indicated, the western farmer has a traditional love of livestock and is very 'cattle-minded'. Many young cattle come from the west and from Munster dairy farms. Dairying is an ancillary activity on some farms. Farther south, as the drift cover thins and limestone nears the surface, drier conditions prevail, cattle are joined by sheep, and tillage, mainly for fodder crops but with some wheat, oats, barley, potatoes and sugar-beet grown for sale, becomes more common. East of the Shannon, the fattening of store cattle for slaughter or export is a notable feature of West-meath, Longford, Meath and north Kildare. Large farms are common, pastures are rich provided they are not overgrazed, and large numbers of store cattle are drawn in from outside the region. Heavy clay soils hinder tillage and neither dairying for the Dublin liquid milk market nor horse-breeding and sheep-rearing in north Kildare cause any break in the vast extent of pasture.

Sheep-rearing is most important on the uplands of the north and east, on nearby lowlands such as the free-draining Curragh in north Kildare, and in the dry limestone country of east Galway and south Roscommon where over one-fifth of the Republic's sheep population exists. In eastern Ireland, the un-enclosed moorlands that lie above the improved hill pastures can best be exploited agriculturally by using hill-farming methods with mountain breeds of sheep being preferred to hill cattle. Man's direct impact on these moorlands is confined to burning the coarse woody growths of gorse and heather to improve

51. Munster landscape
The enclosed pastures of the Glen of Aherlow contrast vividly with the coniferous plantations and open moorland of the Galtee mountains.

grazing. The Wicklow mountains thus support 150,000 sheep for about eight months of the year but cattle seldom graze above the limits of the gorse, *Ulex gallii*. In winter breeding ewes and some younger stock are removed to lowland pastures to avoid the severe mountain weather. In the west improved land rarely exceeds 300 feet, but the prevalence of bare rock and blanket bog restricts the sheep-carrying capacity of the moorlands while the smallness of farms discourages extensive sheep-rearing.

Although a high proportion of commercial tillage gives eastern Ireland a distinctive farming personality, livestock are nowhere unimportant. In Wexford and the Barrow corridor, oats, feeding barley and turnips are widely grown for winter fodder and large open cattle sheds are prominent. In Laois, Offaly and Louth, where cash cropping is also very important, fodder crops, grassland and cattle give farming a very mixed character. Specialization and co-operation are currently increasing farm efficiency in Northern Ireland where most tillage crops are now destined for marketing in the form of fat cattle, dairy products, pigs, poultry and eggs. In east Ulster and around Dublin, the proximity of large urban markets for fresh food and liquid milk produces many specialized farm enterprises varying from cattle-fattening and dairying to intensive pig and poultry production and market gardening. Glasshouses are remarkably conspicuous around Rush, a former fishing village in north Dublin, and vegetable production has recently transformed the demesne land of nearby Kenure Park.

In recent years, the traditional farmyard industries concerned with pigs and poultry have been augmented by the growth of mass-production units around the larger urban markets. In the Republic pig numbers have recovered from their wartime low of 380,000 and now total 1·25 million, being notably prominent in the dairying regions. Specialized pig units are important within the city of Dublin where abundant garbage is available and where many pigs are also kept on a part-time basis in backyards. In Northern Ireland guaranteed prices have greatly stimulated pig-farming and many landholders with comparatively few acres have become big farmers on concrete as sow units and stall-housing systems have accommodated more animals and cut the work of feeding and management. Poultry-farming in the Republic has declined recently but in Northern Ireland the industry has expanded rapidly and thirty persons now

52. *Leinster landscape*
The middle Barrow valley near Graiguenamanagh.

own 10,000 birds each and intensive production units with between 3,000 and 5,000 layers dominate egg marketing.

Rural settlement

Origins and distribution

The distribution and density of the rural population, the type of farming practised and the size of individual holdings are all closely related. Thus the prosperous cattle-fattening lands of Meath with their large farms have only 50 people to the square mile whereas along those parts of the Atlantic seaboard where cottage farming persists there may be 400 persons to a square mile. Between these two extremes, similar if less dramatic contrasts exist. For instance, population densities are much higher in the indifferent drumlin country that stretches across the north midlands from Down to Sligo than in the more favourable farmlands of Leinster and east Munster where farms are consequently larger. Clearly, apart from the uninhabited uplands and bogs, the physical resources of the environment are inversely proportionate to the distribution and density of its human resources. As we have seen, this paradox is explained by the varied social and economic forces that have shaped Ireland during its turbulent past and, in particular, by the way in which successive colonists have displaced their predecessors.

Irish rural settlement is today dominated by isolated family farms dispersed across the improved land. From earliest times isolated farmsteads have formed a recurrent element in the landscape, as the abandoned raths and cashels of the early Christian farmers and the compact farms of the seventeenth-century colonists clearly indicate. In many areas, however, the present dispersed pattern was produced or accentuated by the sweeping changes that transformed the face of Ireland during the nineteenth century. At that time, famine, emigration, landlord activity and state intervention all played a part in breaking up the farm clusters and rundale practices that survived, mainly in the north and west. The population dispersed to new holdings scattered at intervals over former estates, across hillsides and along roads. The redistribution of land by the Congested Districts Board, the Estates Commissioners and now the Land Commission has contributed in no small way to this movement and the addition of drab but functional Land Commission cottages to the rural scene is one of several improvements in the quality and design of smaller country dwellings that have characterized the present century. The many picturesque varieties of thatched cottage that once expressed the individuality of a region and its people are fast disappearing, abandoned in favour of unspectacular, better-equipped bungalows of brick or concrete blocks which are gradually imposing a dismal uniformity on the landscape. Thatch gave way to imported slate, slate in turn yielded to the manufactured tile. Many old thatched cottages now serve as

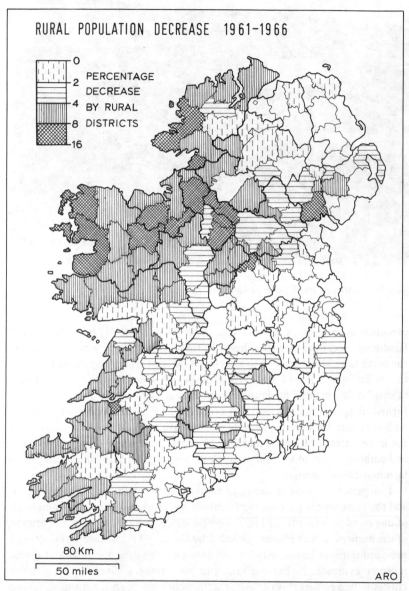

RURAL POPULATION DECREASE 1961–1966

PERCENTAGE
DECREASE
BY RURAL
DISTRICTS

0
2
4
8
16

80 Km

50 miles

ARO

53. Rural population decrease, 1961–6

In the Republic, the decrease was most marked in the northwest midlands and along the Atlantic seaboard. Although the decrease was less pronounced in Northern Ireland, the border districts and certain other areas lying beyond the immediate influence of Belfast lost appreciable population. Compare with Fig. 58.

54. Dereliction of small farm in Connemara

cowsheds or stores but others have mouldered into unsightly ruins. Dispersed farmsteads occur nearly everywhere but their greatest density naturally lies in the small farm areas: notably in the congested west where dispersion followed the redistribution of land, and in the drumlin belt where the frequent repetition of small hills, enclosed fields and homesteads gives the landscape a cosy, well-furnished appearance. Densities decrease as farm size increases, though the widening gaps between farmsteads may contain a few labourers' cottages. On the larger farms of Leinster and east Munster, modest two-storey farmsteads and outhouses built of local stone have long been typical. Many simple Georgian farmhouses still survive.

Two principal forms of nucleated rural settlement – the simple farm cluster and the more sophisticated agricultural village – survive within this framework of dispersed farmsteads. Although comparatively few now remain, the origins of the numerous farm clusters revealed by the early Ordnance Survey maps of pre-famine times have excited much interest. Assessing the field and documentary evidence, E. Estyn Evans and his followers have shown the farm cluster to be a remarkably persistent settlement form of great antiquity, having often coexisted with isolated homesteads of one kind or another. Throughout early Christian Ireland, farm clusters occupied by lowly cultivators apparently existed alongside the raths of their Gaelic overlords. When the raths were later abandoned, the clusters survived but the term *baile* or homestead by which they were known was corrupted to 'bally'. The disruption that followed each phase of colonization eventually yielded a majority of clusters in the physically less favoured north and west. As revealed by the 6 inches to 1 mile Ordnance Survey maps prepared between 1825 and 1841, their farm dwellings and associated outhouses were commonly grouped together without any formal plan and clusters varied in size from as few as three dwellings to as many as forty. Although they normally lacked both inn and church, communal life and exchange of services were still typical, since their inhabitants were frequently related (Johnson, 1961). They worked the surrounding land as a joint farm along rundale lines, and also enjoyed common rights of grazing and peat-cutting. Farm clusters were remarkably flexible in the face of fluctuating population, the number of dwellings expanding or contracting as population rose or fell. Nevertheless, the collapse of rundale farming during the early nineteenth century signed the death warrant for most clusters and for their distant booley huts. The subsequent dispersal of the rural population executed this sentence.

Today, farm clusters survive in a few refuge areas in the north and west, sometimes with still open infields as at Ballyhillin near Malin Head in Donegal, but commonly with the small scattered plots of individual farmers enclosed by stone walls. The vast majority are but shadows of their former selves. Menlough, on the Corrib just north of Galway, now consists of a dozen farms clustered amid the ruins of others but with its open infield still tilled in strips: in 1845 it is said to have had 2,000 inhabitants while lacking a 'centre, market, church, chapel or school'. Along the north shores of Galway Bay, for 10 miles west of Barna, forty-eight farm clusters still function even if only in a very attenuated form (Mac Aodha, 1965). They commonly lie midway between the unenclosed moorland and the coast, to which they are connected by 'seaweed' lanes. Population density locally exceeds 250 per square mile of enclosed land. Reliable tradition asserts that most clusters grew up around one or two homesteads and that early marriages, high fertility rates and the traditional Irish practice of subdividing the cultivable land among all male heirs in a household all contributed to the rapid expansion of the settlements. A century ago their lands were held entirely in rundale and even now many persons hold land in scattered plots. Isolation, the difficulty of imposing consolidation, the poverty of the land, and the kinship, traditions and cultural homogeneity of the occupants, have all favoured the survival of clusters. Even so, many inhabitants have recently abandoned their old thatched cottages for new houses strung out along the main coast road.

In contrast, a more sophisticated form of nucleated rural settlement appears in those areas where, over the past 800 years, outside influences have established their firmest roots. Such villages are commonly arranged around a central open space or along a wide main street and contain a church, chapel, school, shop, garage and one or more 'bars', thus covering a range of social and commercial

55. Deserted village near Cashel, County Tipperary
The south and east of Ireland abound with such traces of former rural settlements whose date of desertion varies from later medieval times through to the eighteenth century.

activities. Some are formally planned settlements of the plantation and landlord eras whose designs clearly express their origins. Plantation villages are common in Ulster, estate villages occur everywhere with Blessington and Enniskerry providing good examples near Dublin. Many landlord settlements now languish beside derelict demesnes but others, like Maynooth and Castlepollard, were villages in conception that have become towns in function without alteration to their original plans. During the eighteenth and nineteenth centuries, much rural settlement also gravitated towards the new roads that were being constructed through the countryside and thus, in a less systematic fashion, linear and crossroads villages arose. In Northern Ireland, several villages are products of the industrial revolution having grown up, like Sion Mills in Tyrone and Darkley in Armagh, near rural textile mills during the nineteenth century. The model village built by a Quaker family at Bessbrook near Newry in 1845 has since grown into a small town. Similar villages survive farther south.

Apart from these comparatively late creations whose origins are well documented, most agricultural villages in the physically more favoured south and east are apparently of medieval origin. Within the area colonized by the Anglo-Normans, medieval charters clearly reveal that villages containing a church and mill and surrounded by large open fields with regular strip-holdings were of fundamental importance in rural life. Many such villages later disappeared and their traces are only now being revealed by aerial photography. Those that survived gradually lost their open fields although modern field patterns that presumably evolved from open-field strips can often be traced, for example around Rush, Swords and Newcastle in County Dublin. At Doornane in south Kilkenny, the fine courtyard farmsteads may once have been grouped around a central open space, recalling similar settlements in Europe so well suited to joint tillage and herding. Similar Anglo-Norman imprints are stamped on settlements throughout south Kilkenny, southeast Wexford, the Cooley peninsula in Louth, and elsewhere. Throughout the southeast, townlands are frequently named after Anglo-Norman families for whom the 'town' was a personal estate, as at Whitestown in Louth, often focusing on pre-existing *bailes*. Other place-names preserve the *baile* element, normally reflecting homesteads of feudal betaghs as at Ballybetagh in south Dublin. Several villages of medieval origin were subsequently redesigned by improving landlords during the eighteenth and nineteenth centuries, some being transformed in function into small towns.

In their many varieties, Irish rural settlements thus commonly preserve in clay and stone something of the skills, ideals and traditions of the people by whom they were originally created. These legacies were severely disrupted by the sweeping rural changes of the nineteenth century but those forms of settlement that were able to adapt to changing circumstances survived – within an expanded framework of dispersed farmsteads. Other settlements became redundant, either because there was little or no room for them in the new order or because famine and emigration had deprived them of their population. A melancholy assortment of ruins and redundancies, comprising abandoned cottages, derelict country houses and decaying farm clusters set amid weed-infested fields, still remains a distinguishing feature of the Irish rural scene.

The thatched cottage

In his penetrating discussion of *Irish Folk Ways* (1957), E. Estyn Evans has lucidly shown how traditional, single-storey thatched cottages vary subtly from one region to another in response to local climates, conditions and contacts. Although such cottages are now rapidly disappearing, sufficient examples survive to express the influence that physical environment, folklore and regional traditions had on their builders. Custom and superstition have given nearly all these dwellings a long rectangular ground plan and when country folk later

56. A Connemara cottage with projecting gable ends and thatch tied down by ropes weighted with stones resting on the eaves

drifted into the towns this shape was perpetuated in the humble, whitewashed cabins that were strung end to end along straggling suburban streets. Simple rectangular designs have been a persistent feature of cottage construction since Neolithic times but oval and round shapes of similar antiquity now survive only as animal byres, stores or derelict booley huts. The rectangular dwelling was well suited to the custom of housing man and beast together, and numerous 'longhouses', in which the family occupied one end and cattle the other, survive in the north and west and in the Wicklow mountains. Many are now in ruins; others are still occupied, but cohabitation by man and cattle is now a thing of the past and a partition has converted the byre into a bedroom, store or dairy. In contrast, the traditional cottage of lowland Leinster, east Munster and south Ulster, with its central chimney and fireside partition which did not easily permit keeping livestock in the house, may be a more sophisticated design introduced by settlers from Britain.

Building materials give further regional expression to traditional country dwellings, although variations are less marked than in England with its wider range of materials, craftsmanship and rural wealth. The clay-walled cottage is typical throughout lowland Ireland, wherever stone is concealed by bogs and glacial deposits and the transport of materials was once difficult. Built upon stone foundations, such walls were constructed with a mixture of damp clay and sour rushes, and later trimmed with a sharp spade to a thickness of 20–30 inches.

They had to be massive for stability, doors were kept narrow and windows small. Thick coats of limewash renewed annually and thatch overhanging at the eaves gave protection against the weather. The roof was commonly hipped for it was difficult to build sturdy walls above about 6 feet high at the gable. Where stone was more readily available, notably at intervals along the Atlantic seaboard and in the Wicklow and Mourne granite country, stone-built cottages are typical. Older dwellings are generally small and crudely constructed by dry walling methods. Newer buildings have mortared walling, larger dimensions, more rooms and, in the gabled variety, loft bedrooms.'

Roofing and thatching styles also vary from one region to another. The hipped roof is particularly common in the south midlands and throughout the southeast coastlands, areas in which medieval colonists were most successful. This roof style is well suited to thatch, which can easily be carried round its corners, but slate and tile have now frequently replaced the original thatch. Gabled dwellings are widespread, being particularly amenable to extension by adding rooms at either end, but they probably developed later than the hipped-roof cottage. The roof frame of these rectangular houses is composed most commonly of coupled rafters, traditionally of bog oak chosen for its strength as well as from the scarcity of live oak trees. This design may have evolved from the older cruck-framed wattle dwelling or have been borrowed from the box-framed house of the seventeenth-century English planters. The coupled rafters are joined by one or two cross-ties, and pegs driven into the rafters secure the long purlins which support a layer of branches or thin laths. On these rests a warm blanket of carefully fitted sods which serve to anchor the rods with which the overlying thatch is generally secured. These rods or scallops are commonly hidden to prevent water seeping through the sods but it is customary to leave a row exposed at the eaves, ridge and gables where the uppermost thatch should lie snugly. The thatch may consist of oat, rye or wheat straw, reeds, rushes, sedge, marram grass or heather. It is finished in a variety of ways. In east Down, the thatch is plastered down at the eaves, gable and ridge with mud or clay. Along the Antrim coast, horizontal ropes are laid across the thatch at 1-foot intervals parallel to the eaves and pegged to the underlying sods with wooden pins; pegged sods protect the rather sharp ridge to the roof. Along the wet and windy Atlantic seaboard from north Antrim to west Cork, the thatch is commonly tied down by ropes that are secured either to small boulders resting on the eaves or to stone pegs below the eaves. In Donegal, where roped thatch reaches its finest development, the thatch and its supporting frame are rounded at the ridge to throw off the winds. In some districts, the ropes run both down and across the roof to provide a tight network; in others, projecting gable ends protect the thatch and horizontal ropes are omitted. Traditional ropes of twisted straw, heather, willow or bog-fir root fibres have now given way to ready-made sisal ropes. Sometimes the thatch may be decorated with straw

57. A Donegal cottage
The thatch is characteristically tied down by cross ropes secured to stone pegs protruding below the eaves and at the gables. The thatch and its supporting frame are rounded at the ridge to throw off the winds.

bobbins at the ridge, eaves and gables, thus protecting the roof at its most vulnerable parts.

In the past, simple thatched cottages were common throughout the country-side and in most small towns. At worst, they were cramped, insanitary and, without chimneys, often likened to smoking dunghills. At best, they formed a picturesque component of the landscape, forcibly expressing the customs and traditions of their occupants and the environmental influences to which the people were exposed. Built from local materials, they blended harmoniously with their surroundings and lacked the vulgar obtrusiveness of many modern bungalows. Inside, the kitchen with its furniture and fittings and the hearth with its continuously burning turf fire were the very core of Irish life. Outside, many an ancient custom was expressed in terms of spades, ploughs, slanes and other implements, cars and carts, stacks and fishing and kelping gear. Many of these traditional features survive today despite the violent assault that modern society with its new techniques and attitudes has made on them in recent years. As E. Estyn Evans has emphasized, 'the past never wholly dies: it lives on buried in the minds of men and in the landscapes they have fashioned'.

Chapter 12
The urban landscape

Almost without exception, the towns of Ireland were founded between the mid-ninth century and the mid-nineteenth. Prior to the Viking incursion, Gaelic Ireland's preoccupation with family groups and economic self-sufficiency created no need for towns and the people possessed no urban traditions. The towns that subsequently intruded into this rural setting did not meet with unqualified success because, as colonizing instruments designed to secure and exploit the neighbourhood for alien settlers, they found little favour with Gaelic society. Many towns failed to acquire any lasting role while those that did survive could hardly be considered expressive of the national way of life.

Nevertheless, by the early nineteenth century the country's present urban framework was largely complete and most towns, doubtless facilitated by the improved road network constructed during the preceding hundred years, had found grudging acceptance as service centres among the rural population. After the great famine the continuing loss of population through emigration and the poverty of industrial development outside east Ulster motivated against the creation of further new towns and, while the railways transformed several small coastal settlements into seaside resorts or into outports and residential satellites for the larger towns, most existing country towns stagnated or decayed. Townscapes which had been developed or renewed during the Georgian era were fossilized, thus preserving the eighteenth- and early nineteenth-century fabric that makes such a striking contribution to the modern urban scene. In some instances, town plans and buildings of earlier origins were also preserved. Meaningful expressions like 'medieval core', 'plantation town', 'landlord settlement' and 'Georgian development' thus recall at once the salient features of many existing townscapes. Only the manufacturing towns of northeast Ireland experienced any appreciable growth during the later nineteenth century but for the majority, as for most towns farther south, the early decades of the present century formed a period of uncertainty and stagnation.

Today, new towns are once again being created, notably at Craigavon south of Lough Neagh, while many existing settlements are having their suburban fringes expanded by organized housing developments and their central areas transformed or even renewed in a piecemeal fashion. In the smaller towns, this transformation is limited outwardly to modernizing the street fronts of shops, hotels and licensed bars or to adding garish neon signs to outmoded buildings.

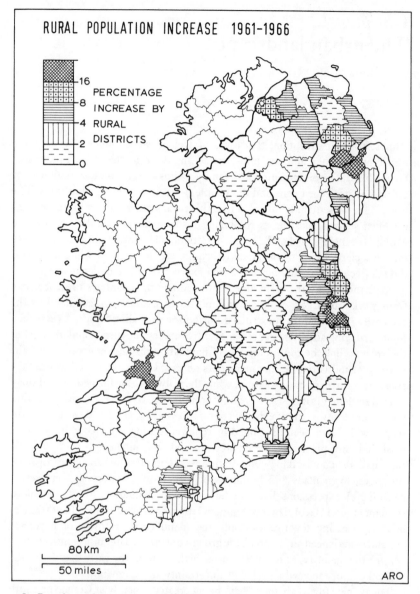

58. *Rural population increase 1961–6*
Apart from the spectacular growth of population around the Shannon Airport industrial estate, the most pronounced increases simply represented the overspill of the suburban populations of Belfast, Cork, Dublin, Limerick, Londonderry, Waterford and certain smaller towns beyond their official limits into adjoining Rural Districts. Compare with Fig. 53.

In many larger towns, functional concrete and glass office blocks are replacing decayed eighteenth- and nineteenth-century dwellings and car parks are engulfing slum clearance sites, at least temporarily. Former town residences, large and small, continue to be converted internally to professional, commercial or administrative uses but their unaltered shells retain the outward expression of another era. In fact, most Irish towns share a common heritage of buildings which are either near the end of their useful lives, or even past it, and are destined for demolition – if they do not fall down in the meantime. Many central areas are riddled with dereliction or with rubble-strewn wastes that lie unsuspected behind main thoroughfares. Urban renewal has as yet left the town plans untouched and, instead of catering for the needs of the motorcar era by creating new arterial routes and multi-storey car parks, most local authorities appear content to cram ever-increasing volumes of traffic into existing street patterns which in most cases were designed more than 150 years ago and may even retain a medieval framework.

Urban functions and hierarchy

Functional base

The most common type of urban settlement in modern Ireland is the small service centre bearing a distinct functional relationship to its rural surroundings. The largest towns, however, are all ports which were designed in the first instance for trade but have since acquired considerable importance as regional centres. These ports, in common with several inland towns, have long generated a variety of craft activities and have more recently attracted some large industries, but only Belfast can claim to have a dominant industrial role. Thus, in terms of function, most Irish towns are expressions of a pre-industrial order which in most other west European countries was largely submerged by the industrial revolution of the nineteenth century. Unlike some nearby countries with a more sophisticated urban framework, towns whose main roles lie in mining, manufacturing or railway activity or which function only as holiday resorts are the exception rather than the rule. Manufacturing towns are mainly found in northeast Ireland, but even there the majority developed from rural service centres catering for the scattered farmers and linen-weavers of the pre-industrial age and, despite altered circumstances, still provide important services for the surrounding rural community. Elsewhere factories have often been superimposed on existing urban structures in recent years, but, although some industries have come to dominate employment in a town, their existence has rarely affected the town's service capacity.

Most rural service centres have developed from medieval or plantation settlements whose situations initially owed much to the dictates of military strategy. With the expansion of commercial agriculture during the eighteenth

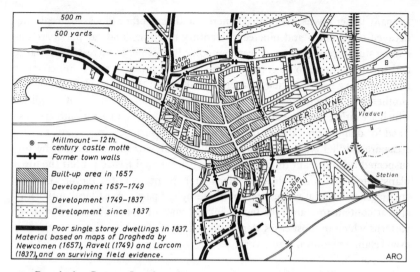

Scale:
500 m
500 yards

Millmount — 12th. century castle motte
Former town walls

Built-up area in 1657
Development 1657–1749
Development 1749–1837
Development since 1837

Poor single storey dwellings in 1837.
Material based on maps of Drogheda by
Newcomen (1657), Ravell (1749) and Larcom
(1837), and on surviving field evidence.

RIVER BOYNE
Viaduct
Station
30 m. (100 ft.)
ARO

59. Drogheda, County Louth
Founded and walled by the Anglo-Normans as one of their most important strongholds
and ports in eastern Ireland. Drogheda originally consisted of two separate boroughs
north and south of the river Boyne until these were united under one corporation in 1412.

century, those towns whose outmoded strategic situations could be exploited
to the advantage of the developing farming community began to acquire their
present service character. Divested of their walls, they were frequently remodelled and, like the entirely new service centres created by improving landlords at that time, were provided with remarkably wide main streets and prominent market places to cater for the marketing requirements of the surrounding
rural population. A close interdependence of town and country was at last
established – a development which had been restricted previously by the turbulent state of the countryside and by the fact that the towns had been founded
and settled by colonists who were often out of touch and out of sympathy with
the rural population who, in their turn, reciprocated these feelings.

When pasture replaced tillage after the famine, many produce markets died
out, but livestock fairs, traditional gatherings far older than the towns into
which they had gravitated, became even more firmly entrenched in the life of
the countryside. On fair-days the country towns erupted into a jostling throng
of cattle, sheep, pigs, horses, farmers and their families, dealers, drovers and
travelling craftsmen. Nevertheless, with emigration draining away the very
lifeblood of the countryside, urban decay was inevitable. Furthermore, the
country towns had flourished by serving the marketing and milling needs of
farmers who lived within a radius of 8 to 10 miles – a comfortable journey by
horse and cart – and were thus spread at fairly regular intervals through the

countryside. Consequently, the advent of motor transport has seen the traditional functions of many smaller towns wither away as fairs and markets have concentrated on larger, better-equipped centres like Carlow, Enniscorthy, Mallow or Longford. Droving has been superseded by livestock lorries and farm trailers. Animals have been removed from the streets into less colourful livestock marts and much of the old fair-day congestion relieved. Private cars and bus services have also presented farming families with a wider range of options: they can now go to the larger towns for their agricultural machinery and for many clothes, household utensils and other consumer goods. The small town shopkeeper suffers because he is rarely able to stock a comparable range of products. Recent decades have thus seen many smaller towns like Boyle, Callan, Cashel and Macroom stagnate and decay as their service functions have been usurped by larger centres with expanding hinterlands. These centres have in turn been able to provide better employment, cultural and recreational facilities and have acquired a social and economic vitality which is forcefully expressed in the bustling townscape. Some small towns, notably in the agriculturally less favoured west, appear destined to achieve new prosperity from tourism.

Many Irish ports were founded as fortified trading posts by the Vikings and Anglo-Normans to secure and exploit the nearby farmlands and forests over which they held uneasy sway. During later medieval times, many less privileged ports fell victim to various restrictions placed on their foreign trade and to repeated attacks by land and sea. Galway, Dingle, Kinsale and others that had once traded extensively with Spain and Portugal never fully recovered because the English reconquest, by redeeming Ireland for the English Crown, naturally favoured the more secure ports nearer Britain. The subsequent export boom in wool, cattle, provisions and grain destined mainly for the British market brought considerable prosperity to the older ports along the south and east coasts while new outlets developed at Belfast, Coleraine, Londonderry and elsewhere to serve the Ulster planters. As ships grew steadily larger during the nineteenth century, however, the dangerous approaches to several smaller harbours led shipping to concentrate on ports where continuous deep water could be provided up to and against the quays.

Furthermore, the vagaries of Irish railway politics deprived several old ports of improved communications until it was too late and silting and dereliction had overtaken their harbours and facilities. Youghal thus yielded its trade to Cork and Waterford and, until the dangerous sand bar that had grown across the Bann estuary was nullified by retaining walls towards the close of the century, Coleraine lost much trade to the new harbour at nearby Portrush. Alternatively, the railway era favoured those ports where lines could be extended to the dockside and also generated new outports designed to exploit the shortest sea crossings to Britain. Kingstown (now Dun Laoghaire), which had

60. *Youghal, County Cork*

A defunct seaport which is now finding new prosperity from manufacturing and tourism. From medieval times onward, the port was an important outlet for the produce of the Blackwater valley and during the later eighteenth century was one of Ireland's leading grain exporting ports. Nearly all the warehouses, quays and buildings to the right (east) of the main street lie on ground reclaimed from the Blackwater estuary, mainly during the late eighteenth century. In the distance the Youghal mudlands were enclosed as a famine relief project in 1846.

replaced Howth as Dublin's packet station in 1826, attracted Ireland's first railway in 1834. Railways to Passage West in 1850 and to Queenstown (now Cobh) in 1862 seriously threatened Cork's role as a deep-sea port, a situation only retrieved by deepening the inner harbour approaches to Cork during the later nineteenth century. Larne grew rapidly after regular rail-served steamship crossings to Scotland were established in 1872. The London and North Western Railway Company actually created Greenore on Carlingford Lough by constructing dwellings, hotel, school, co-operative store, port facilities, and rail links to Dundalk and Newry to serve the new seaport that they opened in 1873. The creation of the Border and other factors later curtailed Greenore's trade, rail and sea services were withdrawn in 1951, and the population had dwindled to 150 by 1956. In 1960 the port was reopened for container traffic. If Greenore was hardly a town, the railways constructed to Valencia Harbour to serve emigrant ships and to Rosslare Harbour to serve the Fishguard packet were even less successful in stimulating urban growth. Railways also made inland navigation superfluous, so that many river towns lost their port functions: Enniscorthy yielded to Wexford and Rosslare Harbour, Carrick-on-Suir yielded to Waterford.

In recent years, many smaller harbours have become virtually defunct as trade has concentrated on a few major ports with superior handling and distribution facilities. Belfast and Dublin not only dominate the industrial, commercial, administrative and cultural life of Northern Ireland and the Republic respectively but also the import–export activities of their territories. Lesser ports at Londonderry, Waterford, Cork and Limerick also function as important regional centres; Dun Laoghaire, Rosslare Harbour and Larne maintain their traditional short sea connections with Britain, Drogheda is an important alternative to Dublin, and several small harbours like Arklow, New Ross, Fenit and Galway trade in a few specific commodities. The remarkable success of the container traffic passing through Larne, now Northern Ireland's second port, has encouraged Londonderry, Coleraine, Portrush, Belfast, Warrenpoint, Newry, Greenore, Waterford and Dublin to offer similar facilities. In contrast, several formerly prosperous seaports like Youghal, Passage West and Kinsale are now utterly defunct, their quays abandoned, their warehouses derelict or converted to some other use, and many of their once fine houses in ruins. The tendency for trade to forsake the smaller harbours in favour of a few larger ports is admirably illustrated by recent developments in the cattle trade. Of the 660,000 cattle exported annually from Ireland between 1960 and 1964 – incidentally the largest international movement of cattle anywhere in the world – Dublin accounted for two-thirds while the rest left from Londonderry, Larne, Belfast, Drogheda, Waterford and Cork (Coppock and Gillmor, 1967). Ports through which cattle had been exported in 1938, when Dublin accounted for only 45 per cent, but which were not used for this purpose in 1964 were

61. Waterford
An important port and manufacturing centre on the south bank of the river Suir near its
confluence with the St John's river, 24 km (15 miles) from the open sea. The broad mile-
long quay and the elegant Mall converge on Reginald's Tower which marks the northeast
angle of the walls that enclosed both the Norse and Anglo-Norman settlements.

Newry, Greenore, Dundalk, Rosslare, Limerick, Galway, Westport, Ballina
and Sligo. Like the country towns, therefore, major ports tend to grow even
larger and in turn generate a wider range of manufacturing and service enterprises, employment opportunities, and cultural and recreational facilities.

Although many ports and inland towns have recently acquired secondary
functions, notably as manufacturing centres, settlements which do not cater
primarily for the service and trading needs of the farming population are comparatively few in number. Many Ulster market towns owe their emergence as
manufacturing centres to the centripetal forces of the industrial revolution
which gathered scattered country folk into new textile mills located on nearby

streams. The subsequent application of steam power first to spinning and then to weaving, the increased migration of domestic weavers into town factories after the famine, and the expanding railway network which could carry large quantities of coal and manufactured goods to and from the inland towns all stimulated further urban growth. By 1900 Belfast contained 350,000 people; Londonderry, with its flourishing entrepôt trade and shirtmaking industry, numbered 40,000; and Ballymena, Lisburn, Lurgan and Portadown each contained over 10,000 persons. Despite recent industrial diversification, these and other Ulster towns like Banbridge, Randalstown, Dungannon and Bessbrook, together with Balbriggan, an old fishing settlement north of Dublin which the Hamiltons transformed into a cotton town in 1780, still maintain vigorous textile manufacturing functions.

The scant success of the industrial revolution elsewhere meant that few towns outside east Ulster had an opportunity to broaden their functional bases

62. Belfast

A major seaport, commercial and industrial centre at the head of Belfast Lough. The rectilinear Georgian development around Donegall Square is highlighted in the foreground. Most of the industrial land, including the important shipyards, engineering works and docks, to the north and east of the railway lies on ground reclaimed from the estuary.

during the nineteenth century. Neither the canals nor the railways brought new industries to enliven the country towns while the few industrial villages that arose were commonly shortlived. The railway system was built to serve established centres of population but, as many towns have declined more or less continuously over the past 120 years, most railway lines had little chance to generate significant traffic before their role was usurped by road transport. Although Dundalk and even distant Claremorris did acquire certain railway functions for a period, major railway towns like England's Swindon or Crewe are unknown in Ireland. Even main-line junctions like Limerick Junction in Tipperary have never attracted much settlement while railway engineering is now confined to a few major regional centres. On the other hand, the railways did stimulate the rapid growth of many seaside resorts. Because wealthier folk had begun visiting the seaside for pleasure during the eighteenth century, most of Ireland's resorts were already well furnished with lodging houses and bathing machines before the railway era, but the railways subsequently placed the seaside within reach of all sections of society. New hotels were built, often by railway companies, and in the summer months these towns were a hive of activity. Resorts like Bangor, Malahide, Bray, Greystones, Tramore, Cobh, Monkstown and Crosshaven have since broadened into residential satellites for their nearby cities and have attracted a large proportion of retired people. Bangor, Bray, Cobh and Buncrana have acquired new industries while Portrush maintains its port activities. Other resorts like Newcastle, Bundoran, Kilkee and Ballybunion, now deprived of their rail links, remain narrowly dependent on tourism.

Apart from decaying service centres and defunct seaports, Ireland contains other towns which have lost their once distinguishing roles. Some of these have acquired new functions: the Ulster plantation port of Donaghadee, having relinquished its cross-channel port role to Larne and Belfast, has become a manufacturing and residential town; Newbridge, which originated with the erection of extensive cavalry barracks in 1816, has avoided the social and economic decay which beset other garrison towns after British forces departed in 1921 by acquiring new manufacturing industries; Youghal, despite a defunct port and market and withering retail and wholesale services, is also finding new prosperity as a manufacturing town; and Rush lost its fishing fleet, to be revived by market gardening. Other towns have also acquired new functions but have been unable to arrest urban decay: despite the replacement of the former British garrison centre at Templemore – enshrined in the song 'It's a long way to Tipperary' – with a police training college, the town's population continues to fluctuate; despite its expanding industrial and residential functions, Cobh's population is still several thousand lower than in the days when it flourished as an elegant seaside resort, bustling transatlantic port and major British naval base; and Castletownbere, which grew up in 1813 to serve the copper mines at nearby Allihies but later came to depend on commercial fishing and still later on

63. *Templemore, County Tipperary*
A town designed and fostered by the Carden family during the landlord era. The former British infantry barracks in the foreground is now a police training college.

the nearby British fleet anchorage, now operates once again as a fishing port. Finally, there are several neglected towns which have lost their principal functions but have yet to find another successful role, other than as ill-equipped service centres: the defunct port of Kinsale has seen its population fall from 6,404 in 1870 to 1,748 in 1966; Fermoy, built in 1791 and formerly a British garrison centre whose extensive barracks once housed 3,000 troops, likewise saw its population dwindle from 6,863 in 1911 to 3,667 in 1961, but is now beginning to revive; Swanlinbar owes its origin to mining and metal-working, later became a spa but is now a small Border village; Lisdoonvarna is a melancholy reminder of a gentler age when the sick came from far afield to seek cures from its spa waters and when farmers flocked to the renowned 'marriage market' after the harvest in search of a wife; Stratford-on-Slaney, whose now dismantled textile mills employed 1,000 workers in 1830, is now barely a hamlet. While these settlements do not yet qualify as 'ghost towns', the large number of part-empty towns throughout the country suggests that Ireland now, in the motor age, has more service centres than its population merits, particularly as these centres formerly expanded to serve a population twice that of today.

'Townhood' and urban hierarchy

In Ireland the physical distinction between town and country is easily recognized because most town limits are quite abrupt and only around Dublin and Belfast is there any kind of urban-rural continuum. Even Dublin was until recently a compact city giving suddenly on to green countryside, but this stark transition is now confined to its western limits. On the other hand, it is very difficult to distinguish between towns and villages on a statistical basis. The Republic's census enumerators are currently instructed to define a town as a cluster of twenty or more occupied houses. Thus many rural settlements, some containing fewer than 100 persons, are designated as towns even though they possess few if any urban functions and most of their inhabitants are directly dependent on agriculture. Such designation is clearly incompatible with the normally accepted concepts of 'townhood' and should therefore be ignored. Nevertheless, the functional bases of most Irish towns as rural service centres and the even distribution of these 'central places' suggest a close correlation between population size, townhood and urban rank, although it appears that the population qualifications for townhood in Ireland diminish from east to west and are everywhere appreciably lower than in other west European countries.

The seventy-two service centres in the Republic and the thirty-one centres in Northern Ireland with populations exceeding 2,500 in 1961 clearly qualify as reasonably well-equipped towns, many of which also serve as bus centres. By 1966 the Republic contained 104 service centres with more than 1,500 inhabitants, together comprising 49 per cent of the country's population. Throughout the south and east, where urban traditions are most firmly rooted and where long-established agricultural villages can rarely be mistaken for towns, the possession of around 1,500 inhabitants may well be a reasonable qualification for 'townhood'. Most places of this size and larger have a significant proportion of their population engaged in service occupations and offer a broad range of services comprising shops, hotels, licensed bars, banks, primary and secondary schools, professional services, garages, churches of more than one denomination, sports facilities and at least one cinema and dance hall. The majority lie astride the country's main road system which was indeed constructed to link them. Even so, despite their large and expanding non-agricultural populations, residential satellites like Greystones–Delgany (3,952), Tallaght (2,476), Lucan (2,100), Blanchardstown (1,784) and Celbridge (1,514) might well be denied townhood because, lying within easy reach of Dublin, their limited services cannot compete with the city's superior facilities and they have yet to develop as subsidiary shopping centres within a metro-

64. Clifden, County Galway
A 'landlord town' founded around 1812 by John Darcy in an attempt to provide a growth point and service centre for the scattered rural population of bleak Connemara. The Twelve Pins lie in the background.

politan framework. Rush (2,488) also lacks many basic services and a large section of its population is engaged directly in market gardening.

In contrast, western Ireland contains several settlements with populations well below 1,500 which function as towns. Many were planned during the landlord era as growth points and service centres for the scattered rural population of remote areas previously lacking towns of any description. Belmullet (694), established in 1825, serves the Mullet and Erris regions of northwest Mayo and has no nearer rival than Ballina, 40 miles to the east. Clifden (989), founded around 1812 and now the self-styled capital of Connemara, lies 50 miles west of Galway. Castletownbere (729), containing four schools, two banks, a cinema-hall and several shops, is the focal point of the Beara peninsula. The landlord town of Kenmare (1,113) and the Ulster plantation settlement of Killybegs (1,062) provide an even wider range of retail, educational and professional services and each contains an Electricity Supply Board showroom, an important measure of urban status in Ireland. No doubt the functional significance of the western towns, large and small, is enhanced by the absence of sophisticated agricultural villages from their areas. When the traditional farm clusters were broken up during the nineteenth century and kinship and family subsistence collapsed, crossroads with a chapel and general store became the local foci of country life while towns, no matter how small, became major focal points for the scattered rural population. When the rural population later dwindled, the towns maintained their functions as central places for those country folk remaining, but urban prosperity declined. Today, road transport enables country folk to shop in better-equipped service centres farther afield and, as many industrial promotions are not meeting with unqualified success, most smaller western towns are coming to depend increasingly on the uncertain and markedly seasonal tourist trade.

Recognition of 'townhood' leads naturally to a discussion of the status of these towns within an urban hierarchy or, put another way, of the relative importance of these 'central places' as revealed by the extent of their trade areas and other criteria of influence. Clearly, population alone provides no real indication of status for most centres achieve importance within a regional environment rather than a national framework. For example, Sligo (13,424) is undoubtedly more important to the northwest, where service centres are fewer and farther between, than Waterford (29,842) is to the southeast with its closer mesh of competing centres. Belfast's dominance over industrial east Ulster restricts the functional significance of many nearby towns with quite large populations, producing a situation analogous to a British industrial region. Nevertheless, the largest cities – Belfast and Dublin – are incontestably supreme in the hierarchies of their respective states. Each has generated several subsidiary shopping centres within the extensive residential zones that surround their highly specialized commercial cores. These subsidiary centres, catering for the immediate daily needs of the suburban population, are frequently similar in functions and appearance, having been profitably colonized by chain stores, banks and cinemas. Belfast County Borough (415,856 in 1961) contains almost 30 per cent of Northern Ireland's population while a further 25 per cent live within 20 miles of the city, many in major satellites like Newtownabbey (37,448) and Bangor (23,862). Londonderry (53,762) is the only major regional centre beyond Belfast but several smaller towns like Newry (12,429), Coleraine (11,901), Omagh (8,109) and Enniskillen (7,406) possess sub-regional significance.

In the Republic, the surviving pre-industrial order produces a simpler urban hierarchy, at least in a regional context. Dublin County Borough (650,153 in 1966) dominates the social, economic and political life of the whole country and is the focus of a metropolitan sprawl which includes Dun Laoghaire (84,814) and Bray (13,668), embraces well over one-quarter of the Republic's population, and is currently expanding at a rapid rate. Cork (125,283), Limerick (58,082), Galway (26,295), Sligo and perhaps Waterford are outstanding regional centres although, unlike the major focal points of provincial life in Britain, none is associated with a conurbation. Lower in the hierarchy are important sub-regional centres like Wexford (12,744), Kilkenny (12,030), Clonmel (11,457) and Carlow (9,765) in southeast Ireland, Dundalk (21,678) and Drogheda (17,908) in the northeast, Athlone (10,987), Mullingar (7,943), Thurles

(6,949) and Tullamore (6,874) in the midlands, and Castlebar (5,629), Ennis (9,181), Tralee (11,976) and even Skibbereen (2,028) in the west. Most regional and sub-regional centres publish a weekly newspaper, an important criterion of urban status, and also function as administrative centres for their counties. In fact, only a few county towns are not the largest service centres in their counties. This pre-industrial order contrasts well with east Ulster where the administrative centres of Downpatrick and Armagh are appreciably smaller than the largest towns in their counties. Significantly, there is no one major regional centre for the midlands, a reminder perhaps of the political fragmentation, difficult communications and general insecurity that hindered urban development in central Ireland until the eighteenth century. During the medieval period, for example, the colonial farming population soon gravitated back towards the peripheral seaports in search of markets, services and protection. Lower still in the hierarchy lie the numerous small towns. Some, like Loughrea and Newbridge which no longer depend solely on the farming population, are flourishing, but many are stagnating. Others, like Castleblayney, Clones and Ballyshannon for whom the Border is hardly an asset, are declining as service centres.

Townscapes

Town plans
Whatever their origins, the plans of most Irish towns have proved to be remarkably durable features which, once laid out, have persisted into the present to reveal much about the phased growth of their related townscapes. Even the widespread renewal of town fabric during the later eighteenth and nineteenth centuries did not erase pre-existing street patterns. Instead, Georgian buildings were either fitted into surviving medieval or plantation frameworks or constructed along the new rectilinear street grids that arose, either as planned extensions to existing settlements or as the centrepieces of new landlord towns. In the larger towns, distinct medieval or plantation cores surrounded by Georgian and Victorian sectors may be clearly recognized, notably because contemporary urban renewal has yet to make much impact on their townscapes. In terms of area covered, however, most cities are dominated by Georgian or, in the northeast, Victorian developments, and bounded by distinctive twentieth-century housing estates. Smaller towns are commonly framed within one main design – either medieval or plantation or Georgian in origin – indicating their major period of development.

Walled towns remained a dominant feature of the urban landscape until the close of the seventeenth century, undoubtedly owing to the hostility that long existed between the townspeople and the native country folk to whom towns were instruments of conquest and alien culture. Walls and charters were sym-

65. Carrickfergus, County Antrim

Situated beneath the Antrim plateau near the entrance to Belfast Lough. Following the collapse of Anglo-Norman power over east Ulster after 1333, the powerful fortress with its four-storey keep (1180–1205) survived the medieval period as an isolated outpost of the English Crown. The nearby town was revived and walled in the early seventeenth century and acquired distinctive English, Irish and Scottish quarters. Today the vast Courtaulds textile plant dominates the neighbourhood.

bols of the physical and cultural separateness of the towns and their burgess communities. Walls rarely conformed to any set pattern and usually adjusted to local slope and drainage conditions, elements of which were brought into the defensive framework. The area contained by the walls was small – barely half a mile separated medieval Dublin's east and west gates, Cork's long axis between the north and south gates measured only 720 yards, and plantation Bandon covered only 27 acres. Consequently, while defence remained high on the list of civic priorities, population growth crammed more and more dwellings into intimate networks of streets and passages. When the need for security diminished and town walls were dismantled during the eighteenth century, considerable urban expansion ensued. For instance, when Limerick ceased to be designated a fortress in 1760, the dismantling of the walls and seventeen great gates around the English and Irish towns began immediately; new quays, warehouses, malls and public buildings arose along the Abbey river between the two sectors and, between 1767 and 1769, the broad streets of fashionable Newtown Pery were laid out. Today most town walls have vanished but the narrow, irregular streets of many medieval towns and the more orderly compactness of the plantation settlements still stand in contrast to the broad street grids and formal squares of the Georgian era and the dramatic developments of more recent times.

Wexford, Enniscorthy, Waterford, Youghal, Carrick-on-Suir, Callan, Kilkenny, Athlone, Athenry and several other early towns still maintain central business districts which are basically medieval in plan. Frequently, the main street widens to provide space for a market but, in common with the principal side streets, constricts where the old town gates once stood. The six gates that formerly gave access to Naas are each reflected in street sections appreciably narrower than the present main street. In Fethard, where the town walls largely survive, the situation is similar. Armagh, which inherited the site of its episcopalian cathedral from the framework of an early Christian monastic settlement, owes the location of its market square, the curving lines of English, Castle and Callan streets, and the radiating Scotch and Irish streets to medieval developments. In contrast, Cork's medieval main street has yielded to a newer central business area built over the Lee marshes and distributaries east of the old walls during the eighteenth century. In Dublin and Limerick, the gravitation of their commercial functions into more spacious eighteenth-century sectors has been even more pronounced but, despite later modifications, their fossil medieval cores may still be recognized from the tighter, less organized mesh of narrow streets, and from fabric remnants. Although most fabric is usually of much later date, the houses of many old towns retain narrow frontages to the street and are backed by long narrow plots, reflecting often the typical burgage strips of medieval and plantation settlements.

During the plantation era, formal town planning became more apparent, but the continued need for walls still confined urban growth. Plantation towns were often dominated by the castle and bawn of the grantee or by a market house, but these buildings have mostly perished. On the other hand, the central market square or 'diamond' with which these towns were commonly provided has proved much more durable and good examples survive in Coleraine, Londonderry, Donegal and Clones. Londonderry, whose walls measure over one mile around and average 20 feet in height, is certainly the most complete example of a walled town remaining in the British Isles. Within the walls, four main streets lead from the four gates to converge at right angles on The Diamond, the central square where the Town House once stood and which is still the focus of the central business district. In contrast, Belfast's commercial core has largely forsaken the old plantation town for the more spacious Georgian sector focusing

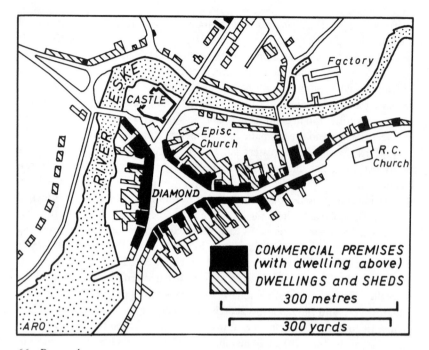

66. *Donegal town*
An early seventeenth-century Plantation settlement in west Ulster as it appears today.
Note the location of the Episcopalian and Roman Catholic churches. See also Fig. 29.

upon Donegall Place and Donegall Square. The seventeenth century also provided additions to several earlier townscapes: Carrickfergus acquired stone
walls, whose line can still be traced around the town, together with Scottish and
Irish quarters; congestion stemming from Armagh's remarkable growth
between 1615 and 1767 was eased by the planned construction of Thomas, Ogle
and Navan streets and later by the tasteful Georgian housing around the Mall;
while Dublin and Cork still retain the ground plans of sectors built beyond
the walls during the century. Elsewhere, the turmoil and uncertainty of the
period often inhibited urban growth. Several plantation settlements were short-
lived or even stillborn, while contemporary features in other towns, old or new,
rarely escaped Georgian reconstruction.

During the later eighteenth and earlier nineteenth centuries, formal town
planning reached its zenith. Urban growth was no longer constricted by the
need for protective walls and their demolition was the signal for major ventures
in design under the patronage of improving landlords. Existing towns like
Dublin, Waterford, Dungarvan, Cork, Limerick, Newry, Belfast and Newtownards were each given planned extensions. The broad, regular streets,

67 Cookstown, County Tyrone

One of the most remarkable essays in town planning ever to be imposed on the Irish landscape. The original settlement founded by planter Alan Cook in 1609 lay towards the far end of the main street. This magnificent main street, 1¼ miles long, 130 feet wide and flanked by 400-foot-deep burgage strips, was largely developed by William Stewart, the then proprietor of the town, around 1750. The building fabric in the foreground is mostly of twentieth-century origin.

elegant squares and treelined malls of this period provide many large towns with sectors of distinctive character. Meanwhile, many smaller towns were radically redesigned and some quite new service centres were born. Consistent with their trading functions in an expanding rural economy, these towns were given ample

213

space for their markets in the form of either a remarkably wide main street or a central open space, furnished often with a classical court or market house. In their many varieties, these market spaces still dominate the morphology of many country towns. Templemore possesses an exceptionally wide main street in the middle of which stands a rather forlorn market house. The planter settlement at Cookstown is now aligned along a magnificent main street, $1\frac{1}{4}$ miles long, 130 feet wide and flanked by 400-foot-deep burgage strips, added to the old town by William Stewart around 1750. Strokestown in Roscommon epitomizes the landlord town – the noble entrance to the demesne lies at the lower end of a 147-foot-wide, treelined main street and the episcopalian church lies at the upper end. Wide main streets are also well displayed in Castleisland, Maynooth and Moate. The classical market square is beautifully developed in Dungarvan but variations include its placing to one side of the main street in Mitchelstown and at one end of the main street, outside the demesne, in Castleblayney and Antrim. Other central open spaces include well-proportioned triangles at Castlepollard and Mountrath, and an octagon in Westport. Kenmare's X street-plan provides for a market place on the northwest limb and a green between this and the northeast limb. This plan reflects a memorandum sent by Kenmare's

68. *Kenmare and Moville*

Two small market centres nurtured during the landlord era. Sir William Petty established English colonists at Kenmare in 1670 but the present town was largely developed by his descendant, the 1st marquis of Lansdowne (1737–1805), in the years after 1775. During the following century, Moville expanded into a fashionable resort and, as a port of call for transatlantic liners until 1939, also became a focus for emigrants leaving the north of Ireland.

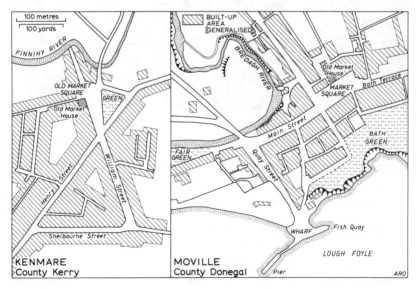

former landlord, the 1st marquis of Lansdowne, to his agent in 1775 which directed that 'the town may be begun by laying out two capital streets 50 feet wide, at right angles'. The industrial settlement which the Malcomsons created at Portlaw in Waterford around 1830 still retains its unique web of five streets converging upon the square and short factory road. Finally, Birr is a landlord-designed town whose wealth of Georgian planning features includes a neat central square, a broad Green, and a Mall with the episcopalian church at one end and the demesne entrance at the other.

The hundred years that followed the Georgian era were renowned neither for the quality nor, outside industrial Ulster, for the quantity of their urban developments. In the north, the industrial revolution packed much mean two-storey terrace housing into drab repetitive streets between factories and mills, notably in Belfast. Later, when tramways brought greater mobility to the growing middle-class populations of the larger Irish towns, the urban mesh sprawled along main roads and engulfed nearby settlements. Intervening suburban spaces were gradually infilled with street grids which had quite lost the corporate elegance of Georgian planning. Not until the planning legislation of the mid-twentieth century were these land-hungry sprawls channelled along more rational lines. One reaction to the errors of the past has seen the enforced segregation of industry from housing. New industries are now commonly restricted to certain localities, such as the planned industrial estates outside Belfast and Waterford, while suburban housing is set tastefully among squares, crescents and avenues garnished with trees and lawns.

Fabric

Owing to the wide extent of Carboniferous Limestone and glacial deposits in Ireland, the country lacks the rich variety of accessible building stones that contribute so much to the regional individuality of field walls, farmsteads, villages and towns in England. Furthermore, by the time the tumult of the medieval and plantation periods had subsided and war-torn towns awaited reconstruction and expansion, bricks were coming into general use. The widespread use of bricks, plaster and roughcast in buildings since the seventeenth century has imposed a certain anonymity on most Irish towns which the addition of concrete and glass to steel-framed structures in recent years has done little to relieve. While many towns may have inherited quite evocative groundplans, therefore, their fabric is generally dull and uninspiring. Even where local stone has been used, it is often crudely hewn and lies ashamedly hidden beneath stucco. Here and there, however, the monotony is relieved by a house or public building constructed of naked local stone. Dublin achieves a certain charm from the granite and limestone used for its monumental, as distinct from its domestic, buildings. Limestone buildings are found in Cork, Limerick and even quite small towns like Kenmare, while Kilkenny owes its marble character to the wide use of polished shelly limestone. Local Carboniferous slate hangs on the walls of many houses in Kinsale, Bantry and Skibbereen. In the geologically more varied north, essays in texture and colour result from the use of granite in Newry, Kilkeel and Newcastle, of warm Triassic sandstone in the Newtownards district, of marbled limestone in Armagh, of Carboniferous sandstone in Dungannon and Draperstown, and of other localized rocks. Eighteenth- and nineteenth-century warehouses, mills and cornstores are nearly everywhere built of unconcealed local stone, but, like the domestic houses of the period, are often roofed with imported Welsh slates.

Owing to the Georgian building boom and the sporadic turbulence of preceding centuries, very little fabric in Irish towns is more than 200 years old. Medieval remnants are generally confined to churches and to pieces of monasteries, castles, fortified town houses, walls and gates, all stone-built because the timber and timber-framed dwellings have long since perished. Athenry not only retains its medieval plan but possesses tolerably well-preserved walls, a gate, a small castle and a friary. Gates at Kilmallock and Drogheda and the walls around Youghal also linger on, mainly because they were in constant use and repair until after 1690. Among the finest pieces of medieval military architecture to survive are the castles at Carrickfergus and Trim and the shell to King John's castle in Limerick. Some ecclesiastic buildings, like the now Protestant cathedrals in Dublin, Kilkenny and Limerick, survived the Reformation and its aftermath reasonably intact, but the churches and monasteries of most smaller towns were less fortunate. The timber-framed and brick buildings of the plantation era have largely vanished, as also have the seventeenth-century Flemish-style houses of ports like Limerick and Youghal.

Because social and economic conditions largely inhibited town growth outside industrial Ulster after 1850, Georgian fabric makes a striking contribution to many existing townscapes. During the landlord era architectural taste was influenced by the publication of design folios and builders' guides which effectively restrained creative eccentricity and imposed a classical uniformity on evolving townscapes. Architects of large buildings sought inspiration from Italy and, later, from Greece and often gave their works great stone columns and pediments. Many surviving town halls, churches, court houses, hospitals, customs houses and private mansions bear witness to their ability. The more restrained domestic architecture of the period, stemming directly from the Anglo-Dutch tradition instituted by Wren in England, is beautifully expressed in the four-storey Georgian terrace blocks of Dublin and Limerick. Each red, pink or yellow brick-faced house, restrained outside to the point of anonymity but decorated inside with ornate plasterwork and marble overmantels, gains its visual effect not as an individual but as a member of a formal terrace. These commanding buildings, now often worn and tattered, are fitting monuments to the Anglo-Irish ascendancy, the favoured minority of eighteenth-century Ire-

69. Dublin looking northeast
The lower part of the photograph is dominated by the rectilinear street grids, superb
public buildings, four-storey red brick houses and elegant squares of the Georgian city.
The well-wooded St Stephen's Green was laid out initially in 1664–5. Merrion Square
farther northeast was laid out in 1762 for the Fitzwilliam estate, and the buildings and
parks of Trinity College (1591) were reconstructed on a grand scale after 1700. The
industrial and port facilities lying north and east of the main railway line are built almost
entirely on ground reclaimed piecemeal from the Liffey sloblands since the North Wall
was first extended seawards in 1714.

land. The beautiful red facing bricks which are so common in Dublin's Georgian
buildings are Bridgwater bricks from Somerset, brought in as ballast by ships
plying on the Bristol trade. Grey stock bricks were produced locally (Craig,
1952). Because the country was little influenced by the industrial revolution
which released so many bizarre currents of taste in England, eighteenth-
century classicism continued to mould the façades of many churches, hospitals,
banks, railway stations and new residential areas into the mid-nineteenth century. In the conservative country towns, stone or brick houses of debased

Georgian simplicity, often faced with stucco, persisted even longer, imposing a dismal monotony on existing townscapes which garish paint hardly relieves.

In other respects, the nineteenth century saw many changes. Dwindling urban prosperity, the centrifugal movement of wealthier people into expanding suburbs and the centripetal movement of the poor in the larger towns soon relegated many formerly elegant residences to the status of overcrowded tenements. The migration of poor country folk into all towns during the 1820s and 1830s gave birth to squalid rows of single-storey thatched dwellings built end to end along suburban streets. These mud and rubble dwellings, their thatch commonly replaced with slates, still survive in many towns. Similar migration into the expanding mills and factories of the north produced a spate of industrial housing whose quality, at least initially, was no better. Fortunately, this gloomy scene was relieved by several beneficial changes. Thatch gave way to slate and rubble yielded to brick as bulk transport by rail and canal ended regional contrasts in the use of building materials. Whereas Cavan had almost no slated dwellings in 1820 and two-thirds of Enniskillen's houses were still thatched in 1845, bye-laws have since largely removed thatch from the urban scene. Street lighting, sewerage schemes, piped water supplies and playing fields were also introduced, at least to the larger towns. With the establishment of religious freedom, numerous Roman Catholic and Nonconformist chapels sprang up on available urban sites, usually on the edge of the built-up area. Railway stations likewise arose on town outskirts or, where landlords objected to railways passing across their lands, some distance from the towns.

During the present century slate has yielded to tile and stucco has given way to roughcast. More recently steel, concrete, aluminium and glass have provided the basis for a new approach to building design. In the larger towns problems of overcrowding have been met by the planned development of suburban housing estates and by the erection of modern flats on slum clearance sites, usually by local authorities but sometimes by philanthropic bodies like the Iveagh Trust. Dublin inherited an appalling slum problem from the nineteenth century and, as late as 1938, Georgian tenements near the city centre averaged eighteen persons to a house. This situation was eased by the council housing estates built at Ballyfermot, Cabra, Crumlin and elsewhere, but, despite a rapid rate of demolition and reconstruction in the central areas, many squalid wastes remain to be tidied. The older parts of Limerick, Kilkenny, Youghal, Kinsale and many other towns are also riddled with blight and dereliction. Despite new council projects and much renewal, one-quarter of the houses in the Republic are over 100 years old and over half were built before 1918. With such figures in mind, the National Building Agency is now stimulating the building boom by providing 3,600 dwellings at Ballymun outside Dublin and a further 2,000 dwellings in Cork. In Northern Ireland, where a quarter of all houses built since 1945 have been provided by the Housing Trust, there remains a backlog of

40,000 houses totally unfit for habitation. As the towns grow, so the demand for water for domestic and industrial uses grows and, through the provision of large water-supply reservoirs such as those in the Wicklow and Mourne mountains, urban populations consciously impose new changes on distant rural landscapes.

Chapter 13
The industrial landscape

Despite successful attempts by both governments to attract new industries to Ireland in recent years, industrial landscapes remain few and far between. The industrial revolution of the nineteenth century created nothing comparable with the industrial and urban sprawls that engulfed most British coalfields. Ireland's rural coalfields generated no equivalent of the Black Country's 'black by day and red by night' landscape, no desolate waste like the lower Swansea valley, and no jungle of collieries, factories and industrial slums entwined within a complex railway network as in northern England. The industrial revolution remained an intrusive element in an agricultural country and did not spread far beyond its footholds in east Ulster. Even the textile mills around Belfast were less dark, less satanic than their English counterparts, while the factories that arose in outlying towns and villages were often built of local stone like the houses around them and soon blended with their surroundings.

More recently, the creation of new industrial estates, the continuing growth of port industries, diversification among the agricultural industries and the expansion of various extractive enterprises have made noteworthy contributions to the changing scene but their impact on the landscape remains localized. The provision of electricity throughout Ireland has added power stations, pylons and high-voltage cables to the countryside and has made industry more foot-loose in respect of power requirements. In the Republic, the hungry appetite of the peat-fired power stations introduced since 1950 has radically altered the face of the bogs, while hydroelectric power stations are making good use of the country's ample water resources. Developments over the past twenty years have imposed several miniature industrial landscapes on Ireland, the impact of which may be locally quite startling where new factories have been set amid rural surroundings.

Extractive industry

Mining and quarrying
Extractive industries have played a far greater role in eroding the Irish landscape over the past twenty years than during any previous period. The exploitation of limestone, chalk, sand, gravel, clay and igneous rock, mainly for building materials and road metal, and the recovery of peat for power generation and

household use have been the main processes involved. The countryside has become pock-marked with limestone quarries, gravel pits and cutaway bogs which have raised in turn serious problems of reclamation and land use. Clay pits and opencast mines are less common but likewise offer little hope of concealment where they do occur. From the amenity viewpoint, however, Ireland's lack of extensive coal and iron-ore reserves has at least spared the countryside the devastation that has frequently accompanied their extraction elsewhere.

The history of metalliferous mining in Ireland goes back nearly 4,000 years, to when Early Bronze Age folk first sought copper in west Cork and Kerry. Later centuries saw the sporadic development of mining and metal-working at many sites scattered through the countryside, but the impact of these early ventures has been blurred by subsequent events. During the seventeenth century, when the avid demands of the expanding charcoal-iron industry hastened the destruction of the last native woodlands, mining's influence on the landscape became more apparent. The eighteenth and nineteenth centuries saw numerous mining enterprises flourish and, as technological advances replaced old shallow workings with deeper, more extensive mines, the output of copper, lead, zinc, pyrites and manganese reached unprecedented peaks between 1830 and 1880. The legacy of derelict engine houses, mining waste, old shafts and ruined miners' cottages that may still be seen at several scattered localities is a reminder of this activity. The old adits, mining waste and ruined buildings in Glendasan, Glendalough and Glenmalure recall the pre-eminence of their lead-mines at a time when lead was being mined, commonly with zinc and silver, at over 150 sites throughout Ireland. The picturesque chimney and nearby riddling and 'poison' houses of the Ballycorus lead works, where smelting operations used Wicklow lead for nearly a century, are familiar landmarks southeast of Dublin. The nineteenth-century copper-mines in the Vale of Avoca, along the east Waterford coast and around the mining village of Allihies in west Cork have left a melancholy collection of abandoned shafts, ruined engine houses and old mine cottages. Place-names like Silvermines in Tipperary, Gold Mines valley in south Wicklow and Swanlinbar in west Cavan – named after four miners who once produced iron on nearby Cuilcagh for the furnaces and forging mills around which the village arose – are similarly evocative. By 1880 many mines had become exhausted or had met geological situations too complex for their technical and financial resources, but the majority ceased production around this time because, with cheaper overseas minerals flooding on to world markets, falling prices had rendered them uneconomic. The next seventy years saw comparatively little mining activity, although lateritic iron ore and bauxite in northeast Ireland, copper at Allihies and Beauparc, and barytes in west Cork were among minerals worked on and off well into the present century.

Since 1940, the government of the Republic has done much to revive interest

70. *The Allihies copper mining landscape at the western end of the Beara peninsula, West Cork*

in the country's mineral resources by removing complications related to mineral rights and land ownership, by providing tax concessions to new mining enterprises, and by giving grants and technical aid to private prospecting. Sophisticated geophysical prospecting and geochemical sampling techniques have revealed the true extent and nature of previously little-known deposits, while advances in mining and concentration methods have encouraged the re-examination of ore bodies previously abandoned as unprofitable. The shortage of sulphur during the 1940s led to renewed mining for pyrites at Avoca, which in turn revealed several million tons of low-grade copper ore. Production of copper concentrates from this deposit began in 1958 and, despite its subsequent erratic history, this enterprise soon added to the devastation in the Vale of Avoca. Meanwhile, high base-metal prices during the Korean war brought three old lead-zinc mines at Glendasan, Silvermines and Abbeytown into temporary production during the 1950s. These events stimulated further exploration, notably in the west-central lowlands, which has culminated so far in the discovery of excellent lead–zinc–silver ores at Tynagh in east Galway, Silvermines and Gortrum in Tipperary, and Keel in Longford. Copper also occurs at Tynagh and Gortrum. Opened in 1965, the half-mile-long Tynagh opencast pit will reach an ultimate depth of 340 feet. Apart from opencast pits, mine shafts, site concentrators and mining waste, these activities are having wider repercussions: the Tynagh development has revitalized the nearby town of Loughrea and generated new storage and handling facilities for its concentrates at the port of Galway; Silvermines has also revived and its concentrates are sent by rail to a new jetty at Foynes, 45 miles away on the Shannon estuary.

Ireland's thin impersistent coal seams have been worked commercially for between 250 and 350 years but the small scale of these operations has made little impression on the landscape, save quite locally, and most of the country's needs have always been imported. The coalfields have remained largely rural and miners have commonly grown crops and reared livestock in their spare time. Even today, the small anthracite fields near Castlecomer and Ballingarry and the bleak semi-bituminous coalfield near Arigna recapture something of the atmosphere of the British coalfields before the industrial revolution. Barren shales underlie poor, rush-infested pastures, scattered mine workings are partly concealed by trees and hedgerows, and mine cottages blend with their rural surroundings. The distinctive personality of the rather isolated Castlecomer plateau expresses more than three centuries of mining and agricultural activity in an indifferent physical environment. Abandoned adits near the plateau edge, recent shafts, spoil heaps and opencast pits nearer the centre, miners' cottages at Clogh, the estate village at Castlecomer planned by the colliery-owning Wandesfords, and settlements with exotic names like Moscow, Bilboa, Gazebo and Crettyard all contribute to this personality. Around remote Lough Allen in east Connacht, derelict adits, mining waste and ruined ironworks recall former industrial activity, but sufficient coal is still mined to feed the small Arigna power station and other outlets. Between 1720 and 1833, mining of the badly faulted bituminous coal seams beneath Antrim's northeast tip stimulated urban and industrial growth in nearby Ballycastle. As the mines were gradually exhausted, Ballycastle achieved new prominence as a small tourist centre. In contrast, the Coalisland district in east Tyrone still maintains a tradition of extractive industry dating back to the early eighteenth century. At that time, coal-mining encouraged the growth of the settlement and the provision of a canal from Lough Neagh in 1787. Coal power and canal transport in turn attracted cotton and linen factories to the town during the nineteenth century and one of these, dating from 1868, still produces linen cloth. As late as 1924, the Annagher collieries were opened with an immigrant labour force of 200 Scottish and Cumberland miners in a renewed but shortlived attempt to mine coal. In recent years, a few thousand tons of coal have been produced annually in conjunction with fireclays from a single deep mine. Another mineral whose extraction is strongly localized is the gypsum deposit at Kingscourt in Cavan, which feeds a local plasterboard industry and a substantial export trade. Silica clays at Cloyne in southeast Cork and barytes near Sligo have been worked on and off since 1937 and 1942 respectively.

In contrast, few parts of the countryside lack pockets of devastation resulting

71. *Sand and gravel workings in the terminal moraine of the last glaciation near Blessington, County Wicklow*

In the middle distance lies Blessington, a broad single-street village laid out in the 1670s by Michael Boyle, Protestant Archbishop of Dublin, who also built the conspicuous parish church in 1682. Blessington was incorporated as a borough between 1669 and 1800. The village was rebuilt by the marquess of Downshire after the destruction wrought by the 1798 rebellion. Between the village and the Wicklow mountains lies the large water supply reservoir serving Dublin and the Pollaphuca hydro-electric station.

from the surface working of commoner minerals. Limestone is widely quarried for cement and agricultural lime; the large quarries supplying the conspicuous cement works on the Boyne estuary below Drogheda and at Mungret near Limerick are notable expressions of this activity. In northeast Ireland chalk quarries have much the same purpose and effect, notably at Magheramorne near Larne. Sand and gravel pits are even more widespread and where the thicker moraines of the last glaciation have been worked extensively, as at Killumney west of Cork city, near Blessington and Enniskerry in north Wicklow, and west of Lough Gill in Sligo, the devastated landscape has assumed lunar characteristics. In face of current heavy demands for building materials in Ireland, the country's vast limestone, sand and gravel resources more than compensate for

the paucity of good brickclays, although extraction of the latter is locally significant at Kingscourt and in the northeast. Gravels, together with basalt and
dolerite chips from several impressive quarries, also cater for the needs of road
construction and repair. Quarries for building and ornamental stone and roofing
slate are largely relics of the past, but some granite is still worked in the Wicklow
and Mourne mountains while the serpentine marble quarries in Connemara
are noteworthy. Finally, mention should be made of the remarkable transformation that the extraction of fireclays, brickclays, sands and gravels by
large-scale opencast methods has brought to the Coalisland landscape over the
past thirty years. Not only have these workings devoured large areas of country,
but allied manufacturing industries have remodelled the skyline. The fireclay
works, which date back to 1890 and today manufacture glazed pipes for the
building industry and duct pipes for telephone cables, are dominated by their
nineteen beehive kilns and several tall chimneys; the extensive brickworks,
dating from 1939, contribute more chimneys and buildings.

Peat production

Ever since nature, possibly with the unconscious help of man, created the bogs
of Ireland, man has been consciously destroying them. Handwon peat or turf
has long formed the traditional fuel of a large part of the population. Until
recently, this peat was harvested almost exclusively by farmers for their own
domestic uses and turbary rights were an important item in tenancy agreements.
Even today 2 million tons of handwon peat are produced annually in the Republic and the allocation of turbary plots and rights is a continuing activity of the
Land Commission. Over the past 250 years, however, much thought and effort
have been directed to the problem of making better use of the bogs. At first the
solution was thought to lie in drainage and reclamation to render them fit for
agriculture, but during the nineteenth century their commercial exploitation as a
source of fuel and power came more and more to be discussed and, indeed, in a
few instances this was seriously attempted. Reclamation rarely passed beyond
the discussion stage and early efforts at producing peat commercially all ended
in frustration and failure.

In the 1930s, peat production entered a new dramatic phase and over the
past forty years the deeper raised bogs of Offaly, Laois, Kildare, Westmeath and
Longford in particular have diminished rapidly under the onslaught of man and
machines. The state-directed Turf Development Board, created in 1934,
stimulated machine turf (sod peat) production and soon launched into the production of milled peat for the briquette factory that it acquired at Lullymore in
Kildare in 1940. In 1946, the state-sponsored *Bord na Mona* was established to
produce and market peat and peat products in the open market, its aim being
to earn enough revenue to meet expenditure. Its first programme had three
objectives: to produce 1 million tons of sod peat annually for use in electricity

225

72. Derrygreenagh milled peat bog, County Westmeath
This *Bord na Mona* operation involves 4,800 km (3,000 miles) of drains and 128 km (80 miles) of narrow-gauge railway. The four harvesting machines in the foreground are gathering ridges of wind-dried milled peat into one large storage rick.

generating stations, factories and homes; to manufacture 20,000 tons of peat briquettes annually at Lullymore for industrial and household use; and to produce 50,000 bales of peat moss annually at Kilberry in Kildare for use as a soil conditioner in horticulture and as bedding material for livestock, thereby utilizing the light *Sphagnum* peat which forms the upper layers of many midland bogs. These objectives would clearly lessen Ireland's dependence upon imported fuels, provide work in country districts to combat emigration and, through reclamation of the cutaway bogs, eventually increase the area of improved land. Suitable bogs were thus drained and mechanized production began. Three sod peat power stations were commissioned at Portarlington (37·5 MW, 1950), Allenwood (40 MW, 1951) and Lanesborough (20 MW, 1958), which now devour 545,000 tons of sod peat annually. Increasing consumption of electricity soon led *Bord na Mona* to expand its activities in order to produce 2 million tons of milled peat annually, the production of which, being more highly mechanized, yields a cheaper cost per unit of electricity than sod peat. Five milled peat power stations have been commissioned at Ferbane (90 MW,

1957), Rhode (80 MW, 1960), Bellacorick (40 MW, 1962), Shannonbridge (40 MW, 1965) and Lanesborough (40 MW, 1966), currently consuming 2,140,000 tons of milled peat annually. Further briquette factories have been built at Croghan and Derrinlough in Offaly, each capable of producing 135,000 tons of peat briquettes annually, while the Lullymore output has been increased to 50,000 tons per annum. The Kilberry peat moss factory now produces 400,000 bales annually and a second factory with similar capacity has been built near Portlaoise.

These events have had a devastating impact on the bogs. Prior to harvesting the moisture content of the raw peat is reduced by drainage from about 95 to 90 per cent, thereby lessening the risk of sinking for the giant excavating machines that follow. After the drained raw peat has been excavated, air drying further reduces the moisture content to 35 per cent in the sod peat process and to 55 per cent in the milled peat process. Peat can thus be harvested only in spring and summer when air drying is possible but if rainfall during the April–August period is higher than average, as it was in 1958, 1960 and 1965, then production is reduced drastically. Sod peat is cut by giant bucket dredgers or 'baggers' from vertical faces about 12 feet deep, fed into macerators, and then extruded on to attached arms for spreading on the bog surface where it is chopped into sods by cutting discs behind the spreaders. The sods then lie for three to six weeks before being dry enough to lift into small piles called wind-rows, where they remain for another one to four weeks before being collected into storage ricks protected from rewetting by polythene film. Weather permitting, two harvests are obtained each season. Mechanical windrowing caters for about 60 per cent of the crop, the remainder being harvested by hand. The milled peat process involves cutting 50-foot-wide strips of the bog surface to a depth of $\frac{3}{8}$ inch with a rotating drum fitted with small spikes. This milling machine leaves very small pieces of peat on the bog surface which are later harrowed to accelerate drying. An angle-dozer then scrapes the loose peat into small ridges which are in turn transferred by harvesting machines into storage ricks. Milled peat stockpiles need special protection against rewetting and wind erosion which, since 1961, has been provided by polythene film. The milled peat harvesting cycle, which is wholly mechanical, takes only two or three days in good weather and allows about eighteen harvests each season. A combination of the above two processes is now being developed. Peat is transported from the storage ricks on the bogs to the power stations and loading depots by light railways. Clearly, mechanization on this large scale is suited only to large, deep bogs free from obstacles. Hand labour, or at best semimechanized methods, still provides the only practicable approach to the exploitation of the shallower mountain and western bogs; donkey carts still form the vital transport link.

Bord na Mona currently employs about 5,000 permanent workers, some of whom are accommodated in eight housing schemes comprising 572 houses.

73. *A cutting machine spreading machine turf (sod peat) after it has been cut and macerated. A single cutting machine can win over 20,000 tons of turf in a four-month season.*

These occur at Coill Dubh (156 houses) near the Timahoe sod peat bogs in Kildare, at Kilcormac (104 houses) near the Boora milled peat bogs in Offaly, at Rochfortbridge (100 houses) near the Derrygreenagh milled peat bogs on the Westmeath–Offaly border, at Clontuskert (68 houses) and Lanesborough (64 houses) serving Shannonside bogs, at Bracknagh (50 houses) near Clonsast sod peat bog in Offaly, and at Derraghan (22 houses) in Longford and Ballivor (8 houses) in Meath. These settlements are tastefully laid out and consist of semi-detached single storey and two-storey terrace houses without individual front gardens but facing on to open lawns and paths maintained by *Bord na Mona*. Some, such as Kilcormac and Rochfortbridge, are attached to pre-existing villages where service and social facilities are available. Others are islands of organized housing without these facilities and only Coill Dubh, with its four shops, vaguely resembles a model village in conception. They are not integrated industrial villages in the nineteenth-century sense.

Peat is not an inexhaustible resource. The overall life expectancy of the bogs now worked by *Bord na Mona* is about thirty years and most of Ireland's deeper raised bogs will have been cut away by the year 2000. The total peat resources of the Republic are expected to last between sixty and ninety years; in Northern

Ireland, the feasibility of commercial peat production is still being studied. The problem of what to do with the Republic's cutaway areas has long occupied *Bord na Mona*, and in 1960 the Agricultural Institute took over this research. Their work has shown that cutaway, with careful fertilization and adequate shelter, is suitable for a variety of agricultural, horticultural and industrial crops, and for afforestation. An average depth of 18 inches of peat will be left on the bog floor to assist reclamation and soil-forming processes. In sod peat production, this will be an admixture of young surface peat, stripped and laid in the cutaway initially, and old decomposed peat from the base of the bog; in milled

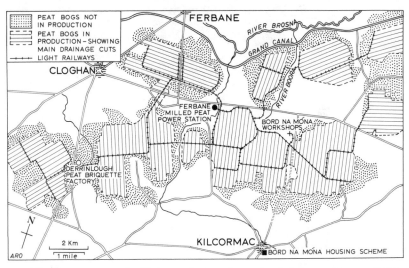

74. *The Boora group of milled-peat bogs and associated features, County Offaly*

peat production, only basal peat will be available. Those uncut blanket bogs in the west, too shallow and uneven for commercial exploitation, offer similar agricultural and afforestation possibilities after drainage, though excessive wetness and high winds may retard growth. If the blanket bogs and cutaways are eventually brought into extensive agricultural use, man will have given the landscape a truly remarkable facelift. Indeed, where he may once have triggered off peat-forming processes, his activities will have run full circle.

Manufacturing industry

Power

Both Dublin and Limerick had electricity supplies as early as 1892, but thirty years later some 300 towns and villages throughout Ireland still lacked elec-

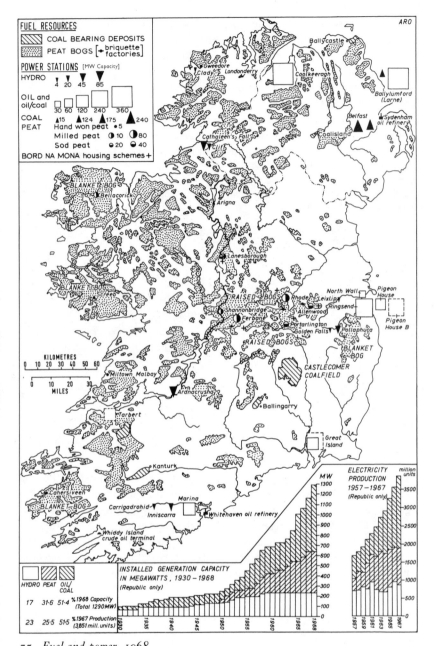

75. *Fuel and power, 1968*
(Information for the Republic based upon successive annual reports of the Electricity Supply Board, Dublin; Northern Ireland data supplied by the Joint Electricity Authority, Belfast.)

tricity of any kind, and industry was still confined to the eastern seaboard where British coal could be imported most cheaply. Cheap electrical power, preferably from native resources, was recognized to be a prime economic need by the nascent Irish Free State and a scheme for harnessing the unused energy of the Shannon was implemented in 1925. The Electricity Supply Board was created in 1927 and since its transmission grid was completed in 1960 power has been available for the spread of industry throughout the country. Motivated by a desire to provide work in the under-developed west, the government is now concerned with making industrial dispersal attractive in economic terms, for industrialists continue to favour the eastern seaboard nearest to their chief export market, Britain.

Of the total electricity produced in 1967, 23 per cent was generated by water, 25·5 per cent by peat and 51·5 per cent by coal and oil. These proportions vary from year to year according to weather conditions, although fluctuations in stream discharge and peat harvesting tend to complement each other. For two decades after commissioning in 1929, the Shannon hydro-electric scheme at Ardnacrusha (85 MW since 1934) supplied the bulk of the country's power. Eight smaller plants, commissioned between 1943 and 1959, later augmented this supply. These comprise the 65 MW Erne plant with hydrostations at Cliff and Cathaleen's Fall; the 38 MW Liffey plant with hydrostations at Pollaphuca, Golden Falls and Leixlip; the 27 MW Lee plant at Inniscarra and Carrigadrohid for which 17 miles of the beautiful Lee valley were drowned; and the 4 MW Clady plant in Donegal which uses a 190-foot fall of water supplied by canal and pipe from the Clady river. These hydro-electric stations account for about 75 per cent of the country's total water-power potential. Apart from the peat-fired power stations supplied by *Bord na Mona* whose combined capacity in 1968 was 387·5 MW, four small 5 MW stations using handwon peat occur at Cahersiveen, Miltown Malbay, Screeb and Gweedore but their output is negligible and uneconomic. The 15 MW Arigna power station, commissioned in 1958, uses 50,000 tons of native coal annually from the nearby mines. Thermal stations using imported coal and oil are located at the coast. These comprise the 90 MW Pigeon House, 48 MW North Wall and 270 MW Ringsend stations in Dublin port, within 25 miles of which 40 per cent of the national electricity output is used, and the 120 MW Marina station at Cork. The Republic's ventures in utilizing native water, peat and coal resources have nearly reached their practicable limits – comprising 50 per cent of the country's total installed capacity of 1,290 MW in 1968. As extensions to existing coal/oil plants are completed and the new oil-fired stations at Great Island (240 MW) near the Barrow–Suir confluence, Tarbert (120 MW) in the Shannon estuary, and Pigeon House B (240 MW) at Dublin are commissioned, generation from local resources will inevitably fall. Imported fuels provide cheaper electricity than the costly peat-fired stations. Northern Ireland relies wholly on imported fuels for its coal-fired power stations at Belfast East (175 MW), Belfast West (240 MW) and Ballylumford A (124 MW), and for the more recent 360 MW Coolkeeragh oil-fired station on Lough Foyle and the oil-fired Ballylumford B whose capacity will ultimately reach 960 MW.

Manufacturing landscapes old and new

East Ulster emerged from the nineteenth century as the most industrialized part of Ireland and, despite subsequent developments elsewhere, it is here that industry still makes its most striking contribution to the landscape. In 1961, one-third of Northern Ireland's employed population were engaged in manufacturing compared with only 17 per cent in the Republic. In 1964, manufactured goods accounted for three-quarters of the value of Northern Ireland's exports but for only one-quarter of the Republic's exports. Since 1921 the Border has served as a tariff barrier on either side of which industrial development has been strongly influenced by distinct political entities motivated, at least initially, by contrasting economic ideals. In recent years, however, the industrial policies pursued by the Belfast and Dublin administrations have revealed similar social and economic objectives. Both governments have obtained wide powers to attract new industries and thereby diversify their industrial structures. In order to overcome geographical isolation and lack of capital, grants and loans have been made towards the cost of factories, plant, machinery and training schemes, rate concessions have been provided and, in the Republic, valuable tax relief has been given. Northern Ireland's policy of industrial diversification stems from the need to stabilize its economy while countering chronic unemployment. The Republic looks to new industries to combat critical under-employment and emigration, notably from the underdeveloped north and west.

In 1921 the Northern Ireland industrial scene was dominated by shipbuilding and other engineering concerns, employing mainly men and concentrated in Belfast, and by a declining linen industry which employed mainly women and, although well represented in Belfast, was more widely distributed. These slump-vulnerable industries formed too narrow a base on which to maintain a stable economy during the recurrent trade depressions of the 1920s and 1930s. Unemployment became chronic, poverty and malnutrition racked working-class families, barefoot children roamed the streets of Belfast, and grass grew on the unused slipways of its shipyards. Furthermore, the Irish Free State's tariff wall crippled Londonderry's entrepôt trade and accentuated social and economic decay along the Border. By 1938 102,000 workers, or 30 per cent of the insured population, were unemployed. The establishment of an aircraft factory in Belfast in 1937 and the wartime boom in traditional industries and construction trades temporarily relieved the situation but postwar mechanization in agriculture and industry soon threatened to revive the spectre of high unemployment. The government acted immediately and, as a result of industrial development acts, capital grants, fuel subsidies and other incentives, 230 new firms employing over 60,000 workers have so far been attracted to Northern Ireland since 1945. The majority are British-owned but thirty-four are American. With its resources of skilled labour and its superior services and port facilities, Belfast continues to dominate the industrial scene and 60 per cent of these new industries lie within 20 miles of the city centre. Belfast, together with the Castlereagh factory estate, employs half the industrial population of Northern Ireland while adjacent Antrim and Down employ a further quarter. It has proved difficult to steer private industries to remoter areas of high unemployment such as Londonderry, Omagh and Newry. Unemployment in Londonderry is three times the Northern Ireland average which in recent years has fluctuated between 5 and 9 per cent, still appreciably higher than the average for the United Kingdom as a whole.

Some new industries, like the oil refinery on Belfast Lough and the synthetic rubber and chemical plants at Maydown near Londonderry, clearly proclaim their identities. Others, engaged in making synthetic fibres, toys, motor-car components, computers, oil-drilling equipment and other light engineering products, conceal their activities in spacious factories designed and built by the government. These include standard single-storey factories built on sites chosen by the firm, more advanced factories erected without a specific tenant in mind but capable of doubling their size, and special factories constructed to a manufacturer's specifications. These factory styles are widely distributed through Northern Ireland but are most striking where grouped into industrial estates. The 100-acre Castlereagh site is the largest of six industrial estates in or near Belfast. The declining passenger and freight role of the diminishing railway network and the closure of all inland waterways, except the Lower Bann navigation, have been met by improving the flexibility of road transport and by implementing a motorway programme which aims to bring every town in Northern Ireland within an hour's run of modernized ports where drive-on ferries and facilities for container traffic are available.

In contrast, memories of the industrial revolution are evoked by many older factories and workshops which have been sustained by their own inertia on sites whose initial attractions are now of negligible importance. For example, water power is now an insignificant locational factor but large volumes of water are needed for the disposal of treated effluent and other industrial purposes, thus rendering coastal sites particularly attractive to some new industries. Older industries owe their survival to modernization, to the adoption of new materials and production techniques, and to the elimination of marginal factories. The textile industry, employing 45,000 persons in 1963, now blends traditional linen with new synthetic fibres; viscose rayon is made at Carrickfergus, Terylene at nearby Kilroot, Acrilan near Coleraine, and nylon at Antrim. Some nineteen flax-spinning mills, thirty-four weaving factories and nineteen bleaching and

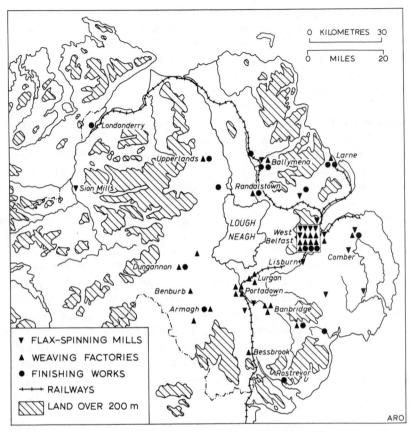

76. *Distribution of the linen industry in Northern Ireland, 1968*

finishing works survive in Northern Ireland, the majority being located in Belfast and nearby towns in the Lagan and upper Bann valleys. The nineteenth-century industrial villages at Sion Mills and Bessbrook are losing their distinctiveness as mill extensions and modern housing estates intrude upon the scene but their mills, employing 950 and 750 persons respectively, carry on a worthy textile tradition. The industrial scene around Belfast Lough continues to change as the reclaimed sloblands attract fresh industry and witness modernization to existing concerns. Extensive modernization in the crisis-ridden shipbuilding industry has reduced the labour force from a World War II peak of over 25,000 to around 9,000 men today but the gantries, slipways, workshops and products of the Musgrave and Abercorn yards are still impressive. The recently commissioned 191,000-ton oil tanker *Myrina* is the largest ship yet launched in the British Isles. Diversification has saved the nearby aerospace factory while grain silos, timber ponds, power stations and a fertilizer plant add variety to the scene. Resulting from recent port improvements, Belfast now has 8 miles of quays, five graving docks and transit sheds covering 31 acres. Fortunately, gone are the days when the level of activity in the shipyards determined the prosperity or lack of it throughout Northern Ireland. Industrial diversification has introduced new opportunities to the male labour force in particular and new personality to the industrial landscape generally.

Government policy has also played a major role in stimulating recent industrial growth in the Republic. In 1921, many towns and villages possessed some manufacturing traditions, but their industries, most of which were allied to local farm production, were limited in scale and made negligible impact on the landscape. Stone-built flour mills and woollen mills, scattered along streams from which they obtained power, blended easily with their rural surroundings. The larger ports contained a few notable factories processing local or imported commodities, but workshop activity, hidden in back streets, was more common. Less successful than their northern counterparts, many industrial villages in the midlands and the south had long since lost their manufacturing functions. Prosperous, in Kildare, where Robert Brook had established a cotton factory and workers' houses between 1776 and 1784, soon deprived its creator of his fortune. Stratford-on-Slaney, a model manufacturing town created by Lord Aldborough between 1783 and 1785, had lost its linen and cotton printing industries by 1838. Apart from tariffs to protect certain industries, independence brought little immediate change to this situation for the Irish Free State government was concerned primarily with fostering agriculture.

After 1932 the government embarked upon a new industrial policy, aimed at achieving economic independence, stemming emigration and reviving the decaying country towns. New industries were established to supply the home market with consumer goods; heavy tariffs and import quotas afforded protection from outside competition while the emphasis on Irish capital investment and management dissuaded foreign firms from opening factories in Ireland. This era of protected industrialization, lasting without change for twenty years, had a significant geographical expression. The encouragement given to factory dispersal prevented any major manufacturing complex from developing and produced a rather incoherent pattern of industrial location. It was an era of small town industry during which many midland towns with good labour and distribution facilities, such as Newbridge, Portlaoise, Tullamore, Athlone and Nenagh, acquired new industries. Some factories were large, at least for Ireland, but they commonly stood alone. The leather tannery established in Portlaw, an old industrial village in Waterford, in 1935, the Athlone cotton factory opened the same year, and the worsted spinning mills established in Tullamore and Cork in 1938 are impressive examples of this activity. Some industries, like the Youghal textile factories opened in 1946 and 1952, occupied attractive modern

77. Silent Valley reservoir in the Mourne mountains provides Belfast with some of its water requirements

premises. Others, by adapting abandoned buildings, added nothing to the land-scape: the large worsted mill at Tullamore is housed in an old prison, the tannery opened at Milford in Carlow in 1948 occupies an old malting mill, the small woollen mill established in Cootehill in 1949 occupies an old workhouse, and the Youghal carpet factory began operations in 1954 in disused cornstores built in the 1780s. Despite the emphasis on dispersion, however, many new industries were attracted to the vicinity of Dublin, Drogheda and Dundalk on the east coast and to the Cork Harbour neighbourhood in the south by the superior labour and distribution facilities and excellent markets of these regions. The policy of protection and decentralization was thus only partly successful. Local consumer products did dominate the home market but quality often varied. Emigration continued and, while places like Newbridge and Youghal did revive, other towns continued to decay.

In the 1950s, with the limited home market nearing saturation, the government removed some protection from home industry and, with generous grants, loans and tax concessions, encouraged local and foreign firms to establish export-orientated industries in Ireland. The opportunities for supplying the British market were obvious and have since been enhanced by the Anglo-Irish trade agreement of 1965 which gives nearly all Irish manufactured goods duty-free entry to Britain. By 1976, when British manufacturers will have duty-free access to Ireland, protection for Irish industry will have finally ended and, with this and possible entry into the European Economic Community in mind, the Republic is now reviewing its economic policies generally. Currently, new factories pay no income tax and no corporation profits tax on their profits from exports for their first ten years. Since the Undeveloped Areas Act of 1952 first directed industry into the west, the other industrial incentives have acquired a strong geographical expression. In the underdeveloped north and west of the Republic, firms can now obtain grants of up to two-thirds of the cost of the site, building, machinery and any special training that workers may need. Although new factories continue to be dispersed throughout this problem area, regional centres like Sligo, Galway and Tralee have been more successful in attracting new industry than the smaller towns. The Shannon Free Airport scheme is a special case where freedom from customs restrictions, tax exemptions on profits from exports until 1983, generous grants for buildings, machinery and training programmes, and certain other benefits have produced an important industrial estate. Elsewhere in the Republic, grants of up to one-half of the cost of the site, building and equipment are payable. Consequently, much new industry continues to focus on Dublin, Drogheda and Cork Harbour, but it has proved difficult to attract further industry to the midlands and the southeast. It is now accepted that many inland towns offer few attractions to industrialists and that regional prosperity is best served by developing specific growth centres, for which purpose new industrial estates have been established in Waterford and Galway. Since 1955 foreign participation has been a notable feature of industrial growth, accounting for 80 per cent of the capital invested in all new industries established between 1959 and 1966 inclusive (Tarrant, 1967). Of the 152 new firms established with foreign participation during this period, forty-nine were British, thirty-nine German and thirty-three American.

At present, manufacturing contributes significantly to the landscape in three principal areas, each of which possesses facilities for distribution by road, sea or air superior to other parts of the Republic. These are the Dublin–Drogheda–Dundalk region whose main industrial complex centres on the port of Dublin with its extensive quays, transit sheds, railway facilities, power stations, oil storage tanks and fertilizer plant; the Cork Harbour neighbourhood whose principal factory zone lies on the south bank of the Lee just below Cork city; and the Limerick–Shannon–Ennis region dominated by the Shannon industrial estate producing high-value goods such as electronic equipment, industrial diamonds, garments, pianos and business machines suitable for export by air. Industrial growth at Shannon stems from the creation in 1957 of a development authority designed to save the airport and its employees from the redundancy threatened by the introduction, proposed for 1958, of long-range jet aircraft

78. Shannon Free Airport with its industrial estate and housing complex, 1967

that could overfly Shannon on North Atlantic routes. By 1967, in response to the attractions laid before industrialists, eighteen manufacturers, eight warehousing firms and eight service concerns had been established and spacious premises covering 1 million square feet of the industrial estate had been completed. These firms employed 3,244 persons and produced almost one-third of the Republic's manufactured exports in value. A further 2,087 persons worked in the airport and in the nearby community, a tastefully designed but as yet stark collection of bungalows, houses and multistorey flats that currently house 1,800 persons.

Not one of the three regions constitutes anything like a continuous manufacturing zone. Indeed, many factories are concealed in congested back streets or lie beside spacious suburban housing estates. Other enterprises lie amid rural surroundings – the Whitegate oil refinery, the Haulbowline steelworks and the Rushbrooke shipbuilding yard disrupt the pastoral backcloth to Cork Harbour. Outside these regions, some industries, like the fertilizer plant in the Vale of Avoca, the crane factory at Killarney and the oil storage tanks on Whiddy Island, in Bantry Bay, seriously detract from the recreational amenities of their scenic settings. On the other hand, the many creameries that dot the countryside in the dairying counties and the food-processing plants and woollen mills

79. *The Whitegate oil refinery on Cork Harbour, 1966*

that occur in several country towns seem natural extensions of the agricultural scene.

Finally, it should be noted that the industrial and commercial fabric of many modern ports often lies on land that man has reclaimed from the sea. Limited reclamation of the slob has long featured in the growth of ports like Youghal,

Kinsale, Bantry, Londonderry and Drogheda, but has reached dramatic pro-portions in Belfast and Dublin. Most of Dublin's industrial fabric and dock installations east of the railway line from Fairview to Sandymount lie on land reclaimed piecemeal from the Liffey estuary since the North Wall was first built seawards in 1714 and the South Wall constructed between 1708 and 1762.

Chapter 14
Regional expressions and planning

The Irish landscape is now changing more rapidly than at any time since the great famine. Road transport, new industries, television and tourism are exposing formerly remote areas to fresh ideas and material benefits. Modern farming and building techniques are replacing traditional methods. Economic and physical plans sponsored by the Dublin and Belfast governments are attempting to mould their respective resources into national frameworks. New planning and tourist regions are supplementing administrative units of longer standing. Under these stimuli, the landscape is acquiring a homogeneity which is fast destroying local regional expressions. Nevertheless, two categories of regionalism appear to be strengthening: on the one hand lies the uneven north–south contrast which is deeply rooted in Ireland's turbulent past and since 1921 has found fresh if rather artificial expression in political partition; on the other hand lies the widening rift between east and west which is common to both Northern Ireland and the Republic. These inherited landscape contrasts, which stem largely from differing cultural endowments, are now being exaggerated by government action or inaction as the case may be.

Regionalism

Local expressions
Ireland is a compact, mainly low-lying country upon which climate, drainage conditions, vegetation and soils bestow a distinctive physical personality. Within this framework, however, major contrasts do exist, notably between the physically better-endowed south and east and the less favoured north and west, and also between the extensive lowlands and harsh peripheral uplands that comprise the country's main physical regions. These contrasts have long been recognized by man and have been emphasized by human activities of widely varying character. The favoured lowlands of the southeast understandably fell to colonists who were technically better equipped and more organized than their predecessors while the more difficult country of the uplands and the north-west became a place of refuge for displaced peoples and traditional ways of life. In these less favourable regions, where the limits of glacial drift and the bog edge are critically important to agriculture and settlement, close relationships between natural conditions and human activity may still be found. Many smaller

physical units like the Lough Neagh basin, the Castlecomer plateau and the Burren also exert a powerful influence on man, but some regions with a distinctive physical endowment, such as the drumlin belt and the Atlantic seaboard, exhibit landscapes which cannot be interpreted solely in terms of natural conditions. Even the broad central lowlands possess little cultural unity because, although forest clearance and agriculture may once have been directed towards the better lands, any rational relationship between land quality, farm size, land use and population distribution has long since been obscured by the selective colonization practices of the past 800 years. Thus, although physical conditions may evoke a rudimentary regionalism, the diversity of local expressions within Ireland cannot be explained without reference to past human events as reflected in present economic, social and administrative arrangements.

It has long been fashionable to interpret local differences in the Irish landscape in terms of economic activity. Physical and historical circumstances combine with practical economics to produce one of the most fundamental contrasts in the present landscape – between the mixed farming economy of the southeast where commercial tillage traditions are rooted in the medieval period, and the dominantly pastoral economy of the midlands and the northwest where, apart from the need for subsistence crops, cattle have reigned supreme in rural life since before the coming of Christianity. This contrast is not confined to the purely agricultural sector. The landscapes of the southeast are rich in medieval market towns and ports and in villages, farmsteads and cottages of sophisticated design, all of which serve as reminders of the alien origins of mixed farming. Furthermore, town and country are more fully integrated here than they are in the pastoral northwest where, for example, livestock transactions were once commonly conducted at bare crossroads while rural life focused traditionally on simple farm clusters and isolated homesteads, settlement forms of great antiquity. In the latter area therefore, there was little inducement to the growth of market towns and villages and even those imposed on the landscape during the plantation and landlord eras did not meet with unqualified success. Even in the midlands, many traditional fair sites were remote from any form of nucleated settlement. Today, as in the past, subtle contrasts in the nature and aims of livestock production and tillage within this broad framework give rise to agricultural regions of smaller dimensions such as the cattle-grazing east midlands, the mixed farming country of Wexford and the Barrow valley, and the dairying country south of the Shannon estuary where the co-operative creamery movement began in the late nineteenth century. Many such regions have a strong physical basis, but, owing to powerful historical and economic factors, physical and agricultural boundaries rarely coincide and the latter are more commonly blurred as farming undergoes a subtle change of emphasis from one region to another. These agricultural regions are continuously fluctuating in both character and extent in response to varying economic controls. Nowhere is this better expressed than in the Golden Vale of south Tipperary where commercial cereal cultivation, so important in the landlord era, has contracted in the face of an expanding dairying industry.

Regionalism of an industrial nature is of limited significance for only east Ulster can claim a meaningful industrial personality. The Republic has indeed recognized the geographical imbalance of its economy by designating the country west of a line from Dundalk through the Fergus estuary to Ross Carbery as an undeveloped area wherein government grants to industry exceed those offered elsewhere. As yet, however, this policy has had little impact on regional expression for, although new factories continue to be dispersed throughout the problem area, they are commonly exceeded in both size and number by the new premises favouring the south and east. Even so, the growth of manufacturing in the Dublin–Drogheda–Dundalk coastal strip, around Cork Harbour and in the Limerick–Shannon–Ennis zone has yet to impose a dominant industrial personality on these three regions.

Another form of regional expression is provided by the administrative unit for where such arrangements are of long standing they are often reflected in

80. The evolution of the county system

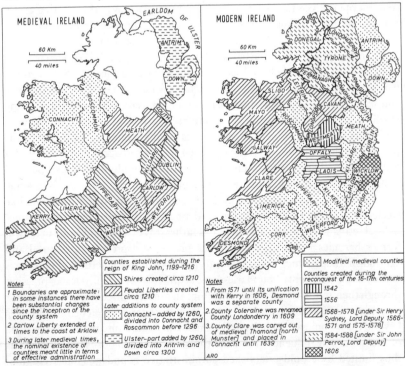

local sentiments while their boundaries, being limits of executive power, are sometimes revealed in the landscape. Probably the most far-reaching influence on modern regionalism in this respect was the introduction of the county-barony-vill administrative hierarchy by the Anglo-Normans, a scheme based originally on units of landholding. The county system was completed only when Laois and Offaly were shired in 1556, when the outstanding parts of Ulster and Connacht were subdivided during the 1568–88 period, and when Wicklow was created by statute in 1606. Counties frequently took as their boundaries major rivers like the Shannon, Barrow and Lagan or notable watersheds such as the Blackstairs, Knockmealdown and Derrynasaggart mountains. Despite its alien origin and its lack of a close equivalent in Celtic society, the county has left a deep impression upon Irish life and today an Irishman identifies himself first and foremost as a man of his county. One may speak of Mayomen, Kerrymen or Louthmen as if they possessed distinctive personalities. Similarly, county names evoke mental images of distinctive landscapes and ways of life although, more often than not, the only tangible expression of a county boundary is a change in the quality of the road surface. Somewhat ironically, loyalty to the county, an alien imposition which was little more than an administrative convenience for immigrant landholders, finds its most virile expression in the support given to Gaelic football and hurling teams in the sporting arena. Equally strange, hurling is most deeply rooted in those counties of the south and east where outside influences have always been strongest.

In a more local context, the barony may still evoke powerful regional impressions and, although abolished as an administrative device in 1898, many a barony name survives in use locally, notably where linked with a distinctive landscape. Many Anglo-Norman baronies or cantreds were based on existing Gaelic *tuatha* or petty kingdoms, having been formed after the submission of the ruling chieftains; others were newly created as colonization from outside progressed through the centuries until each county had been subdivided in this fashion. Some baronies were linked with distinctive physical landscapes and took expressive names like Burren, Corkaguiny, Imokilly and Murrisk; some, like Barrymore and Courceys, revealed Anglo-Norman family links or, like Decies and Deece, were named after earlier peoples; others acquired the names of local settlements. Forth and Bargy in southeast Wexford and Lecale in Down, former baronies based upon still older *tuatha*, still preserve a cultural and agrarian heritage which owes much to medieval English settlers. Sometimes barony and even county boundaries have acquired a certain physical expression through their influence on land ownership. In nineteenth-century Wicklow, for example, the Fitzwilliam and Carysfort properties rarely stretched southwards beyond the baronies of Shillelagh, Ballincor and Arklow into the adjoining parts of Wexford. The influence of some of the most active landlords in Leinster was thus limited by an old-established administrative boundary (Jones Hughes,

1965). The third and smallest unit introduced by the Anglo-Normans was the vill which, like the barony, was based to some extent on pre-existing divisions and changed and multiplied in later centuries. As units of landholding whose inhabitants had certain collective responsibilities, vills no doubt once produced local contrasts in land use. They survive today as townlands, of which there are 62,202 in Ireland. Although townlands are the smallest territorial divisions used for administrative purposes and country folk are commonly located by the townland in which they reside, these units have no local government role.

Alongside the county-barony-vill hierarchy, the territorial units that have survived in modified form from before the Anglo-Norman invasion rarely evoke strong regionalism. The seven provincial kingdoms of early Christian Ireland are now represented by four provinces but, although Leinster, Munster, Connacht and Ulster each possess certain unique qualities, provincial loyalties are mainly reserved for the sporting arena. Many Celtic over-kingdoms, units into which *tuatha* were formerly grouped, served to outline the dioceses that were formed in the twelfth century but, despite the great attachment to church and chapel in modern Ireland, diocesan and parochial loyalties are often but weakly developed. Indeed the Reformation and its aftermath made the parish, as a long-standing social and administrative entity, meaningless to the overwhelming majority of the Irish population. When the Roman Catholic Church came to rationalize its local government structure in the early nineteenth century, it chose the growing towns fostered by landlordism as its focal points rather than the hallowed, if alienated, diocesan centres whose cathedrals had fallen to the episcopalian church at the Reformation. Thus Downpatrick yielded to Belfast, Cashel to Thurles, Cloyne to Cobh and Killala to Ballina. In similar vein, existing Roman Catholic parishes rarely possess stable or historically justifiable boundaries. Even the medieval parishes that were later inherited by the Church of Ireland and also formed the basis of many civil parishes rarely provided a framework within which the settlement pattern evolved. Unlike some other west European countries, the Irish landscape contains few villages which have been nourished over many centuries as centres of wealthy parishes. On the other hand, over much of Ulster existing Church of Ireland parishes originated with the seventeenth-century plantations and were synchronized with land grants so that, even today, parishes and their churches are still identifiable in terms of the estates which they accompanied. Civil parishes were abolished as administrative units in 1898.

The Poor Law Unions established under the Poor Relief Act of 1838, together with their subdivisions – the Dispensary Districts created after the Medical Charities Act of 1851 and the Registrars' Districts outlined in 1864, were other interesting attempts at relating administrative units to the evolving pattern of villages, towns and communications, as well as to the general distribution of population. With the choice as Union centres of towns like Banbridge,

Boyle and Killarney which had been nurtured as the urban foci of large estates, the correlation between major units of landholding and administrative divisions was often reinforced. The Poor Law Unions later provided models for the rural districts which, together with the new urban districts, replaced the baronies under the Local Government Act of 1898. Although thirty-one rural districts survive in Northern Ireland, where they are mainly concerned with sanitation and housing, the 160 rural districts elsewhere were abolished as administrative areas in 1925, or in the case of County Dublin 1930, and thus had little time in which to generate local efforts and loyalties. As for the towns, the Republic currently contains four county boroughs, one borough, six municipal boroughs and forty-nine urban districts while Northern Ireland has two county boroughs, ten boroughs and twenty-four urban districts. These urban units have a wide range of responsibilities and thus considerable opportunity to mould distinctive townscapes. Boroughs and urban districts are responsible for the provision of water supplies, sewerage, street lighting and cleansing, for the upkeep of harbours and most roads, and for slum clearance, planning and redevelopment within their areas. They also build houses for letting and may provide parks, recreation grounds, markets, museums, art galleries, libraries, gas undertakings and other amenities. County boroughs have the functions of both counties and urban districts.

Finally, Ireland is rich in regional sentiments and expressions which, although rooted deeply in the past and acknowledged by the survival of regional names, have rarely been revealed in administrative arrangements. Fingal is one such area in north Dublin where strong tillage traditions date back to medieval times. Cooley in north Louth long retained certain distinct qualities, partly as the last refuge of Gaelic-speaking peoples in eastern Ireland and partly because its landscape bore the imprint of several centuries of landlordism and mixed farming (Jones Hughes, 1961). Equally evocative regional names survive along the Atlantic seaboard. In the Rosses and Gweedore in Donegal, Mullet in Mayo and Cois Fharraige, the narrow coastal strip between Barna and Cashla Bay in Galway, the harsh physical environment and the cultural heritage of the surviving Gaelic-speaking population are firmly interwoven, both in the landscape and in the mentality of the inhabitants. Despite its Anglo-Norman name, Joyce's Country in west Galway is similarly rich in Gaelic relics while nearby Connemara, where the Irish language has now largely disappeared although it was spoken by nearly everyone in the 1850s, also retains many traditional landscape elements. Nevertheless, the most remarkable loyalties and sentiments in modern Ireland are those which find micro-regional expression in the drab streets and industrial housing of the northern towns. Here, religious beliefs provide a basis for powerful social and territorial affiliations which are sometimes given forceful expression in the townscape. In the Shankill area of Belfast, for example, 99 per cent of the population is Protestant and, predictably, most people support Linfield football club, read the *Belfast Newsletter* and *Belfast Telegraph*, and marry, shop and visit within Shankill or use buses operating along Shankill Road for visits to the city centre (Boal, 1968). On the twelfth of July each year, this neighbourhood erupts with colourful displays of bunting, kerb painting, Union Jacks, decorated arches, wall slogans and other dubiously artistic manifestations designed to commemorate William III's decisive victory over James II on the Boyne in 1690 and to reaffirm loyalties to Protestant and Unionist ideals. In adjacent Clonard on the other hand, the population is 98 per cent Roman Catholic and most persons support Glasgow Celtic football club, read the *Irish News* and perhaps the *Belfast Telegraph* (the only integrating force), make their grocery purchases, visits and marriage ties within the Falls Road area, and visit the city centre on buses operating along the Springfield and Falls roads. Periodic displays of papal and republican flags serve to emphasize local Roman Catholic and nationalist loyalties. Finally, the memory of distinct English and Irish sectors in towns like Limerick, Athlone and Kilkenny with Scottish quarters added in Carrickfergus and other northern towns, together with the survival of English, Scottish and Irish streets in places like Armagh and Downpatrick, adds fuel to the old fires of segregation that still smoulder, at least in the minds of men.

North and south

Several years of sporadic and at times bitter fighting between a section of the Irish people and British armed forces – euphemistically called 'the troubles' – culminated in 1920–21 in a compromise political settlement which has since had far-reaching repercussions on the shaping of the Irish landscape. In 1920, the United Kingdom Parliament passed the Government of Ireland Act partitioning Ireland. This led, in June 1921, to the establishment of a separate government with limited powers for six of Ulster's nine counties – henceforth known as *Northern Ireland*. These six counties – Antrim, Armagh, Down, Fermanagh, Londonderry and Tyrone – together had a Protestant majority which favoured continuing union with Great Britain, although a strong and locally dominant Roman Catholic minority largely favoured a more independent course. On 6 December 1921 the articles of agreement for a treaty between Great Britain and Ireland were signed. These allowed Northern Ireland the option of remaining part of the United Kingdom while the remaining twenty-six counties became a self-governing British dominion named the *Irish Free State*. Thus, the unhappy legislative union established between Great Britain and Ireland in 1801 was finally dissolved. The term *Irish Free State* was abolished in 1937 when the Dublin government insisted that the name *Ireland*, or in the Irish language *Éire*, should apply to the whole island even though 'pending the re-integration of the national territory' its jurisdiction remained confined to the twenty-six counties. In 1948 the state was restyled the *Republic of Ireland*, a

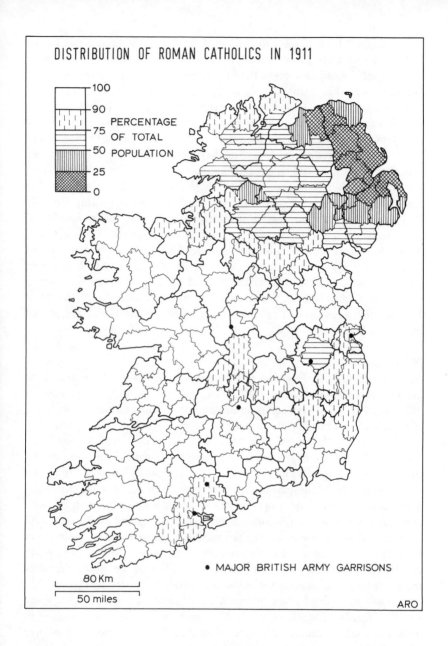

DISTRIBUTION OF ROMAN CATHOLICS IN 1911

100
90
75 — PERCENTAGE
50 — OF TOTAL
POPULATION
25
0

● MAJOR BRITISH ARMY GARRISONS

80 Km

50 miles

ARO

81. The distribution of Roman Catholics in Ireland in 1911
The presence of large British army garrisons commonly had the effect of inflating local
Protestant populations.

step which the United Kingdom government regarded as placing the country outside the British Commonwealth.

The roots of this partition may be traced back to the seventeenth century when, in order to consolidate Britain's hold over the recently defeated Gaelic-speaking peoples of the north, Scots and English colonists loyal to the Crown and to the Protestant cause were planted on confiscated lands throughout much of Ulster. What had been the last powerful stronghold of Gaelic society thus became the formidable bastion of peoples whose speech, habits and traditions were far removed from native ways and whose bellicose Protestantism and militant loyalty to the British Crown prepared the way for eventual partition. Compared with the less successful plantation schemes in other parts of Ireland, the Ulster plantation was better planned, more competently executed and thus more durable. While flourishing communities of merchants, artisans and labourers peopled the new towns, immigrant farmers established firm roots in the countryside and stamped their distinctive imprint boldly on the landscape. Ecologically, the various settlement schemes established an immigrant Protestant population on the land which was sufficiently numerous to regenerate from within and sufficiently virile to withstand subsequent overcrowding by a still vigorous native Roman Catholic population. Later, the expansion of flax-growing and domestic linen production within a more widely based rural economy, the operation of the 'Ulster custom' which made for happier landlord-tenant relationships, and the spread of the industrial revolution confirmed Ulster on its divergent path. Thus by 1921 the Ulster landscape and a significant component of the population possessed certain inherited characteristics which distinguished them from their counterparts farther south. Such individuality should not, however, be overstressed. The northern plantation policy was not unique to what is now Northern Ireland but also affected Ulster's other three counties and spilled over into Leitrim where, for example, one Scots Presbyterian acquired 5,279 acres in 1620 and founded Manorhamilton. Even today, Protestants still own a sizeable proportion of land in the Republic's Border counties. Furthermore, to agree with M. W. Heslinga's (1962) perception that the Irish land Border is a more effective cultural divide within the British Isles than the Irish Sea, is to ignore the undoubted Celtic contribution to the landscape and population of the north. The basis for partition remains primarily religious – almost 95 per cent of the Republic's population is Roman Catholic compared with 35 per cent in Northern Ireland – but the precise location of the Border cannot be justified on purely religious grounds. In a cultural sense, Northern Ireland's most expressive core may be quite distinct, but the boundaries of this individuality are not.

Nevertheless the Border exists, finding physical expression in Customs posts on the approved crossing roads and in obstacles placed across minor roads. Since its creation in 1921 subtle differences in the attitudes, methods and

82. Carlingford Lough
Looking across the Louth countryside in the Republic from the Border to Warrenpoint and the steep slopes of the Mourne mountains in Northern Ireland.

objectives of the governments on either side have been transmitted to their respective landscapes. The first impression gained in crossing the Border into Northern Ireland is that of passing into a compact, tidy state where hedge-trimming laws are enforced, where many country roads are lined with stone kerbs and footpaths as in England, and where small farmsteads are remarkably neat. No doubt Northern Ireland's compactness and population pressure – 272 persons per square mile in 1966 compared with 106 persons per square mile in the Republic – have generated a keener awareness of land and resources in a people inherently careful and neat by nature. After 1921 the consolidation of Northern Ireland was expressed by the opening of such fine buildings as the Parliament at Stormont in 1932 and the Law Courts building in 1933. South of the Border, on the other hand, the best buildings of the 'colonial' era were converted to government use while the less useful symbols of the British connection were demolished – one way or another. The 1930s were years of persistent depression and unemployment in the north, aggravated by the tariffs erected by the Irish Free State which severely damaged the entrepôt trade and certain industries of ports like Londonderry and Newry. After 1932, the south pursued a vigorous policy of state intervention in economic activity. Where private enterprise failed or was lacking, as in the fields of air and public transport and peat-bog development, the state created public enterprises which often effected substantial changes in the landscape. Having inherited a country which lacked many essential social provisions and whose economy was based almost entirely on agriculture, the Republic can look back with some satisfaction on achievements in the industrial field over recent years. Nevertheless, much remains to be done, notably in the chronically depressed areas of the west. Northern Ireland's active participation in World War II and subsequent British military commitments has provided the landscape with naval facilities, military aerodromes and, indirectly, new buildings on former bombed sites. These features are less evident in the unaligned Republic, neutral in World War II, although the country's defence forces have put many formerly British military establishments to good use. Northern Ireland has undoubtedly benefited from the British connection, notably in the realm of progressive social legislation although much still remains to be done to quench the lingering sectarianism and discrimination which are so deeply rooted in the past.

East and west

The most striking regional contrast in modern Ireland lies between the comparatively prosperous east, long favoured by nature and man, the poorer west with its more limited resources and restricted social and economic opportunities. This is also a contrast between dominantly urban and overwhelmingly rural communities or, in an extreme sense, between metropolitan areas and the rest.

Despite an annual emigration rate of nearly 7,000 persons in recent years, Northern Ireland's 1966 population of 1,485,000 was the highest since 1841. However, this figure conceals the fact that since 1841 the continuing eastward shift of population into industrial east Ulster has allowed Antrim, Down and Belfast collectively to increase their total by over 40 per cent while the remaining area, which has experienced serious economic problems ever since the domestic linen industry collapsed, has lost two-thirds of its population. Even during the relatively prosperous 1961–66 period, when Antrim and Down again showed large increases, Fermanagh's population fell by nearly 2,000 and an average annual net emigration rate of 16·6 persons per 1,000 was recorded for the county. The landscape implications are obvious. Increasing concentration of industry and people around Belfast has created a dangerous imbalance in Northern Ireland's social and economic life which can only be countered by drastic planning action. Pressures on space in the east must be alleviated. The remainder of the state must be developed within a national framework.

The situation in the Republic is no less dramatic. To many observers, the western counties – Donegal, Leitrim, Sligo, Mayo, Galway, Clare, Kerry, west Cork, Roscommon, Cavan, Monaghan and Longford – qualify as a disaster area. For example, while the population of Dublin city and county has expanded from 373,000 in 1841 to 795,000 in 1966, that of dismal Leitrim has fallen from

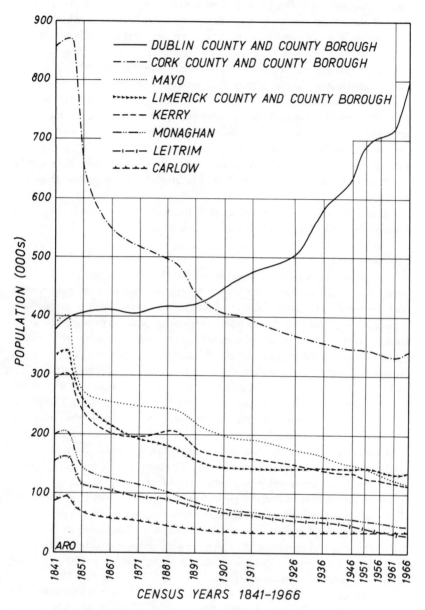

Legend:
- DUBLIN COUNTY AND COUNTY BOROUGH
- CORK COUNTY AND COUNTY BOROUGH
- MAYO
- LIMERICK COUNTY AND COUNTY BOROUGH
- KERRY
- MONAGHAN
- LEITRIM
- CARLOW

POPULATION (000s)

ARO

CENSUS YEARS 1841–1966

83. Population change in selected Irish counties, 1841–1966

155,000 to 30,000 and that of Roscommon from 254,000 to 56,000 over the same period. Connacht's population has fallen from 1,420,000 in 1841 to barely 400,000 in 1966. Largely because of this continuing flight from the west, the Republic of Ireland shared with East Germany the melancholy distinction of being the only European countries to suffer a declining population between 1951 and 1961. Today, Dublin flourishes as its country's social, economic and political capital, most farms in the south and east prosper, but the west continues to lose people. Many farmsteads lie derelict, fields are neglected and small country towns stagnate. The western counties share many problems in common. In general, the agrarian structure is unbalanced, there being a quite irrational relationship between the number of persons engaged in farming – 55 per cent of the employed population – and the available productive resources of the region. Increased farm productivity is inhibited by small farm sizes, fragmentation, soils which are not inherently fertile, and a topheavy age structure to the population. For instance, 35 per cent of the farms are less than 25 acres and in Connacht, despite the continuing efforts of the Land Commission, 41 per cent of the farms are still fragmented. Young persons are generally disinclined to remain at work on holdings which do not yield sufficient cash income or live in areas where social amenities are few. Consequently, owing to the scarcity of off-farm employment opportunities, many emigrate. Between 1961 and 1966, 13·6 persons in every 1,000 in Connacht emigrated and Mayo and Leitrim, with net emigration rates of 17 and 19 per 1,000 lost 6·3 and 8·7 per cent of their population respectively. As many emigrants are reluctant to sell their lands, the pool of useful land available for redistribution is small. The effects of emigration are clearly seen in the age-sex structure of the remaining population: there is a scarcity of young adults in the 20–40 age group; 63 per cent of the farmers in the west are over fifty years old; and there are more men than women for the womenfolk have poor prospects of an early marriage and alternative employment opportunities are few. Half the total farming population consists of unmarried farmers and, owing to emigration, there is a general decline in the number of children being born – Connacht's natural increase of 5 per 1,000 between 1961 and 1966 compares unfavourably with Leinster's 13·5 per 1,000 population. The loss of young adults and the preponderance of elderly farmers are reflected in farming activities: those requiring much labour give way to dry cattle and sheep-rearing. The farming population, 92 per cent of which has had no more than a primary education, is too conservative to adopt new methods, too elderly to initiate the improvements necessary to raise farm income, and too reluctant to accept credit facilities which imply debt. Many farmers live at or just above subsistence level, selling an animal occasionally. Others depend strongly on cash remittances from relatives abroad, on seasonal work in Britain, or on insurance 'stamp collecting' – working thirteen weeks on road construction or some other form of public work in order to qualify for twenty-six weeks'

253

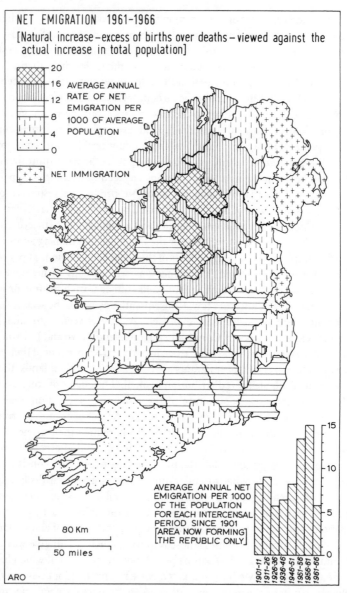

NET EMIGRATION 1961-1966
[Natural increase – excess of births over deaths – viewed against the actual increase in total population]

20
16 AVERAGE ANNUAL
12 RATE OF NET
     EMIGRATION PER
8 1000 OF AVERAGE
4 POPULATION
0

+ + + NET IMMIGRATION

AVERAGE ANNUAL NET
EMIGRATION PER 1000
OF THE POPULATION
FOR EACH INTERCENSAL
PERIOD SINCE 1901
[AREA NOW FORMING
THE REPUBLIC ONLY]

80 Km

50 miles

ARO

1901–11
1911–26
1926–36
1936–46
1946–51
1951–56
1956–61
1961–66

84. Average annual rate of net emigration during the 1961–6 intercensal period
Partial migration of the central-city populations of Dublin and Belfast to the suburbs
and the consequent growth of residential satellites largely explains why those County
Boroughs experienced net emigration while the surrounding county areas experienced
net immigration.

unemployment assistance before commencing the cycle again. In such circumstances, and lacking adequate capital, initiative or education, farming assumes secondary importance.

The western problem has engaged many minds, but their combined efforts have yet to find a workable solution that will stem the flow of emigrants. Undoubtedly the state has inherited a congestion problem in the west which was produced by fateful historical circumstances beyond its control. Furthermore,

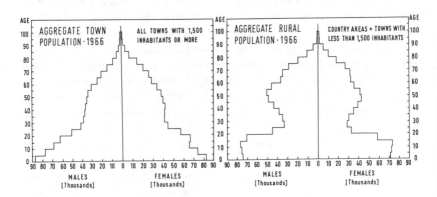

85. Population pyramids for the aggregate town and rural areas of the Republic of Ireland, 1966

the movement from rural to urban areas and from agricultural into industrial and service employment is a normal feature of developing countries. Unfortunately, very little of this movement is currently being absorbed into towns and industries in the west and, although the state recognizes its responsibilities, the central government has yet to implement comprehensive planning legislation for the distressed counties. Several palliatives have been tried: the 1952 Undeveloped Areas Act directed industries into the west, but the effect was not spread evenly throughout the region. Since 1964, pilot agricultural areas have been designated throughout the western seaboard's small-farm country in an attempt to create viable holdings and stimulate rural development through an intensive advisory service, various ancillary activities and, above all, community effort. Tourism, forestry and fishing are being promoted to provide extra employment opportunities. Attempts are being made to intensify agriculture by improving stock and widening the range of crops. Decentralization of the central government, with two departments going to Athlone and Castlebar, is also being implemented. Nevertheless, there is still a backlog of suspicion and ignorance to be cleared away, and a communication gap between the central administration and the people of the west to be closed.

Planning for the future

In recent years, planning legislation on both sides of the Border has paved the way for major controlled changes in the landscape at both regional and local levels. Development plans have been drawn up for several towns and regions, but, in view of past experience, it is important to distinguish between the proposals on paper and the extent to which they have so far found expression in the landscape. Northern Ireland's first halting steps in planning were taken with the permissive but largely ineffective planning act of 1931. In 1944 local authorities secured more effective control over development and land use in their areas, pending the introduction of actual planning schemes. Soon afterwards, the urgent need for countryside conservation was officially recognized. The most important plan to date has been Sir Robert Matthew's *Belfast Regional Survey and Plan*, published in 1964. To prevent the city from destroying the remaining amenities of its fine location, to preserve good agricultural land, and to check the city's absolute dominance over Northern Ireland's social and economic life, this report proposed a 'stop-line', beyond which the Belfast urban area should not expand, bounded by a 'greenscape' in which development was to focus on existing settlements leaving the remaining land for agriculture, forestry and outdoor recreation. The report also recommended the development of alternative growth centres to Belfast, in particular the creation of a new city (Craigavon) based on Lurgan and Portadown adjacent to the motorway system and the Belfast–Dublin rail link, and the expansion of Antrim, Ballymena, Carrickfergus, Larne, Bangor, Downpatrick and Newtownards; the concentration of industry in six key centres elsewhere, namely Londonderry, Coleraine, Omagh, Dungannon, Enniskillen and Newry; the public acquisition or control of amenity areas; the creation of a Ministry of Planning and Development backed by comprehensive planning legislation; and the extension of the survey technique throughout Northern Ireland. The government and local planning committees have since taken steps to implement these recommendations. Craigavon, the first beneficiary of the 1965 New Towns Act, is taking shape in the lowland south of Lough Neagh and hopefully, by 1981, will have added 64,000 persons, 22,000 houses and 15,000 new jobs to the existing twin towns of Lurgan and Portadown. Outline plans for the other growth centres envisage traffic-free shopping centres, tasteful neighbourhood units, industrial sectors and ring roads. Following the recommendations of the Ulster countryside committee, areas of outstanding natural beauty which deserve special protection have been designated in the Lagan valley south of Belfast, along the Antrim coast with its glens, in the coastal area of north Londonderry and its hinterland, and in south Armagh and the Mourne mountains. Scenic drives, picnic areas, guided walks and other recreational facilities have been provided in the state forests at Gortin Glen, Lough Navar, Ballypatrick, Ballycastle and Portglenone while the tourist potential of the Ulster Lakeland in Fermanagh is being developed. Derelict industrial sites are being cleared, closed railway lines are being converted to public footpaths, and coastal walks are being provided, notably along the south shore of Belfast Lough from Holywood to Groomsport. The greater Londonderry plan, published in 1968, envisages an additional 23,000 people, 12,000 new jobs and 9,600 new houses over the next fifteen years. The expanded urban area, which will include major secondary centres at Waterside and Shantallow, will lie it is hoped at the heart of a crescent of population growth and industrial expansion extending down the Foyle valley from Strabane to Limavady but in which the amenities of the river and the surrounding countryside will be carefully preserved. All the above moves, together with the implementation of the 1965 Wilson report on *Economic Development in Northern Ireland*, should encourage ordered development of the country's potential while ensuring preservation of the best that nature and man have bequeathed from the past and the prevention of disfigurement of the landscape in the future. Planning and conservation of this nature are so important in a state where the land area is so small and the population increasing, where the tourist industry is a valuable asset and where new, much-needed industries may well be a disruptive force.

South of the Border planning also experienced a false start in the 1930s, though radical attempts are now being made to retrieve the situation. The Dublin government first acknowledged the need for planning legislation with the Town and Regional Planning Acts of 1934 and 1939. Local authorities were authorized, but not required, to engage in planning although no time limit was set for the preparation of planning schemes. As a result, in thirty years only one council – Dublin County Borough – reached the stage of preparing and adopting a plan. By the early 1960s, most towns had acute problems associated with conflicting land use, traffic congestion, obsolescence and decay. The urgent need to reconcile urban and industrial growth with the requirements of conservation, amenity improvement and tourism could only be resolved through comprehensive planning. The implementation of the First Programme for Economic Expansion after 1958 had already demonstrated economic planning at a national level. What was now required was physical planning at local and regional levels. Consequently, the wide-ranging Local Government (Planning and Development) Act was passed in 1963 and the National Institute for Physical Planning and Construction Research was created in 1964. The government and ultimately the eighty-seven local planning authorities were now firmly committed to physical planning.

At the local level the 1963 Act required each urban authority to submit within three years a development plan dealing with four principal objectives: land-use zoning for residential, commercial, industrial and other purposes; the improvement of road and traffic conditions; the development and renewal of obsolete areas; and the preservation, improvement and extension of amenities.

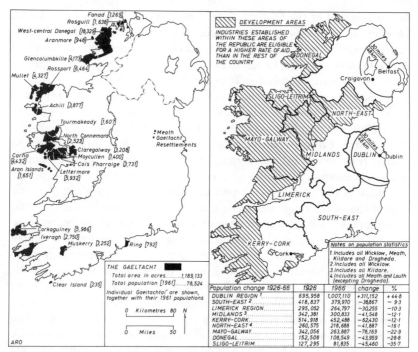

86. *Two facets of regionalism in the Republic of Ireland*
The Gaeltacht and the nine physical planning regions proposed by An Foras Forbartha in 1964.

Rural authorities were required to submit plans to meet the last two objectives and to provide new public services. In addition, the development plans could deal with such items as community planning, the size, density and layout of buildings, the preservation of open spaces, scenery and rights of way to the sea-shore, and the control of advertisements, dumping and pollution. Provisions were made for the acquisition of land, the statement of objections and the pay-ment of compensation. Most local authorities have now submitted their pro-posals, many of which are in the process of implementation.

At the regional level, the Republic was divided into nine regions for planning purposes. The regional ideal was given added emphasis by the economic planners who, in the Second Programme for Economic Expansion for 1964–70, abandoned earlier attempts to spread industry thinly over a wide area in favour of developing poles of economic and social growth focusing on such important regional centres as Waterford, Galway and Sligo. The outline advisory plans for the planning regions have now been submitted – for the Dublin region by Professor Myles Wright, for the Limerick region by Dr Nathaniel Lichfield, and for the remainder by Professor Colin Buchanan. The Dublin regional plan, for example, deals with the critical area within a 30-mile radius of the city, an area which already contains one-third of the country's population and almost half of its industrial and service employees, and which may well have 1·2 million inhabitants by 1980. It is envisaged that most of the additional population will be based on a number of growth centres placed in an arc of country some 7 to 12 miles from the city centre and extending from Malahide and Swords in the north to Clondalkin and Tallaght in the southwest. These growth centres would be connected to the city by means of a new motorway system while cross-city traffic would be relieved by other major bypass arteries to the north, west and south. Towns beyond the arc, notably Drogheda, Navan, Naas, Newbridge and Arklow, would also be developed but the recreational value of the Wicklow mountains, the coastline and the Liffey valley would be preserved and enhanced. The Limerick regional plan covers counties Limerick, Clare and Tipperary (North Riding) with a current population of a quarter of a million, of whom only 100,000 are town dwellers. The problems of reconciling desirable industrial and urban developments with emigration on the one hand and the region's tourist potential on the other are examined. It is envisaged that further industrial growth in the Limerick–Shannon–Ennis complex will be supported by major improvements in housing and traffic conditions, and that the Shannon lakes and estuary, the mountains north and east of Limerick, the Clare coast and the Burren will be developed as tourist areas.

It is as yet too early to view the changes in the landscape that these regional plans envisage although important, and not unrelated, improvements to the amenities of town and countryside alike have already occurred. The Tidy Towns competition sponsored by the Irish Tourist Board has had remarkable success in settlements like Rathvilly, Ballyjamesduff and Virginia. The first State Forest Park with a scenic drive and other facilities has been formally opened at Gougane Barra in Cork, while Killakee and Glendalough forests south of Dublin and Lough Key forest in Roscommon are scheduled for similar development. With the adoption of systems building in many urban renewal projects, blighted townscapes are rapidly diminishing in extent. After a late start and a reluctance to accept new ideas and materials, some fine contemporary churches, rural schools, regional technical colleges, university buildings, hotels, motels and prestige office blocks have been built. Nevertheless, the landscape keenly awaits the implementation of man's proposed intentions for its future.

References and further reading

ANDREWS, J. H. (1956), 'Notes on the historical geography of the Irish iron industry', *Irish Geog.*, **3**, 139–49.

ANDREWS, J. H. (1964), 'Road planning in Ireland before the Railway Age', *Irish Geog.*, **5**, 17–41.

BECKETT, J. C. (1966), *A Short History of Ireland*, 3rd edn., Hutchinson.

BOAL, F. W. (1968), 'Territoriality on the Shankill-Falls divide, Belfast', Paper read to Second Conference of Irish Geographers, Dublin.

BUTLIN, R. A. (1967), 'Urban genesis in Ireland, 1556–1641', in *Liverpool Essays in Geography*, ed. R. W. Steel and R. Lawton, Longmans, pp. 211–26.

CAMBLIN, G. (1951), *The Town in Ulster*, Belfast, W. Mullan.

CHARLESWORTH, J. K. (1963), *Historical Geology of Ireland*, Oliver & Boyd.

CLAPHAM, A. R., TUTIN, T. G., and WARBURG, E. F. (1962), *Flora of the British Isles*, 2nd edn., Cambridge University Press.

Climatological Atlas of the British Isles (1952), H.M.S.O.

COLE, GRENVILLE A. J. (1922), *Memoir and Map of Localities of Minerals of Economic Importance and Metalliferous Mines in Ireland*, Stationery Office, Dublin.

COLE, GRENVILLE A. J., and HALLISSY, T. (1924), *Handbook of the Geology of Ireland*, Thomas Murby.

COMMON, R., ed. (1964), *Northern Ireland from the Air*, Queen's University, Belfast.

CONNELL, K. H. (1950), *The Population of Ireland, 1750–1845*, Clarendon Press.

COPPOCK, J., and GILLMOR, D. (1967), 'The cattle trade between Ireland and Great Britain', *Irish Geog.*, **5**, 320–6.

COUSENS, S. (1966), 'The restriction of population growth in pre-famine Ireland', *Proc. Roy. Irish Acad.*, **64**, 85–99.

CRAIG, M. (1952), *Dublin 1660–1860*, London, Cresset Press.

DE PAOR, MÁIRE and LIAM (1958), *Early Christian Ireland*, Thames & Hudson.

EDWARDS, R. D., and WILLIAMS, T. D., eds. (1956), *The Great Famine: Studies in Irish History 1845–52*, Dublin.

EVANS, E. ESTYN (1957), *Irish Folk Ways*, Routledge & Kegan Paul.

EVANS, E. ESTYN (1958), 'The Atlantic ends of Europe', *Advancement of Science*, **15**, 54–64.

FLATRÈS, P. (1957), *Géographie Rurale de quatre Contrées Celtiques, Irlande, Galles, Cornwall et Man*, Rennes.

FREEMAN, T. W. (1957), *Pre-famine Ireland: A Study in Historical Geography*, Manchester University Press.

FREEMAN, T. W. (1965), *Ireland – A General and Regional Geography*, 3rd edn., Methuen.

GILLMOR, D. (1967), 'The agricultural regions of the Republic of Ireland', *Irish Geog.*, **5**, 245–61.

HESLINGA, M. W. (1962), *The Irish Border as a Cultural Divide*, Assen., Van Gorcum.

JESSEN, KNUD (1949), 'Studies in late Quaternary deposits and flora-history of Ireland', *Proc. Roy. Irish Acad.*, **52** B, 85–290.

JOHNSON, J. (1961), 'The development of the rural settlement pattern of Ireland', *Geografiska Annaler*, **43**, 165–73.

JONES, EMRYS (1960), *A Social Geography of Belfast*, Oxford University Press.

JONES HUGHES, T. (1959), 'Landlordism in the Mullet of Mayo', *Irish Geog.*, **4**, 16–34.

JONES HUGHES, T. (1961), 'Landholding and settlement in the Cooley peninsula of Louth', *Irish Geog.*, **4**, 149–74.

JONES HUGHES, T. (1965), 'Society and settlement in nineteenth-century Ireland', *Irish Geog.*, **5**, 79–96.

KILLANIN, LORD, and DUIGNAN, MICHAEL V. (1967), *Shell Guide to Ireland*, 2nd edn., Ebury Press.

LEWIS, SAMUEL (1837), *A Topographical Dictionary of Ireland*, S. Lewis. (2 vols.)

MACAODHA, B. (1965), 'Clachan settlement in Iar-Connacht', *Irish Geog.*, **5**, 20–8.

MACCRACKEN, E. (1959), 'The woodlands of Ireland *circa* 1600', *Irish Hist. Studies*, **16**, 271–96.

MCEVOY, T. (1958), 'Forestry in Ireland', *Advancement of Science*, **14**, 307–16.

MAXWELL, CONSTANTIA (1949), *County and Town in Ireland under the Georges*, rev. edn., Dundalk, Tempest.

MAXWELL, CONSTANTIA (1956), *Dublin under the Georges*, rev. edn., Faber.

MEENAN, J., and WEBB, D. A., eds. (1957), *A View of Ireland*, British Association for the Advancement of Science, Dublin.

MITCHELL, G. F. (1956), 'Post-boreal pollen diagrams from Irish raised bogs', *Proc. Roy. Irish Acad.*, **57** B, 185–251.

MOODY, T. W., and BECKETT, J. C., eds. (1955, 1957), *Ulster since 1800*. British Broadcasting Corporation, London: 2 series – A political and economic survey (1955); A social survey (1957).

MOODY, T. W., and MARTIN, F. X., eds. (1967), *The Course of Irish History*, Cork, Mercier.

MOVIUS, HALLAM L. (1942), *The Irish Stone Age*, Cambridge University Press.

Ó RÍORDÁIN, S. P. (1964), *Antiquities of the Irish Countryside*, 4th edn., Methuen.

ORME, A. R. (1964), 'Planation surfaces in the Drum Hills, County Waterford, and their wider implications', *Irish Geog.*, **5**, 48–72.

ORME, A. R. (1966), 'Youghal, County Cork – growth, decay, resurgence', *Irish Geog.*, **5**, 121–49.

ORME, A. R. (1966), 'Quaternary changes of sea-level in Ireland', *Trans. Inst. Brit. Geogr.*, **39**, 127–40.

OTWAY-RUTHVEN, A. J. (1965), 'The character of Norman settlement in Ireland', in *Historical Studies*, **5**, ed. J. L. McCracken, London.

PIGGOT, STUART (1954), *The Neolithic Cultures of the British Isles*, Cambridge University Press.

PRAEGER, ROBERT LLOYD (1950), *Natural History of Ireland*, Collins.

PROUDFOOT, V. B. (1958), 'Ancient Irish field systems', *Advancement of Science*, **14**, 369–71.

PROUDFOOT, V. B. (1959), 'Rural Settlement in Ireland', *Advancement of Science*, **15**, 336–8.

RYAN, PIERCE (1963), 'The soils of Ireland', *Irish Forestry*, **20**, 2–16.

SIMMS, J. G. (1958), 'Connacht in the eighteenth century', *Irish Hist. Studies*, **11**, 116–33.

SIMMS, J. G. (1961), 'County Sligo in the eighteenth century', *J. Roy. Soc. Antiq. of Ireland*, **91**, 152–62.

Statistical Abstract of Ireland 1966. Stationery Office, Dublin, 1966.

SYMONS, L. J., and CRUICKSHANK, J. G. (1964), 'Agricultural geography in Ireland', in *Field Studies in the British Isles*, ed. J. A. Steers, Nelson, 462–81.

TARRANT, J. R. (1967), 'Recent industrial development in Ireland', *Geography*, **52**, 403–8.

Ulster Year Book 1963–65. Her Majesty's Stationery Office, Belfast, 1965.

WOODHAM-SMITH, C. (1962), *The Great Hunger*, Hamish Hamilton.

YOUNG, ARTHUR (1780), *A Tour in Ireland in the years 1776, 1777 and 1778*. (2 vols.), London, 1780; ed. A. W. Hutton (2 vols.), 1892.

Appendix
The place-names of Ireland

The Celts, Vikings, Normans, English, Scots and others who have helped to fashion the Irish landscape have all left their mark on the place-names of the country. Most modern place-names are anglicized versions of Gaelic words and clearly relate to the physical nature of the local countryside, to the former vegetation cover, or to features of settlement, land use and other forms of human activity. Others have been so modified throughout time as to obscure their original meanings while the spellings that appear on maps, derived as they often were from the mouths of local dialect speakers in the early nineteenth century, may vary greatly from reality. The study of these place-names is thus fraught with many difficulties, but this appendix lists some of the commoner elements and may assist the reader in his understanding of the Irish landscape. The list provides the Gaelic place-name element, its English meaning, and one or two examples of place-names in which the element appears. The appendix concludes with brief reference to those place-names of non-Gaelic origin, most of which trace their roots to the colonists who came after the Celts. It should be remembered that, just as English-speaking peoples of recent times have modified Gaelic place-names, so the Gaelic-speaking invaders probably acquired by word of mouth some place-names familiar to the pre-Celtic peoples whom they overran over 2,000 years ago.

Gaelic place-name elements

abha, river. Ow, Owenboy, Avonmore.
achadh, field. Achonry, Aghavannagh.
aill, cliff, rock. Oyledarrig, Aellevore.
aitinn, furze. Coolattin.
aonach, fair. Nenagh (*an aonach*=the fair).
árd, high, height. Armagh (*árd Macha* = Macha's height), Ardagh (*árd achadh* = high field), Ardattin (height of the furze).
áth, ford. Adare (*áth dara*=ford of the oak); the old Gaelic name for Dublin, *Ath Cliath*, relates to the 'ford of wattles'.
baile, place, land, homestead, town. One of the most common place-name elements in Ireland, *baile* is generally corrupted to 'bally' and often linked with a personal name: Ballybunion, Ballyferriter, Ballymacoda, Ballyquin.

Liam Price (1967) provides the following notes on the use of *baile* at different times:

1. a piece of land held by a family group – the usual sense in monastic charters of the twelfth century.
2. the land and holding of an individual – this sense came into general use after the Anglo-Norman invasion.
3. farmstead, frequently described by its situation – this was a later use, developed from the spread among the English settlers of the word 'town' from the thirteenth century onwards. 'Town' was used as the equivalent of *villa* in the sense of a manor or farmstead, and the Gaelic *baile* was similarly used to correspond to *villa*.
4. town – the word had acquired this sense by the beginning of the fourteenth century.

bealach, pass, way, road. Baltinglass, Ballykeeran. Usually refers to a road through mountain or wooded country.

beann, peak, mountain. Ben Bulben, Benbaun, Benburb.

bearna, gap, pass. Barnesmore, Barna.

bó, cow. Drumshanbo, Annamoe. *Bó-daingean* = cattle fortress, later anglicized to 'bawn', a fortified enclosure.

boireann, stony place. Burren.

bóthar, cattleway, road. Bohereen, Boherboy, Butter Mountain.

buaile, summer dairying place. Ballyknockan, Boola. Booleying, or the use of summer pastures by cattle, was a fundamental part of Celtic farming practice and persisted until quite recently in the Wicklow and other mountains. Ruins of cowherds' booley huts may still be seen.

cabrach, rough bad land. Cabra.

caiseal, stone structure, fort. Cashel, Cashelgarran. *Caislean* = castle.

carn, pile of stones. Carnew, Carntogher.

carraig, rock, rocky place. Carrick, Carrigtoohill, Carrickfergus.

carrán, rocky land. Carran, Cawrawn.

ceall, *ceallóg*, cell, little church. A common element, commonly anglicized as 'kil-' and often linked with the name of an early Christian missionary: Kilkenny (*ceall Chainnigh* = cell of St Canice); Kilgarvan, Kilcormac, Kilmore, Kildare.

ceann, head, end, peak. Kinsale, Kinvarra and Kenmare each mean 'head of the sea'.

ceapach, tillage plot. Cappagh, Cappoquin.

cloch, stone. Clogh, Clogheen, Clogher.

clochog, *clocharán*, stepping stones, stone causeway. Cloghan, Cloghran.

cluain, clearing, meadow, pasture. Clonmel (*cluain meala* = meadow of honey), Clonard, Clonmacnoise, Cloonlara. In its anglicized forms 'clon' and 'cloon', this element is particularly common in the northwest midlands.

cnoc, hill. Knockmealdown, Knockboy, Knockaderry.

coill, coillidh, wood. Killylea, Killadreenan, Quilty, Lugnaquillia.

corcagh, marsh. Cork.

cruach, cruachán, steep hill, mountain. Croghan, Croagh Patrick.

daingean, firm, strong. Rathdangan. Also refers to a strong place or fortress as in Daingean in Offaly and Dingle (*Daingean Uí Chúise*) in Kerry.

díseart, hermitage. Dysart, Desertmartin.

doire, oakwood. Derry, Derrytrasna, Knockaderry.

droichead, bridge. Drogheda, Droichead Nua (Newbridge).

druim, druimín, ridge. In its anglicized forms 'drum' and 'drom', this element is very frequent: Drumcondra, Dromore, Rathdrum. The term 'drumlin' was coined in 1833 by J. Bryce to describe low ridges of superficial debris in the north of Ireland and has since been adopted into geographical literature generally as describing streamlined ridges of glacial till.

dubh, black. Dublin, Slieveduff, Knockdoo.

dún fort. Occurs in several hundred place-names, for example Donegal, Dundrum, Dungarvan, Dunmore, Donard.

eanach, marsh. Appears in over 360 townland names, usually in the form 'ana', or 'anagh': Annaclone, Annaghmore.

eas, waterfall. Glenmacnass, Assaroe, Ballysadare.

eiscir, ridge, elevation. In the form 'esker' this word sometimes appears as a place-name but is better known as describing the many winding ridges of sand and gravel, fluvio-glacial in origin, that occur in Ireland and other countries.

fearann, land, estate. Farran, Farranfore, Ballynerrin.

fiodh, wood. Fiddown, Fethard.

fir, men, people. Fermanagh, Fermoy.

glas, glais, glaise, stream. Glasnevin, Clashmore, Lugglass.

gleann, glen. Glendalough, Glencullen, Glandore.

gort, guirtín, tilled field. Gort, Gorteen, Gortnahoo.

inbhear, river mouth, estuary. Inveran.

inis, island. In the form 'inish' and 'ennis', this element is very common: Inishfree, Inishowen, Enniskillen, Enniskean, Inishmore.

iubhar, iubhrach, yew, place of yews. Killinure, Newry.

lios, enclosure, fort. In the form of 'lis' this element is widely found, but is least common in Leinster. Lismore, Liscannor, Lisburn, Lisbellaw.

loch, lake. Usually found anglicized to 'lough'. Lough Neagh, Lough Derg.

longphort, fortress – particularly on the coast or river. Longford, Rathlangford.

maigh, plain. Usually found in the form 'moy': Moycullen, Moyard, Maynooth.

maol, maoilín, bare hill, little bare hill. Mweelrea, Carrignamweel.

muine, thicket. Moneymore, Moneygall.

mullach, summit, height. Mullaghcleevaun, Mullaghareirk.

páirc, field, demesne. Parknasilla, Parkbawn.

poll, pool. Pollaphuca, Poulanass. In the limestone country of Clare, Galway and other counties, 'poll' meaning a hole is a common prefix in words describing swallow holes where drainage disappears underground.

ráith, *ráithín*, fort, rath. 'Rath' is a particularly common place-name element and refers most frequently to the former existence of a Celtic cowlord's homestead and its enclosure, rather than an actual fort. Rathdrum, Rathvilly, Rathkeale.

rinn, point, headland. Ring, Rinmore, Rinvyle.

ros, grove, wood. Roscommon, Roscrea, Rosnakill. *Ros* meaning headland is also found, as in Rosslare, Rosmuck and The Rosses.

scarbh, rocky ford. Scarriff.

sceillig, crag. Skellig, Templenaskellig.

sliabh, mountain, mountainous land. As 'slieve', this word prefaces many mountains and hills throughout Ireland: Slieve Snaght, Slieve Aughty, Slieveardagh, Slievenamon, Slieve Donard.

sráid, street. Stradbally, Acrenesrade.

teampull, church. Templemartin, Ballintemple, Templemore. After the Anglo-Norman invasion of 1169, this word came to denote the principal church of a parish.

tír, land, territory. Tyrone (*Tir Eoghain*=the land of Owen), Tirconnell.

torc, wild boar. Kanturk, Inishturk.

tráigh, strand. Tramore, Tralee.

tulach, *tulachán*, *tulai*, mound, hill, slope of a mountain. Tully, Tullow, Tulla, Tullamore, Tullagher.

turloch, dry lake. Although Turlough does occur as a place-name, the word is more commonly used to describe the depressions in the limestone country of Clare, Galway, Roscommon and Mayo that acquire temporary lakes when the water-table is high, notably in winter, only to dry out when the water-table drops.

Common adjectives found in place-names include *árd*, high; *beg*, small; *bréan*, rotten; *coal*, narrow; *críon*, old; *fada*, long; *fliuch*, wet; *garbh*, rough; *gearr*, short; *leathan*, broad; *lom*, bare; *mín*, smooth; *mor*, great; *salach*, dirty.

Colours include *airgead*, silver; *bán*, white; *buidhe*, yellow (usually anglicized to 'boy'); *dearg*, red; *dubh*, black; *fionn*, white, fair; *glas*, green, grey; *liath*, grey; *ruadh*, red.

Ruirthech (the old name for the Liffey), *Sabrann* (the old name for the Lee and still found as the Severn in Britain) and several other river names are considered by some authorities to be pre-Celtic words inherited by the Celts. The Celtic overlords also named some probably pre-Celtic folk such as the *Conmaicne* ('sons of dogs' who have given their name to Connemara – lit. 'sons of dogs of the sea') and the *Déisi* ('vassal people' who have given their name to baronies in Meath and Waterford) whom they found on their arrival.

Non-Gaelic place-names

The handful of Viking and part-Viking place-names around the coast includes such Norse elements as *ay*, *ey*, island (Lambay, Dalkey), *gata*, road (Windgate), *fiord*, bay, harbour (Waterford, Carlingford), and *lo*, meadow near water (Arklow, Wicklow). *Staor*, stead, land, is found in the Gaelic-Norse compounds Leinster (the land of the Laigin), Ulster (the land of the Ulaid) and Munster. Other Norse place-names include Helvick, Howth, Leixlip, Skerries, Smerwick and Wexford, while Norse personal names such as Torcaill (Curtlestown, Rath-turtle) and Gunnhildr (Stagonil) have been incorporated in some place-names, notably in Wicklow.

The most important place-name element to follow in the wake of the Anglo-Norman invasion was 'town' which spread among the English settlers from the thirteenth century onwards. 'Town' was used as the equivalent of the Norman–French 'vill' to denote a manor or farmstead and its associated land, and was frequently linked with a personal name. 'Town' and 'vill' were translated by the native Irish as *baile*, but, in the place-names that have come down to us, 'town' elements remain predictably conspicuous in those parts of the south and east effectively settled by the English colonists while 'bally' elements, though more widely ranging, are relatively more important in areas of persistent Irish settlement.

Certain material features of the Anglo-Norman invasion generated similar Gaelic words which survive as place-names. For instance, the *motte* became the Gaelic *móta* and is revealed in place-names like Moate and Killamoat; the *bretesche* or timber palisade and blockhouse became the Gaelic *briotás* and the modern element 'brittas'. Hospital in Limerick derives its name from a hospital of the Knights Templars founded in 1226.

During and since the plantation era, many new settlements have been given names which are distinctly English and need little comment. Several 'newtowns' of the seventeenth and eighteenth centuries simply added the names of their creators: Newtown Forbes (1619) in Longford, Newtownstewart in Tyrone, Newtown Mount Kennedy in Wicklow, Newtownhamilton (1770) in Armagh. Cookstown, Edgeworthstown (also called Mostrim), Hillsborough and Mount Bellew Bridge have similar origins, but not all landlords have achieved lasting memorials: Parsonstown has reverted to its former name Birr, Bagenalstown has become Muine Bheag. Some towns were named after the ruling monarch of the period: Jamestown (1621) in Leitrim, Charleville (incorporated 1671 but now officially renamed Rath Luirc), Kingwilliamstown (an experimental farming settlement founded on the Cork–Kerry border in 1832, now Ballydesmond). Important towns like Maryborough (now Port Laoise), Kingstown (now reverted to Dun Laoghaire) and Queenstown (now Cobh) could not expect their imperial names to survive long after Independence in 1921.

References

o'brien, m. a. (1957), 'Place-names', in *A View of Ireland*, ed. J. Meenan and D. A. Webb, Dublin, 187–96.

price, liam (1967), *The Place-Names of Co. Wicklow*. Dublin Institute for Advanced Studies, (Part 7, The Baronies of Newcastle and Arklow).

Index

Numbers in italic type refer to illustrations